STANDARDIZED
TEXTBOOK
OF BARBERING

Fifth Edition

IN THREE PARTS

Part I — The Fundamentals of Barbering

Part II — Barber Science

Part III — Business Principles

With 276 Illustrations

PUBLISHED BY

ASSOCIATED MASTER BARBERS AND BEAUTICIANS
OF AMERICA

PRICE $6.00

GENERAL OFFICE
537 SOUTH DEARBORN STREET, CHICAGO 5, ILLINOIS

"There will be no elevation ... *without education"*

THIS Textbook was compiled and is published by the Associated Master Barbers and Beauticians of America so that the barber may improve his position in the business world, and to help him appreciate the higher ideals essential to the recognition of barbering as a professional calling.

CONTENTS

✦

Part I—THE FUNDAMENTALS OF BARBERING

Part II—BARBER SCIENCE

CONTENTS

Preface

IN this modern age it is not sufficient for the progressive barber to know only the practical part of his profession. He must know something about the anatomical structure of that part of the human body upon which he operates; also the functions of the organs of the body that appreciably affect these parts. This knowledge is scientific, hence the term, "Barber Science."

Barbering became a science when interest shifted to the study of the physical makeup of the human entity and the nature of the environment in which the human being lives. The human body is the most interesting object on earth, and to know it, especially the portion upon which the barber operates, is indispensable to the proper practice of the profession.

Today we find every industry spending a great amount of time and money on scientific research. It is well known that discoveries in pure science, through research work for the advancement of knowledge, will sooner or later form the basis of new arts, professions and industries.

With the amazing increase in advertising, with its messages to the public, with the spread of the habit of reading informative magazines and newspapers, watching television, and listening to radio broadcasts, American men and women are becoming expert buyers. They are learning to select service and merchandise solely on their merits. There is no doubt that the great multitudes of purchasers of all things are seeking higher and higher standards of cleanliness, artistry, quality and design. The trend is unmistakable. People are demanding a higher grade of service—a scientific service that will give results.

It is apparent that it is up to the barber profession to educate the public to the necessity of properly caring for the hair, scalp and face. It is important to impress upon the whole family, where there is a tendency toward baldness, that the necessary attention to the scalp and hair cannot be given too early in life or too conscientiously. Also that clear and clean skin is a business and social asset, while a repulsive face ruins opportunities for social and business advancement.

Before an attempt should be made along these lines the organized groups (owners, employes, manufacturers of and dealers in barber supplies, and barber schools), and the State Boards of Barber Examiners, which are the units to which the profession must look for its future welfare, and which are vitally interested in the elevation of the profession, must themselves study progressive and efficient methods and obtain a more scientific knowledge of the business, thereby keeping abreast of the kind of service that the public will recognize as beneficial.

Referring more especially to Part II of this Textbook, "Barber Science," it is not intended to impart a complete understanding of the entire human body, but only to give the barber a comprehensive knowledge of the portion with which he has to deal, and other parts primarily affiliated therewith. It is confined to the subjects that make up Barber Science, and explains the technical terms used in the more advanced books on physiology and anatomy in a more simple manner applicable to the profession of barbering.

Deep appreciation is herewith expressed to all members of the Associated Master Barbers and Beauticians of America who gave their time and minds to the task of improving Standardized Textbook of Barbering and creating the Fifth Edition. These members include school operators and instructors, National Educational Council supervisors, members of State Boards of Barber Examiners, General Officers of the Association, and Chapter officers and members from all sections of the nation. They confidently present Standardized Textbook of Barbering, Fifth Edition, to the profession, convinced that it represents the best medium in existence for the training of the future barbers of America.

PART I

The Fundamentals
of Barbering

Chapter 1

History of the Barber Profession

THE profession of barbering is one of the oldest in the world. Archeological studies indicate that some crude forms of facial and hair adornment were practiced among prehistoric people in the glacial age.

There are in existence many relics, such as combs, cosmetics and razors, the latter made of tempered copper and bronze, which came from the tombs of Egypt. These relics, as well as many written records, reveal that the nobility and priesthood had already become regular patrons for barbers' services 6000 years ago.

In those ancient days the barber's art included shaving, haircutting, beard trimming, hair coloring and facial makeup.

During the time of Moses (1450-1400 B. C.) barber services became available to the general population, as well as to the nobility. However, people governed by Mosaic (Moses') law had definite instructions forbidding them from cutting the hair and trimming the beard in imitation of others who had adopted the custom.

The Bible contains several passages pertaining to the services of the barber. A few of the references may be found in:

Deuteronomy 14:1, prohibiting shaving between the eyes of the dead.

Leviticus 19:27, prohibiting trimming of the beard.

Leviticus 21:5, prohibiting shaving of the head.

The greater part of the 13th chapter of Leviticus gives instructions for the diagnosis and treatment of diseases. In this chapter, the 29th to 37th verses give instructions for the diagnosis and the treatment of scalp and face diseases by shaving and quarantine.

In King David's time (1115-1055 B. C.) barbers played a part in his wars.

In 595 B. C. Ezekiel said: "And thou, son of man, take thee a sharp knife, take thee a barber's razor, and cause it to pass upon thine head and upon thine beard."

In the golden age of Greece, 500 B. C., well-trimmed beards were fashionable. Later, in 334 B. C., Alexander the Great decreed that beards of his troops must be shaved. Thus the shave became a military expediency for the purpose of gaining advantage in hand-to-hand combat. Alexander's warriors were able to grasp an enemy by the beard, but they, themselves, were safeguarded in this customary method of fighting.

Barbering was introduced in Rome in 296 B. C. There the art became further advanced, and Rome became known for its fine baths and barber salons. The barbers became very popular and prosperous, and their shops were frequented as centers for daily news and gossip. All free men of Rome were clean-shaven, while slaves were forced to wear beards. It is from the Roman (Latin) word *barba*, meaning beard, that the word "barber" is derived.

In the early Christian era barbers became assistants to the clergy, who, on sacrilegious grounds, were not allowed to do the surgery of those days. The barbers did blood-letting. Later they pulled teeth, and for centuries this act comprised the whole art of dentistry. Later on, barbers also administered herbs and other forms of medications. For more than a thousand years they were known in history as barber-surgeons.

It was the custom of the barber-surgeon to use a white cloth bandage to stop bleeding on the arm of a person after a blood-letting operation. This blood-stained bandage was then hung up to dry. As time went on, the hanging, blood-stained bandage became recognized as the emblem of the barber-surgeon's profession. Still later the original emblem was replaced by a painted wooden pole of white and red stripes. This symbol is today's *barber pole,* and it is universally used as the sign of a barber shop.

Barber-surgeons formed their first organization in France in 1096 A. D. Soon after this the first formal school of surgery was established in Paris by the barber-surgeons.

In the early years of the twelfth century a guild of surgeons was organized from elements within the ranks of the barber-surgeons. The members of the guild of surgeons applied themselves to research and study of medicines and drugs in efforts to find new methods of healing.

In the fifteenth century, in England, the science of medicine was growing to such an extent that the guild of surgeons surpassed the barber-surgeons in knowledge and specialized skill, and they succeeded, by an act of parliament, in restricting the barber-surgeons to the medical practices of blood-letting, tooth-pulling and simple cauterizing.

The surgeons and barber-surgeons in England were reunited in 1505, and this union existed for two more centuries. However, the restrictions on barber-surgeons continued during this period.

As time went on, medicine continued to advance through science and research, and it greatly overshadowed the ancient and dying practice of blood-letting. The barber-surgeons' medical practice dwindled in importance and repute in the light of advancing science, and finally, in 1745, the alliance between surgeons and barbers was completely dissolved.

The barbers, however, continued to practice blood-letting and tooth-pulling, and they dispensed some simple herb medicines in the villages and small communities because of precedence and because often there were no physicians available.

The year 1745 marks the end of a long and glorious period in the history of the barber profession. Stripped of its former prestige, barbering continued to decline economically, technically and even morally. There was a slow degradation of the art, and by the end of the nineteenth century barber shops had become untidy, unsanitary and undignified. They became characterized as centers for cheap gossip and reading rooms for risque magazines, rather than for their tonsorial services. Barbering in general became an unrespected craft, and barbers were grouped in the lowest social strata.

The Rebirth of a Profession

In the latter part of the 19th century a few barbers who were men of high ideals initiated efforts to lift the craft of barbering from its degraded position to its rightful level of professional, personal service. Barbers began to organize into employer organizations, known as "boss barber" and "master barber" groups, and into employe organizations known as "journeyman barber" groups.

On December 5, 1887, the Journeyman Barbers International Union was formed at its first national convention at Buffalo, New York. Affiliated with the American Federation of Labor, this employes' union is now called The Journeyman Barbers', Hairdressers', Cosmetologists' and Proprietors' International Union of America, with headquarters in Indianapolis, Indiana.

In 1893 Mr. A. B. Moler established the first barber school in the world, in Chicago. Mr. Moler also published the first textbook of barbering, "The Moler Manual of Barbering."

In 1897 the first barber license law was passed in Minnesota. This state legislation was designed to prescribe sanitary practices for barbering, and it stipulated minimum educational and technical requirements for barbers in that state.

On November 19, 1924, the Associated Master Barbers of America was organized in Chicago, Illinois, through the leadership of Louis E. McIlvain. The name of the organization was changed to Associated Master Barbers and Beauticians of America at the National Convention in Cleveland, Ohio, in October, 1941, in recognition of the growing number of beautician shop owners and managers who were becoming members. The Association is now recognized as the national organization representative of barber and beauty shop owners and managers.

On October 19, 1927, the National Association of Standardized Barber Schools, now known as the National Association of Barber Schools, Inc., was organized at its first convention in Cleveland, Ohio. This organization immediately sought to develop co-operative efforts with the National Educational Council of the Associated Master Barbers and Beauticians of America, in a program to standardize the operation of barber schools in the United States and the training of students in these schools.

On October 21, 1929, the National Association of State Boards of Barber Examiners, now known as the National Association of Barber Examiners, was organized at its first convention in St. Paul, Minnesota. Its purposes, expressed in resolutions adopted by the convention, were to standardize qualifications of applicants for barber examinations and to standardize methods of examining applicants. Also, this organization of State Barber Boards declared itself to be a clearing house for information that might be of value to all State Barber Boards.

On April 11, 1943, the Barbers and Beauty Culturists Union of America, at its first national convention, held in New York City, received its charter from the Congress of Industrial Organizations and became the national C.I.O. barber employes' union. This barbers' union remained in existence for only ten years. It was absorbed by the A.F.L. barbers' union in 1954.

In 1925 the Associated Master Barbers and Beauticians of America established the National Educational Council, whose purposes were to standardize school training and to uplift the art of barbering. Some of the outstanding achievements of this Council include: (1) Standardization of the better class barber schools, which must have instructors qualified under the rules of the National Educational Council; (2) training of Barber Science teachers; (3) establishment of a curriculum of Barber Science for the practicing barber, in connection with which several thousand Council diplomas have been issued (Barber Science has also been added to the curricula of the Standardized

Schools, and beginning students today have the advantages of its advanced instruction) ; (4) the formulation of the Model License Bill, in conjunction with the Journeymen Barbers', Hairdressers', Cosmetologists' and Proprietors' International Union of America (a great deal of legislative work has been done co-operatively between the Associated Master Barbers and Beauticians of America and the union, which has resulted in the passage of state barber license laws. Up to the date of publication of the Standardized Textbook of Barbering, Fifth Edition, the District of Columbia and all states of the Union except Virginia have barber license laws. Minimum price laws are now in force in a number of states) ; (5) the creation, in 1930, of a Research Department in the General Office of the Associated Master Barbers and Beauticians of America.

The decade from 1950 through 1959 were years that recorded great economic gains for the barbering profession. During this same decade there was renewed attention given to the provisions in state licensing statutes under which barbers are registered. At the 1952 National Convention of the Associated Master Barbers and Beauticians of America, and again at the 1955 National Convention of the Association, resolutions were approved which recommended that the state laws be amended to provide for a required high school education to qualify one to enter training to become a barber. Also, the Conventions recommended that school courses be extended to nine months, and that instructors be better educated and have special teacher training.

In 1959, Kentucky enacted an amended statute that specifies a complete high school course as a prerequisite of one who enters a school of barbering in that state. Also, the Kentucky law requires a high school diploma and two years of college as a prerequisite of one who qualifies as a barber college instructor. Efforts in other states met with moderate degrees of success, and the goal of higher educational and training standards is gradually being reached.

The first practical achievement of the Research Department was the compilation and publication, in 1931, of the Standardized Textbook of Barbering, First Edition, the first standard, all-inclusive volume ever written that covered and co-ordinated complete instruction in the practice of barbering and the study of Barber Science. Subsequently, the Association published a Second Edition, a Third Edition and a Fourth Edition, all of which met with the approval of the profession.

The current Textbook, the Fifth Edition of the Standardized Textbook of Barbering, has been completely reviewed, re-edited and modernized. Some of the Chapters have been expanded, particularly Haircutting, and some of the subject matter contained in the Fourth Edition has been condensed. The excellence of the Textbook is being maintained in all respects, including the quality of printing and other steps in producing the work. The Textbook has been improved by the addition of 102 new illustrations, making a total of 276 illustrations.

All constructive material contained in the Fourth Edition for training barbers has been retained in this Fifth Edition. Other subject matter that is deemed constructive has been added. Due consideration is given to the need for a comprehensive Textbook that serves for training purposes in all of the states of the Union and which can be used as the basis for examinations by all State Boards of Barber Examiners.

Chapter 2

The Implements of the Barber Profession

ALL the instruments and accessories used in the various phases of the barber's work may be considered as the implements of the barber profession.

The instruments in general consist of razors, shears and clippers.

Accessory implements consist of hones, strops, combs, brushes, mugs, lather mixers, etc.

One of the characteristics of all outstanding artisans is the finesse of choice of the instruments of their art, and so it is with the expert barber. His kit is always graced with the finest instruments he can procure.

The Instruments

THE RAZOR. The first instrument to be considered is the barber's razor, which is one of the keenest cutting instruments used in any profession or craft.

There are seven points to be learned or considered about razors: The style, width, length, grind, finish, balance and temper.

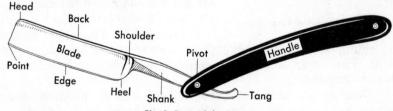

Fig. 1. Parts of the Razor.

STYLE. The style of the modern razor, through a process of slow evolution in its manufacture through the centuries, has become quite standardized.

The illustration shown (Fig. 1) depicts the general style of the modern razor, with back and edge straight and parallel. The head and heel are rounded, while the point is square. When put into use, however, the sharp point is usually rounded off slightly by the barber, because of its tendency to scratch.

WIDTH. The width of the razor is measured in eighths or sixteenths of an inch—most generally in eighths: 4/8, 5/8, 6/8, etc. The nine-sixteenths and five-eighths inch razors are the widths usually preferred.

LENGTH. The length of the blade varies a little with the width, but this variation is not marked and is seldom taken as a criterion in the barber's choice of a razor.

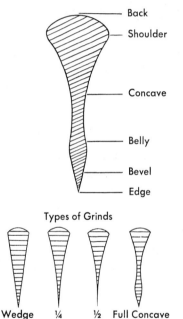

Types of Grinds

Wedge   ¼   ½   Full Concave

Fig. 2. Cross-section of Razor Blade.

GRIND. The "grind" of a razor is a term used to designate the type of grinding on the blade. Grinds vary from a regular wedge to what is known as the hollow-ground, or full concave. (Fig. 2.)

The hollow-ground razor is the most widely used, and it is considered by some authorities as the most efficient type of grind for barbers' razors. However, the wedge razor finds favor with many barbers.

FINISH. By "finish" is meant the polish of a razor. The barber's razor has a polished surface, usually designated as a crocus or rouge finish, because the surface is polished or buffed with crocus or rouge powder.

Nickel or silver-plated razors are not recommended because they are usually of inferior steel.

BALANCE. The finest razors are equipped with a handle whose weight balances that of the blade. This is an important factor in the efficient handling of this instrument.

Handles are made of hard rubber, bone or plastics; most generally of plastics. Atmospheric conditions may sometimes warp the handle so that the edge will strike it on closing. In such cases, moist or dry heat may be used to straighten it.

The blade must not be so tightly riveted to the handle that it cannot be moved with ease, nor should it be so loosely riveted that it moves by its own weight.

TEMPER. Much can be said about individual opinion pertaining to what the proper temper of razor steel should be, but, in general, the barber's razors are quite uniform in this respect, and one can rely on correct hardness and malleability of razors produced by standard manufacturers.

Of course, barbers have varied opinions on this subject, some preferring soft steel, and others hard steel, giving such reasons as that one will give a better edge, one a more lasting edge, etc. However, this is more a matter of personal fancy than actual fact.

Fig. 2A. Electric Shaver.

ELECTRIC SHAVER. This instrument utilizes the principle of the electric clipper. It has exceptionally thin cutting blades. Many modern shops use electric shavers to serve patrons who request this service. (Fig. 2A.)

THE SHEARS. As a razor is indispensable for all shaving purposes, shears are equally indispensable for all haircutting.

There are two types of shears: the German type, with no finger brace, and the French type, with a brace for the small finger. The French type is almost universally used now, because of the greater stability in handling afforded by its design. (Fig. 3.)

SIZE. Shears of 7½-inch total length are most popular with a majority of barbers. The measurements vary as to the length of the blade and the length of the shank, these being a matter of

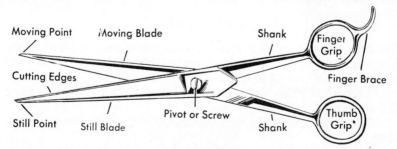

Fig. 3. Parts of the Shears.

choice with the individual, according to his personal fancy, and those proportions which fit the shape and size of his hand. Some operators use shears with short shanks and long blades, and vice versa. The most efficient type, however, are shears with shanks and blades approximately equal in length.

GRIND. The two main types of shear grindings are plain and corrugated, the plain being almost universally used.

Of the plain grinds, there are the polished or smooth (sometimes called "knife edge" grind), the medium, and the coarse. The medium is preferable.

The corrugated grind also varies in coarseness.

The choice of these various grinds depends on the individual and his technique. The plain grinds, however, are preferred by most experts.

THE SET. The set of the shears is just as important as the grind itself, for the shears with the keenest edges may be a very poor cutting instrument if the blades are not set properly.

It is necessary, therefore, that only an expert, experienced shear grinder recondition a dull pair of shears, for the ordinary street grinder may ruin the blades by improper grinding and setting.

THE THINNING SHEARS. Other than the shears for regular haircutting, another type is known as thinning shears.

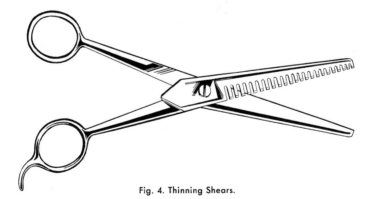

Fig. 4. Thinning Shears.

One type has one smooth blade and one tooth-like, notched blade. Another type has both blades serrated. The thinning shears are of value in thinning heavy hair. (Fig. 4.)

THE CLIPPER. There are two types of hair clippers—hand and electric.

The hand clipper is well-standardized in shape and design. (Fig. 5.)

There are two types of electric clippers. One is motor-driven,

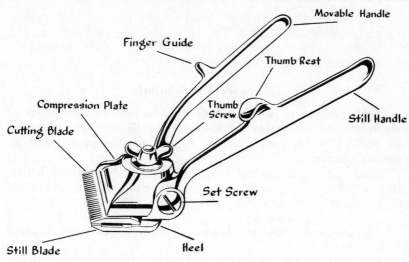

Fig. 5. Parts of the Clipper.

which may be run by a flexible shaft from a motor on a stand, or with a very small motor built into the instrument.

The other type is a magnetic electric clipper, with a compact vibrating mechanism built into the instrument. (Fig. 6.)

Fig. 6. Electric Clipper.

Fig. 7. Attachable Clipper Combs.

The blades of all clippers, hand or electric, are indicated in cutting thickness as follows: The 0000 gives the shortest cut, the 000, 00, 0 and No. 1 give proportionately longer cuts. Attachable clipper combs permit still longer cuts. (Fig. 7.)

Accessory Implements

THE HONE. A barber's hone may be defined as a block of wearable solid substance impregnated with abrasive material that will cut steel. Its purpose is to produce the proper cutting edge on a razor.

There are two general types of hones: the natural hones, often called stones, because they are derived from quarried rocks, and the manufactured hones, also called synthetic hones because they are manufactured.

The natural hones are termed "water hones" and Belgian hones.

WATER HONE. The water hone is a soft, clay-colored stone, which produces a very fine edge through its slow-cutting action. Its "slowness" is a disadvantage, however, that has reduced its popularity with barbers who prefer a "fast" hone.

The fact remains that water hones are very good hones, and they are still used for finishing by many barbers. There is a rule that may be laid down here: The finer the abrasive in a hone, the slower it must necessarily be in sharpening a razor edge.

Conversely, the faster the hone produces an edge, the coarser the edge will be.

BELGIAN HONE. Many barbers still use the Belgian hone. It is a fine-cutting hone, but somewhat faster cutting than other water hones.

The Belgian hone is distinguished by a light-yellow colored cutting surface and a bottom dark red-colored supporting rock. This hone is quarried in Belgium.

Lather or water is used as the wetting agent on water hones.

SYNTHETIC HONES. There is a wide variety of manufactured hones, the first of which was the Swaty, originally produced by an Austrian chemist. It is of hard texture, quite fine, and a medium fast cutter.

A great number of synthetic hones have become popular because they are fast-cutting hones, among which is a class of hones whose abrasive qualities are due to carborundum content.

STROPS. In general, leather and canvas are the two types of strops used. These strops are nearly always used in pairs.

It is not the purpose of the strop to grind the razor, as is the case with the hone, but to align the tiny cutting teeth of the razor edge (as shown in the 100x magnification, Fig. 15).

Leather strops are usually made of horsehide or cowhide.

Those made from horsehide are either designated "horsehide" or "shell," the shell being a very smooth leather made from tanned muscular strips of the horse's rump.

Cowhide is most widely used in strop manufacturing. This strop requires a great deal of work to "break it in," but once the proper stropping surface has been developed it makes an ideal strop.

There are also strops made of pigskin and synthetic leathers.

The "canvas" strop is made either of linen or silk, in coarse, medium and fine weaves, the medium being the most preferable.

COMBS. For the most part, combs are made of hard rubber; a few are made of bone, and now other durable and heat-resistant plastics are being used. They are made in a wide variety of shapes and forms to suit every purpose or fancy. (Figs. 8, 9, 10.)

Fig. 8. Barber's Comb.

Fig. 9. Flat-top Comb.

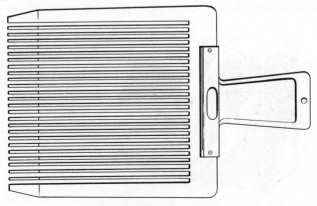

Fig. 10. Wide Flat-top Comb.

Utility is the primary factor to be considered in purchasing combs. The teeth should be smoothly finished, and they should be fine enough and set far enough apart so that they will pass through the hair with the greatest ease.

An important factor to be considered is the ends of the teeth. These should be smoothly tapered, with rounded ends, and should never be sharp. Sharp teeth have a tendency to scratch and irritate the scalp. Barbers should have both light and dark colored haircutting combs, using dark combs for light hair and light combs for dark hair, thus utilizing contrast to make their work easier.

BRUSHES. There are three types of brushes used in the barber's work: the hair brush, the hair duster, and the lather brush.

The ordinary hair brush should have medium hard bristles. It is used to brush the hair or assist in combing the hair, but never to scrub the scalp, either in shampooing or for any other reason. Many modern shops have eliminated use of the hair brush for sanitary reasons.

The hair duster is finding increasing disfavor among barbers in recent years, and some health authorities have banned its use on the grounds of it being unsanitary. Many modern barber shops have eliminated the use of the hair duster by installing compressed air equipment. Others use either a freshly-laundered towel or paper tissue.

The lather brush should be selected for its ability to stand up under long and constant use in hot water, without losing its bristles.

THE MUG. The mug is used for mixing lather with the aid of a lather brush, using cake soap, cream or powder.

LATHER MIXERS. There are several electric lather-making devices now available. They are not only more sanitary than the mug, but also are a means of saving time, since the flip of a lever

Fig. 11. Lather Mixer.

brings instant, warm, sanitary lather. Electric lather mixers are gradually replacing the mug in modern barber shops. (Fig. 11.)

TWEEZER. A good quality tweezer should be a standard item in each barber's equipment. It is used to pluck or shape eyebrows and to extract "ingrown" or infected hairs.

Fig. 12. Tweezers.

The needle-and-tweezer combination instrument serves a double purpose—the needle to help expose the infected or imbedded hair, the tweezer to extract it. This instrument must be sterilized before and after its use. (Fig. 12.)

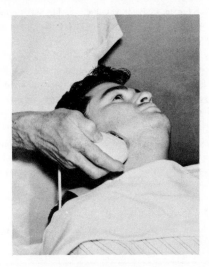

Fig. 13. Electric Razor Shaving.

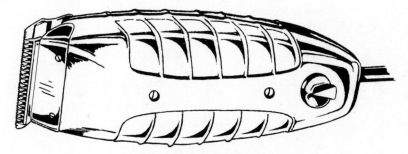

Fig. 14. Electric Outline Shaver.

HOW TO STUDY

It's a lot of fun to study, if you do it right. But it's not much fun if you are whining and grouchy, and have the idea of getting it over as quickly as possible.

Books are interesting things—and just because they are school-books doesn't mean they're less interesting. History is exciting to read. English—putting words together to form different meanings—is a game you can play every day for the rest of your life without ever becoming tired. Numbers are amazing—with them men analyze the stars, the sea, and build bridges, roadways and great buildings.

Every study is mysteriously romantic under its cold surface. When you do your lesson, forget about getting a set amount finished in the shortest possible time. Ask your instructor about something you don't quite understand; get below that cold surface to find the exciting mystery. It's there in every subject, if you have the curiosity to dig it out.

When curiosity arouses real interest, you'll find yourself eager to get to your studies, rather than hate them.

Chapter 3

Honing and Stropping

Honing

HONING is an art that must be carefully learned. Speed and grace, or the general skill that characterizes the expert's honing process, are only acquired through adequate study and practice.

Skillful honing, however, does not lie alone in graceful movements, as some practitioners would lead one to believe, but rather in a combination of graceful movements with scientific principles involved.

One point that cannot be emphasized too much is that, no matter how clever a barber may be, he cannot give a good shave with a dull razor.

For instance, a barber may be ever so fancy in honing a razor, but if he makes such technical errors as taking one long, heavy stroke in one direction, and one light, short stroke in the opposite direction, he will never get a perfect edge on a razor.

All hones contain some sort of fine-to-coarse abrasive particles that actually grind the edge of a razor, just like a piece of sandpaper on a block will grind a piece of wood passed over it.

If a piece of hardwood is passed over a piece of sandpaper, its surface would soon present a multitude of fine, perceptible scratchings.

This is precisely what happens to a razor's edge when passed over a hone, except that in this case the scratches are so minute that they are imperceptible to ordinary vision.

On the other hand, if we view the edge of a razor through a microscope, we see minute scratches, and instead of a perfectly smooth edge, as we would suppose, we find the edge resembles saw teeth. These microscopically fine teeth form the actual cutting edge. (Fig. 15.)

Rules for the Correct Technique in Honing

1. The razor must be stroked edge-first diagonally across the

Magnified Razor Edge
(Side View)

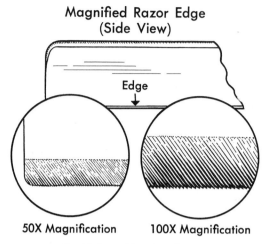

Edge

50X Magnification   100X Magnification

Fig. 15. Razor Edge Magnification.

Fig. 16.   Honing Positions.   Fig. 17.

hone. This is to produce teeth with a cutting edge, which is a very important factor in increasing its cutting quality. (Figs. 16 and 17.)

2. The angle should be equal on both strokes, to insure that the teeth will be set at the same angle on both sides of the blade.

3. The razor must be stroked with equal pressure on both sides of the blade and with equal pressure from heel to point to insure an equal bevel on each side and a uniform parallel bevel from heel to point.

4. The razor must always be kept perfectly flat on the hone while the strokes are made, for if the razor is rocked the least bit the bevel will in time become uneven, and the result will be a

crooked edge instead of one that is perfectly straight. Be sure to give an equal number of strokes on each side.

The Art of Honing

Before beginning the actual honing process,-one should first master the technique of turning the razor without turning the wrist. This may seem a trivial matter to the novice, but it is necessary to insure keeping the razor in perfect condition, and it is one of the many characteristics which will later distinguish the expert from the careless workman in the eyes of the employer.

The first step in the actual honing process is to place the razor with the heel on the hone, and back at a slight angle to the right end of the hone, as in Fig. 18A.

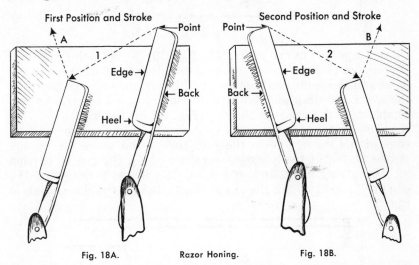

Fig. 18A.   Razor Honing.   Fig. 18B.

Draw the razor diagonally across the hone along the dotted line 1. This is stroke No. 1. When this stroke is completed, turn the razor on its back, and at the same time move it up to the second position, with the back of the blade next to the left end of the hone at a slight angle to the hone, as in Fig. 18B.

Make stroke No. 2 as in Fig. 18B, then turn the razor and bring it up to the first position (Fig. 18A) again. Repeat these movements slowly at first, carefully following the rules given above.

If the razor is quite dull, the first honing strokes should be made with firm pressure, easing up the pressure on the strokes as the razor takes an edge. Experience will prove to be a guide.

It is well to practice on a slow-cutting hone at first, with an old razor, until the action of honing has become an easy and free muscular act. Try to acquire smooth, even strokes, and remember that it is highly important to acquire correct technique at first, for speed and grace will come naturally with practice.

Honing Technique for the Advanced Student

After a student has learned to hone a razor evenly and has mastered the honing motions and strokes, he may direct his attention to the method of maintaining the correct "curve" on the cutting edge. A perfect cutting edge should have its highest point at the center of the edge and should slope very slightly

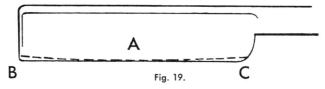

Fig. 19.

(dotted line) from the center (A, Fig. 19) to the point and heel of the edge (B and C, Fig. 19). If the center of the edge is the low point and the point and heel are the high points on the edge, then the razor will drag and fail to cut smoothly, and the patron will complain of the razor "pulling." (Fig. 20, dotted line.)

The average barber has a tendency to hollow out the cutting edge of his razor, due to the fact that as he takes the honing stroke he instinctively exerts pressure along the center portion of the cutting edge, and unless this tendency is corrected the edge will soon take on the shape illustrated by the dotted line in Fig. 20.

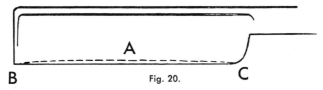

Fig. 20.

To fashion and maintain the correct "curve" on the cutting edge of a razor:

Lay the razor flat on the hone, making sure that the edge and the heel of the razor are flat on the hone surface. Take four short honing strokes with pressure exerted at the *heel* of the razor. Shift the position of the razor on the hone so that the edge and the point of the razor are flat on the hone surface. Take four short honing strokes with pressure exerted at the *point* of the razor. Shift the position of the razor on the hone so that the center portion of the razor lies flat on the hone surface. Take several light strokes with little or no pressure.

It is easily understood that more of the razor edge is honed at the heel and at the point of the edge than is honed at the center portion, which develops the desired "curve," as illustrated by the dotted line in Fig. 19.

Testing the Edge

After the mechanical action of honing has been mastered, the next step is to learn to test the edge. This is an act that requires the training of a delicate sense of touch, and it can only be acquired by diligence and many patient trials. The two rules for testing a razor are:

1. A *honed* razor is to be tested by passing it lightly over the moistened thumb nail. (Fig. 21.) Do not use saliva in these tests. It is not sanitary.

2. A *stropped* razor should be tested by passing it gently over the moistened ball of the thumb or index finger. A stropped razor should never be tested on the nail. (Fig. 24.)

Fig. 21.

Sensations of Testing After Honing

1. Blunt edge: Passes smoothly and freely over the nail without any sensation.

2. Keen edge: Drags or tends to dig in, but it is smooth in sensation.

3. Coarse edge: Drags, and digs in with a slight, grating sensation.

4. Rough or over-honed edge: Tends to stick, and gives a harsh, disagreeable, gritty sensation.

Sometimes one may detect two or more of the above sensations along the razor edge. This indicates that the razor has not been honed evenly, and there is some fault in the technique of the honing process.

A student should consult the teacher in such cases, in order to alter his honing technique immediately, for if a faulty technique is allowed to become a habit it will be very hard to correct. Pains taken while learning will mean ease, speed and perfect results later.

As the razor edge tends to become sharp, gradually lighten the pressure in honing, take fewer strokes and test it more frequently. This will prevent over-honing, for an over-honed razor is no better than a dull razor. A fine, slow-cutting hone is recommended for beginners.

Stropping

After the razor has been keenly honed it is ready to be stropped. Although it may have a perfectly-honed edge, one that will split a fine hair with ease, it is not yet smooth enough to be used on the face. Remember, a razor should never be used for shaving without being stropped.

The purpose of stropping is to smooth the whetted edge, or "finish" it, preparatory to the shaving process.

It must not be thought that expert honing is the only action necessary to put a good edge on a razor. Proper stropping is also essential. A well-honed razor which has been improperly stropped fails to slide smoothly through the beard and give that even-cutting sensation that is so pleasing to the patron.

Most barbers use a pair of strops, consisting of a canvas and a leather. The relative importance of canvas and leather is still a moot question. The viewpoint is accepted by barbers that the leather strop is indispensable, where the canvas may or may not be necessary, depending on the individual's co-ordination of hone and strop. With some types of hones, however, the canvas is considered to be necessary.

The general principles of stropping are little different from those of honing, except that stropping is reversed, *i. e.*, the razor is stroked with the back moving forward, and at a slight angle. The razor must be kept perfectly flat against the strop, with the strop held taut. Guard against sagging. The pressure of the razor must be heavy enough to feel a firm drag or "draw."

The razor is held with thumb on top of the shank and rolled in the hand without moving the wrist. This not only makes for equal pressure on both strokes, but also makes the act more graceful and easy.

First learn to turn or flip the razor by holding it in one position without making the strokes.

After this act has become easy, proceed with the strokes slowly, as illustrated in Figs. 22 and 23.

When the razor is freshly honed, it should be finished on the leather only. Subsequently, it is advisable to use the canvas first, then the leather, each time the razor is stropped.

To test the razor edge after stropping, use the ball of the thumb or index finger (the flesh), touching it lightly along the

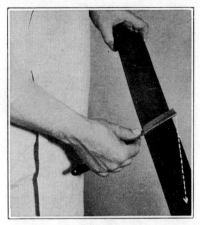

Fig. 22.

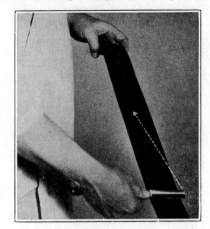

Fig. 23.

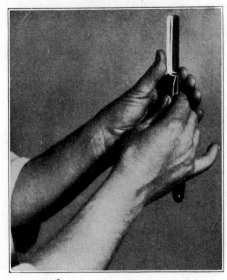

Fig. 24.

edge. (Fig. 24.) If the edge is dull it will not stick or draw. If it has the correct edge, it will have a keen, drawing sensation. This method of testing requires a great deal of experience, but eventually the razor's edge can be tested quite accurately in this manner.

When a razor is properly honed, and the knack of stropping has been perfected, one should be able to give many shaves with the same razor without rehoning, simply by stropping it before and during the shaving process.

Chapter 4

Professional Hands

B EFORE considering the acquisition of manual techniques in the application and execution of barber services, the operator must first realize that in all his work his hands are being applied directly, or indirectly through instruments, *on the living human body.*

A machinist, clerk, carpenter or anyone working with inanimate objects tries to achieve technical skill and acquire manual efficiency to produce the finest workmanship. Barbers must do more than acquire fine manual skill. They must go beyond that. They must achieve an artistry that transcends skill alone, for their hands must reflect artistic ability to their patrons, who sense their every mood.

Like actors, they must nullify any sense of indifference, carelessness or moodiness which will be distracting or displeasing, and convey care, confidence, consideration and deference to their patrons in all their work. They must at all times be considerate of their patrons' well-being, and they should strive to develop pleasant reactions to all their ministrations.

A barber, beginning with the early period of his training, should not only keep his hands scrupulously clean and well-groomed for sanitary reasons, but also he must constantly practice handling his combs, shears, razors, etc., until he has thoroughly mastered handling them, not only efficiently but also in an artistic manner. The artistic musician is an artist because he gives more than a mere correct technical interpretation of his music. In the same sense a barber must develop art in his movements.

A system of hand exercises, massaging and water therapy for the hands is recommended to limber and soften the hand tissues, and to help give them suppleness and artistic dexterity.

Following are a few suggestions for exercising the hands and fingers:

1. Place the hands in a bowl of hot water, contract and flex

them until the water becomes too uncomfortable, then take the hands out for a little while. Repeat the procedure for about five minutes.

2. Spread a generous amount of cold cream on the hands while they are still warm, work the cream in and massage the muscles with deep kneading movements.

3. Exercise the wrists by moving them alternately to and fro and sideways.

4. Exercise the fingers by first opening and closing the hands; then exercise them separately and in different combinations, so that they will become separately limber. (Figs. 25 and 26.)

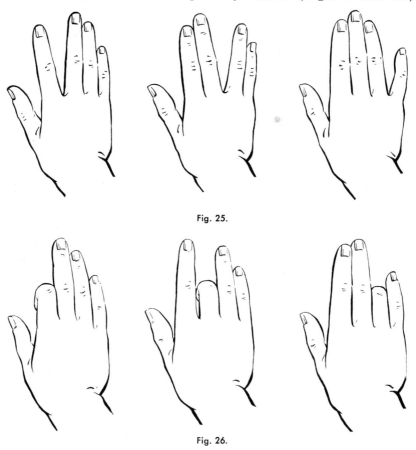

Fig. 25.

Fig. 26.

Exercises With Instruments

The student can best learn the proper technics of handling instruments by practicing exercises with the instruments.

1. Hold a razor in the positions and practice the cutting strokes as illustrated in Figs. 28 and 29.

2. Lather the side of a wide, flat glass bottle and practice cutting strokes by moving the wrist only. This will develop the proper wrist motion, and the shaved area will show the correctness of the stroke. In so far as possible, use shaving strokes explained in Chapter 5.

3. Continue the above procedure, this time executing the movements both from the wrist and elbow.

4. In order to develop the arm muscles in shear-cutting, take the shears in the right hand, hold the arm extended straight out, and move the blades slowly till the muscles become slightly tired.

5. Repeat the fourth movement. This time move the arm up and down in about a one-foot radius.

6. This time hold the comb in the left hand and the shears in the right hand, and with bended arms, as in haircutting, practice shear-cutting by moving both arms up and down together. (Fig. 73, page 70.)

7. There is no better method of developing agile and supple fingers and hands than by finger exercises on the piano. These simple exercises also develop ambidexterity. Students are urged to avail themselves of this suggestion and utilize this means of training, if possible, in order that they may ultimately take pride in knowing they possess artistic and professional hands.

Chapter 5

Shaving

T HE over-all technique of giving a shave indicates to the patron whether or not he is getting good service. The things that are noticeable to the patron with which he will find fault are: Poorly-heated lather or towels, cold fingers, dull razors, rough razors, bad breath of the barber, uncomfortable position in the chair, heavy touch of hand, unclean towels and hands, non-disinfected instruments, sharp, glaring lights overhead, and patches of hair left on the face after shave. A barber cannot command a desirable position in a shop unless he is able to give a good shave.

Before the student begins the actual practice of shaving at the chair, it is necessary to master a few fundamentals in handling the razor.

There are four standard positions for holding the razor, and four types of strokes required in order to get at all parts of the bearded portions of the face and neck with the greatest ease, efficiency and grace.

The four positions and strokes to be learned are: 1, the free-hand; 2, the back-hand; 3, the reverse free-hand, and 4, the reverse back-hand. Before describing these four strokes it is proper to explain what takes place during any kind of cutting stroke.

Everyone knows from experience that in order to cut anything well with a knife, whether it be a piece of wood or a loaf of bread, it is necessary to draw the knife through it with a slicing or sawing movement, for if one tried to press the knife directly through it, no matter how sharp the blade might be, the result would be a poor cutting job.

Through experience we also know that in order to cut whiskers perfectly with the least effort or traction on the hairs, the razor must slide over the surface at any angle with the grain of the hair. By study we know that the most efficient cutting with a razor is done with the point going forward.

The correct angle of cutting with a razor is called the *cutting stroke*. (Fig. 27.)

Technique in Handling Razor

The four strokes explained below should be practiced faithfully by the student. That is, he should hold the razor as described

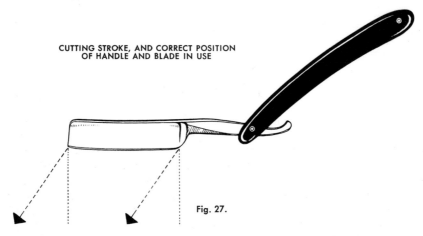

CUTTING STROKE, AND CORRECT POSITION
OF HANDLE AND BLADE IN USE

Fig. 27.

and practice the arm motions by himself for a time before attempting to use them on a patron.

No. 1. The Free-Hand

Take the razor in the right hand with the handle between the third and fourth fingers, the small finger tip resting on the tip of the tang of the razor, the thumb resting on the side of the shank near the shoulder of the blade. Never allow the thumb to slide up on the blade, as this gives an awkward appearance. The third finger should lie at the pivot of the shank and handle, and the first and second finger in front of it on the back of the shank.

Hold the elbow up near the level of the shoulder, and bend the hand at the wrist, slightly outward. Now, placing the left hand in a position in back of the blade, as if stretching the skin, make the cutting strokes about six inches in length, as shown in Fig. 28.

This is called *the free-hand* stroke.

No. 2. The Back-Hand

Place the thumb tip on the back of the shank at the pivot, and the first joint of the first finger in front of the shank next to the shoulder of the blade, the second finger bracing the pivot below the thumb, the third and fourth fingers bracing the handle just alongside the tang.

Hold the elbow slightly away from the body and turn the

razor in a position so that the end of the handle points inward. The palm will be facing inward, and the fingers will be pointing upward and inward.

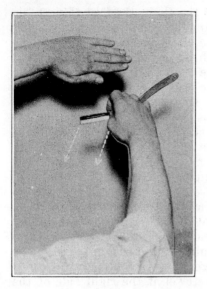

Fig. 28.

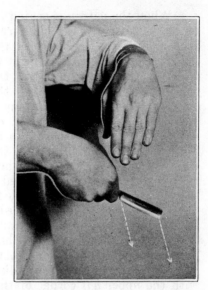

Fig. 29.

Place the left hand in back of the razor, as if stretching the skin, and make several cutting strokes outward about six inches in length. This is called *the back-hand* stroke. (Fig. 29.)

No. 3. The Reverse Free-Hand

In this case the razor is held similarly to the free-hand position, except that the hand is bent downward and the blade is directed upward.

The reverse free-hand stroke differs from the free-hand stroke, in that it is executed by a slight rotation of the wrist, with the blade describing a small arc.

No. 4. The Reverse Back-Hand

The position of holding the razor in this stroke is identically the same as that for the back-hand stroke, except that the elbow is held downward and the forearm upward. The wrist is turned in such a position that the palm and fingers are directed upward and inward.

The reverse back-hand stroke is executed by taking short, cutting strokes in a downward direction and slightly outward.

The Shave

Preparation and Standard Linen Setup

When the patron is seated in the chair, the first thing to do in regular shop practice is to arrange the chair cloth by grasping each side of the neckpiece of the cloth and placing it over the patron from the front. Do not throw it over the patron's head from the back. Make sure that the chair cloth entirely covers the clothing of the patron, but not the neck.

Adjust the head rest paper so that there will be a clean surface; also adjust the head rest to such a position that the patron will not need to stretch his neck. If the lower portion of the head rest is brought up to the level of the patron's shoulder, it will prove to be, as a rule, the most comfortable position. The release should always be pressed in when adjusting the head rest, in order to avoid making a noise from the scraping of the ratchet.

Recline the chair to a position comfortable to the patron. Avoid having the patron lie too flat or too much at a slant. Before proceeding further, wash your hands, using warm water, as warm fingers are more pliable and soothing to the patron.

Place a clean face towel diagonally over the patron's chest, with the upper *left* corner of the towel at the right side of the patron's neck. Now lift the patron's shirt at the neck with the first finger of the right hand and tuck the edge of the towel under the shirt collar with a sliding movement of the first finger of the left hand.

Cross the lower end of the towel over to the left side of the neck and tuck it under the shirt neck with a sliding movement of the forefinger of the right hand, this time without turning the patron's head. Take care that the linen is smoothly and neatly arranged. Never reach over the patron's face in adjusting the face towel, as this is apt to annoy the patron. For more protection, the face towel may be doubled before being tucked in.

(Where lather mixers are used, simply take from the mixer the required amount of lather in the hand, and proceed to lather the face.)

If the barber shop does not have individual lavatories, pick up the shaving cup and brush with the left hand, holding the thumb on the brush so that it will not fall out as it is carried to the lavatory for rinsing. Rinse the brush and mug thoroughly with warm water, leaving enough water to make a creamy lather. If too hot water is used for making the lather, the lather will dry more quickly than if medium warm water is used. Carry the cup back to the workstand and mix up a lather with the brush until the lather forms into a correct, creamy consistency. Avoid making noise by rattling the handle of the shaving brush on the sides of the mug.

Apply the lather to the face with a rotary movement of the brush, starting on the neck just below the jaw bone on the patron's right side. Hold the brush in such a way that the handle rests in the palm of the hand, with the first two fingers of the hand dipped into the bristles. The purpose of this is to control the bristles, thus avoiding getting soap in the patron's nostrils, ears and mouth. (Fig. 30.)

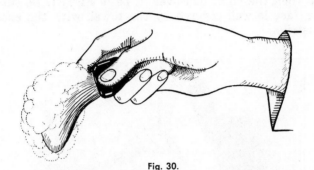

Fig. 30.

After the bearded portion of the face has been covered thoroughly with the lather, hold the brush in one hand and, using the cushion tips of the fingers of the other hand, with a light rotary movement proceed to work the lather into the beard. Avoid a hard, scrubbing movement or use of the backs of the fingers or knuckles in lathering the beard. The hand holding the brush is used to turn the patron's head by grasping the head near the crown. Never turn the head by pushing or grasping the forehead, or allow the hand to rest on the forehead while lathering the beard, as this is annoying to the patron.

The amount of time required for rubbing the beard depends upon its stiffness and density. However, a well-lathered face is an essential of a good shave. Lather packs between the hair shafts and helps to keep them erect, against the slicing stroke of the razor. The rubbing of lather into the beard causes the lather, by its chemical reaction and the mechanical action of rubbing, to detach dirt, hardened oil or any other foreign substances from the face and beard, holding these substances suspended within the soap film. Another important reason for lathering is that the lather film on the skin acts as a lubricant, making it easy for the razor to slide over the face.

Now place the brush back in the cup, and prepare a steam

towel. This is done by folding a clean turkish towel lengthwise; then fold it again by bringing both ends of the folded towel together. Hold it under the faucet and soak it well with hot water. The towel must not be so hot that it will cause discomfort to the patron. Also be sure that the towel is evenly heated, as a towel half hot and half cold feels very disagreeable to the patron.

Wring out the towel thoroughly and carry it folded in the left hand to a position in back of the chair. With both hands above the patron, unfold the towel near the point of the chin and adjust it carefully over the face, placing the left end down on the forehead, and then the right end over it, as in Fig. 31. Be sure that the entire face is well covered by the towel, with the exception of the nostrils.

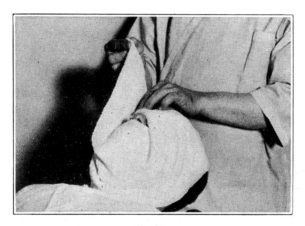

Fig. 31.

The purpose of steaming the face is to further wet and soften the cuticle or outside layer of the hair. The heat of the towel also stimulates the flow of the sebaceous and sudoriferous glands in the skin, causing the oils and sweat to come to the surface, and giving added lubrication for the razor as it passes over the face.

While the face is being steamed, strop the razor. After it is stropped it should be dipped in sterilizing fluid and then placed in the sterilizing cabinet, never in the pocket of the shirt or smock. Remove the towel by grasping the ends on the forehead, one in each hand, and with a soothing, stroking movement wipe first the forehead, then over the eyes, using both hands simultaneously; then over the temples and sides of face; then around the crevices of the nose and mouth; then over the chin, then down the sides of the neck until the soap has been completely removed.

Fold the towel neatly, and for sanitary reasons place it on a sterile paper towel, either on the stand or lavatory.

The face now needs to be relathered. Be sure the lather is still comfortably warm, or warm it again by adding hot water.

After the lathering is completed, wipe the hands free of any soap. Take the razor from the cabinet, open it and grasp it properly, and assume a position at the right side of the patron. Tear a piece of lather paper from the roll at the head rest, about four by six inches, and place it on the patron's chest, with one corner tucked under the face towel. Now proceed with the shave.

Movement No. 1

This is a free hand movement. Before taking this stroke, however, first turn the patron's head gently to the left, and with a finger of the left hand clear the lather away from the side outline of the hair and front of the ear.

Place the edge of the razor in position to make the correct side outline and take a short free hand stroke. Continue with these strokes until the right side of the face has been shaved down to the jaw bone, firmly but gently stretching the skin with the thumb of the left hand, as indicated in Fig. 32. This stroke is a gliding, cutting stroke, from point to heel of the razor.

Movement No. 2

Deposit on the lather paper the lather that has accumulated on the blade, using the center of the paper, as lather on the edges of the lather paper gives an unsightly appearance.

Grasp the razor in the back-hand position and shave the

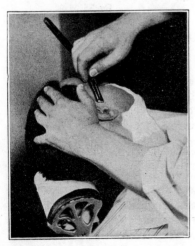

Fig. 32.

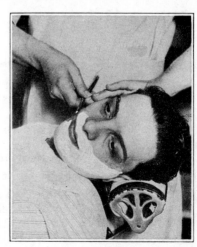

Fig. 33.

area from the angle of the mouth to the right tip of the chin with back-hand strokes, stretching the skin with the left hand, as indicated in Fig. 33. Be sure to shave the angle of the mouth clean with this stroke.

Movement No. 3

Clean the lather from the razor again, and, holding the razor in the free-hand position, shave the right side of the upper lip, stretching the skin between the thumb and second finger of the left hand, placing the second finger on the tip of the nose and the thumb at the angle of the mouth, as in Fig. 34.

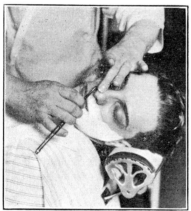
Fig. 34.

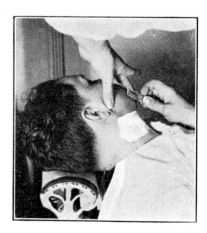
Fig. 35.

Movement No. 4

Without cleaning the razor this time, shave that portion just beneath the right jaw bone, near the chin, on the right side. With the same free-hand and gliding stroke shave down with the grain of the beard to the line where the grain is reversed. (Fig. 35.)

Movement No. 5

Shift to a position back of the chair. Hold the razor in the reverse free-hand position and shave the right side of the lower part of the neck upward, stretching the skin with the left hand, shifting the left hand into position with each stroke of the razor, as shown in Fig. 36. (Note: On some patrons the grain of the beard continues downward and requires use of Movement No. 4.)

Movement No. 6

Clean the razor off the third time, strop and sterilize it. Relather the left side of the face. Experienced barbers do this by grasping the lather brush in the same hand in which the razor is held.

Take a position at the right side of the patron, hold the razor in a back-hand position, stretch the upper lip by lifting the tip of the nose lightly with the thumb and second finger of the

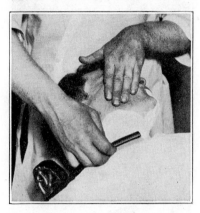

Fig. 36.

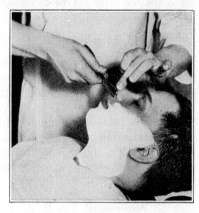

Fig. 37.

left hand, and shave the center and at least half of the left side of the upper lip. (Fig. 37.)

Movement No. 7

Turn the patron's face gently to the right. Clear the lather

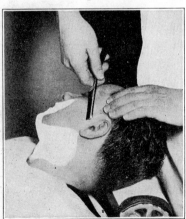

Fig. 38.

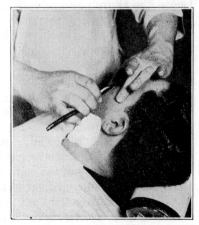

Fig. 39.

from the hairline of the left side outline and in front of the ear. Outline the left hairline and shave the left side of the face with a back-hand stroke, stretching the skin with the left hand. Note that it will be necessary to stand back of the chair in order to execute the stroke easily. (Fig. 38.)

Movement No. 8

Shift position to the right side of the patron again. Clean the razor again, and proceed with a free-hand movement to shave the rest of the left side of the face to the tip of the chin, as shown at left, using the thumb and second finger to stretch the skin. (Fig. 39.)

Movement No. 9

Clean the razor again, and change the position of the razor for back-hand strokes. Shave the area below the jaw on the left side with downward, back-hand strokes, stretching the skin between the thumb and fingers, as shown in Fig. 40, shaving with the grain to the line where the grain is reversed.

Movement No. 10

Clean the razor again and take a position behind the chair. Change the position of the razor to the reverse free-hand, and shave the left side of the neck with upward strokes as far as the grain grows upward, stretching the skin between thumb and second finger of left hand, as in Fig. 41. (Note: On some patrons

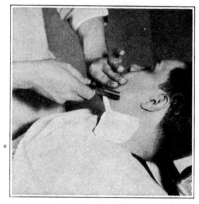

Fig. 40.

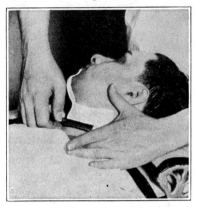

Fig. 41.

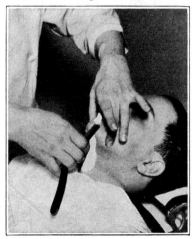

Fig. 42.

the grain of the beard continues downward, requiring the use of Movement No. 9.)

Movement No. 11

Change position back to the right side again, strop and sterilize the razor, and apply more lather. Hold the razor in the free-hand position, stretch the skin over the chin between the thumb and second finger tightly (Fig. 42), and shave the beard with free-hand strokes across the tip of the chin—the first stroke with the point of the razor, the next a little lower on the blade, and so on, until the entire chin has been shaved. The last stroke ends about a half-inch or so below the chin, leaving a clean area from which to start the next movement.

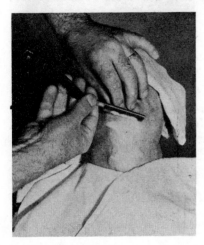 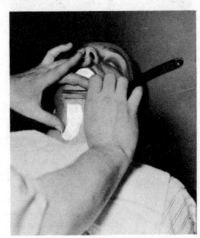

Fig. 43.   Fig. 43A.

Movement No. 12

The area of the face just below the chin is shaved with a back-hand stroke. The finger tips of the left hand stretch the skin by rolling it upward over the chin bone, as shown in Fig. 43. Shave with a graceful back-hand stroke down to the point where the direction of the hairs turn upward. This movement may be performed with free-hand technique (Fig. 43-A).

Movement No. 13

Shift your position to the back of the patron, and shave the bottom of the neck with reverse free-hand strokes upward, following the grain of the beard. Stretch the skin between thumb and second finger of left hand. (Fig. 44.) (Note: On some patrons the grain of the beard continues downward, requiring use of Movement No. 12.)

Movement No. 14

Stretch the skin of the lower lip downward over the chin with first finger of the left hand, and finish the shave with a few

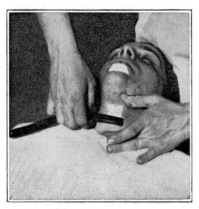

Fig. 44.

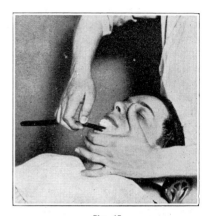

Fig. 45.

short reverse free-hand upward strokes at the lower lip. (Fig. 45.) During Movements No. 13 and No. 14 the barber should avoid breathing into the patron's face, and should likewise avoid receiv-

OUTLINE OF SHAVE MOVEMENTS
A.M.B.B.A. STANDARD

Position	Movement	Direction	Area
1	Free-hand	Down	Right sideburn
2	Back-hand	Down	Right side of cheek, to chin
3	Free-hand	Down	Right upper lip
4	Free-hand	Down	Right side, below jaw
5	Free-hand	*Up or down	Right side of neck
6	Back-hand	Down	Left upper lip
7	Back-hand	Down	Left sideburn
8	Free-hand	Down	Left side of cheek
9	Back-hand	Down	Left side, below jaw
10	Free-hand	**Up or down	Left side of neck
11	Free-hand	Left to right	Across chin
12	Back-hand, or Free-hand	Down	Below chin
13	Free-hand	**Up or down	Middle of neck
14	Free-hand	Up	Lower lip

*Beard must be shaved with the grain.
**Free-hand if shaved up. Back-hand if shaved down.

ing the patron's breath himself, for this is equally annoying and unhealthful to patron and barber alike.

Clean the razor thoroughly, and in doing so fold the lather paper once in half and leave it in its former position.

These fourteen movements constitute what is termed the "once-over of the shave." Some patrons will ask for just a "once-over" shave. In that case a few more strokes than usual may be taken, in order to insure a complete shave, at the completion of the above movements.

However, in all cases one should strive to make the "once-over" as complete and clean as possible, for this will be a good habit that will speed up the shaving service.

If a "once-over" is all that is wanted, proceed from this point with the finish explained further on; otherwise continue with the second part of the shave.

Second Time Over

As soon as the first 14 movements have been completed, lay the razor aside and apply the second steam towel. Then, while the face is steaming, strop the razor for the third time.

After the razor has been stropped, sterilize it and place it in the sterilizing cabinet. Remove the steam towel, in the same manner as before, being sure that all the excess soap is removed from the patron's face. Fold the towel and replace it on the sterile paper previously provided. Never *throw* the steam towel onto the lavatory or work stand, and always pay heed to sanitary procedure.

With the razor palmed, pick up the water bottle with the free thumb and first two fingers and sprinkle a little water in the

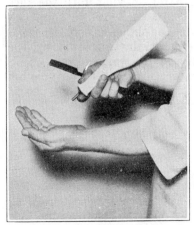

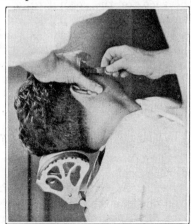

Fig. 46.   Fig. 47.

cupped palm of the left hand. (Fig. 46.) Moisten the bearded area of the face with this water. Take care that the water does not trickle down on the patron's neck. Place the bottle back on the work stand and then proceed to shave the second time over.

A great deal of precaution should be taken in shaving the second time over, especially with a tender face. It is best to begin on the right side of the face by placing the second finger of the left hand over the cheekbone and the thumb near the ear, stretching the skin in this manner and shaving the beard with a free-hand stroke sidewise to the grain of the beard. (See Fig. 47.)

Then proceed to shave the upper lip, working downward to the lower jaw bone, carefully shaving the angles of the mouth; then on the lower part of the neck, following the grain of the beard. Then use the reverse free-hand on the lower portion of the right side of the neck if the grain of the beard grows upwards.

Now turn the head of the patron toward the right and proceed to shave the other side of the face in the same manner, but stretching the skin away from the ear in the first movement with the first three fingers. Only the free-hand and reverse free-hand are needed for the entire face during the second time over.

Be cautious in shaving the second time over across the chin, just beneath the lower lip, the lower portion of the neck and around the Adam's apple, as these portions of the face are usually the most tender and sensitive, and are easily irritated by close shaving. Never give a real close shave to any patron unless it is by his own request.

In order to avoid dry shaving, a sufficient amount of water should be used on the patron's face in shaving the second time over. In some shops a finishing or vanishing cream is used on the face for the second time over. After shaving until the face feels smooth, and no patches of the beard can be felt by the touch of the hand, the patron is ready for the finish. Clean the razor thoroughly, sterilize it, place it in the cabinet, and discard the lather paper. Cleanse the face with a moist, warm towel.

It must be understood that the foregoing outline for shaving is a standard procedure, but it may be amplified by the use of specialized creams used in conjunction with lather.

Finishing the Shave

The finish given in this lesson is used as a standard in most barber shops.

Place a small quantity of face cream in the palm of the left hand and rub both hands together until the cream is spread over the palms and fingers of both hands. Apply the cream to the face by manipulating with both hands with smooth, stroking movements over the entire face, using long, even strokes with the palm and cushion tips of the hands and fingers. Avoid short, jerky or slapping strokes, as they are annoying to most patrons.

Now apply another evenly-heated steam towel. After a few seconds, press gently with the fingers of each hand on the nerve centers over the eyes, at the temples, on the chin and sides of the neck. (Fig. 124, page 180.) Then remove the towel in same manner as before.

This is the proper time to suggest a facial to the patron. (Facials will be described in another chapter.)

After the steam towel has been removed, pick up the bottle containing the after-shaving lotion with the right hand and sprinkle some of the lotion into the cupped palm of the left hand. Replace bottle on stand. Carry the lotion to a position at the back of the chair; pour the excess lotion from the left hand to the right hand, rubbing both hands together, and immediately apply the lotion to the face, in order to avoid spilling.

With a graceful, sweeping movement spread the lotion with both hands, first on the shaved portion of the face, then over the forehead, around the eyes and over the nose. The lotion must be mildly astringent and antiseptic. Witch-hazel is an ideal and popular lotion used in the majority of shops. Witch-hazel may have boric acid, or both boric and salicylic acid, dissolved in it. The correct proportion is 30 to 60 grains of boric acid, and about 3 to 5 grains of salicylic acid, to a pint of witch-hazel. This increases its astringent and antiseptic action.

Now pick up the loose ends of the face towel, fold it over the chin if the patron has a mustache, and underneath the nose if he does not have a mustache. Press and stroke over it with both hands with a medium firm pressure, in order to absorb some of the lotion. Never slap the hands down on the towel, as this jars the patron's head. The towel should be stroked as if blotting the face with the towel. Then take the towel up, spread it out and make a towel pad by wrapping a dry portion of the towel around the right hand. This is done as follows:

Fold the face towel lengthwise and grasp one end between the first and second fingers of the right hand and the other end with the thumb and first two fingers of the left hand. (Fig. 48.) Now bring the side held by the left hand diagonally across the palm of the right hand held upward; then continue with the left hand around to the back of the right, turning the right hand so the palm turns downward.

Then twist the left hand away, bringing the twisted end of the towel around the thumb of the right hand, finally bringing this portion of the towel between the thumb and first finger of the

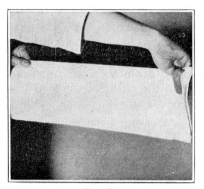

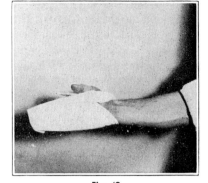

Fig. 48.   Fig. 49.

right hand, pressing the thumb against the towel to hold it in place. Now release the left hand.

Then, with the left hand, tuck the end of the towel at the finger tips backward between the second and third fingers of the right hand. This makes a soft, neat pad, for both drying the face and for applying powder. (Fig. 49.)

Dry the entire face thoroughly, especially the corners of the eyes and angles of the mouth, crevices of the nose, and inside and behind the ears. Change the arrangement of the towel on the hand as often as needed, in order to always have a dry surface.

A hand fan may be used to complete the drying of the face. Some barbers use the towel for this purpose. However, a fan dries the damp face more rapidly. Care should be taken to fan far enough away from the patron's face, to avoid striking him.

Sprinkle and spread a small quantity of powder on a dry portion of the towel. Carry the powdered towel to a position at the side of the patron. Spread the chair cloth up to protect the garments. Start below the chin and right side of the neck, and continue to spread the powder carefully and evenly over the entire face. Do not dab the powder on, as that will leave spots of powder on the face.

Place the face towel finally in the left hand, and raise the patron slowly to a sitting position.

The Neck Shave

In preparation for the neck shave, tuck the face towel around the back of the neck inside the patron's collar band. Only with a haircut is a complete hair outline shave given. The neck shave accompanying the standard shave consists only of shaving the neckline on the back of the neck below the ears.

Warm lather should be used in shaving the neck, after ascertaining the style of neck shave the patron desires. It may be necessary to stretch the skin with the first two fingers or thumb of the left hand in certain areas, especially when the patron has a thin neck, or where there are moles or scars to be avoided.

Cuts or Scratches. If the skin should be cut during the shave or neck shave, clean the area gently with sterile cotton, then apply a very small amount of powdered or liquid styptic to stop any bleeding, before continuing with the shaving procedure.

When finished with the razor, place it in the sterilizer. Wipe the neck with a damp towel, then dry it with the face towel. *Dry thoroughly—but gently.* Now replace the towel around the neck and run the cushion tips of the fingers up through the hair, giving a scalp manipulation for just a moment.

At this point the desirability of a professional scalp manipulation, hair dressing or hair tonic may be suggested to the patron.

Combing the hair is next in order, using the brush in the left hand and comb in the right hand. (Fig. 50.) Care should

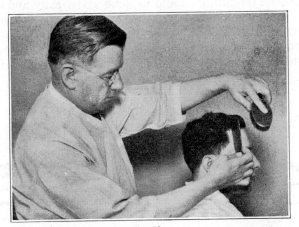

Fig. 50.

be taken to part the hair correctly. Avoid handling the comb and brush in such a manner that they scratch the scalp. This is very annoying to the patron. Combing the hair is the final finish, and a neatly combed head of hair is pleasing to the patron. This helps bring him back to your chair the next time he desires barber service. (Note: Better class shops have eliminated the use of a hair brush entirely, for sanitary reasons.)

Now make out a check for the amount of service the patron has received.

Remove the towels from the back of the neck and also remove any loose hairs, lint, face powder, etc., that may have fallen upon the clothing of the patron. Also gently "towel" the forehead, tip of the nose and behind the ears. Comb out the mustache if the patron has one. Grasp each side of the chair cloth and gracefully remove it. (Do not jerk the chair cloth off the patron.)

Hand the check to the patron as he leaves the chair, and thank him.

If there are no patrons waiting, fold your chair cloth neatly and place it over the arm of the chair, being sure that the neck piece of the chair cloth is exposed, in order that it can be easily spread apart for use on the next patron.

Mustache Trimming

Mustache trimming is one of those services that has many possibilities, and it offers the barber an opportunity to display his skill on this type of masculine adornment. It is always possible that he can suggest an improvement of the style to which the patron is accustomed.

Mustache trimming should be done artistically and carefully, for it is obvious that the patron with a mustache is very particular, since a mustache is worn not for utility, but as a personal adornment. A face towel should be placed across the eyes when giving this service, to protect the eyes against any flying hairs.

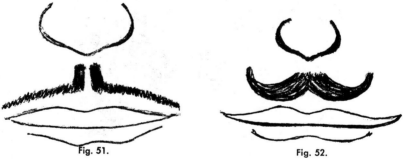

Fig. 51.   Fig. 52.

Mustache styles are almost endless in number, each patron having his own individual preference. For this reason this Textbook offers no special instructions other than to remind the barber that if he displays good judgment in this phase of his work he is apt to gain many steady patrons as a result of his contribution to the patron's appearance.

The student barber should pay particular attention to this item, for early study of correct technique on mustache trimming will repay him many times over when he gets into the active practice of barbering among a discriminating clientele.

Mustache shaping is done with the razor during the shave as much as possible. Then at the end of the shave it is used for final shaping, after required trimming has been done with the shears. (See pages 52, 53, 54, 55 and 56.)

The student barber must learn the fundamentals of trimming beards, as it is a service that he will be called upon to perform when serving the public. Pages 52 through 56 show basic types of beards, and from these basic structures are created the various types of beards worn by men. The student must first study the beard types, and then learn *by doing* under the close supervision of his instructor. Care should be taken by the student to keep the beard hairs too long rather than too short when first learning to trim beards—more hair can always be removed, but cutting the hairs shorter than intended will result in a poor beard trim and a dissatisfied patron.

VAN DYKE   VAN DYKE WITH SIDE BURNS

ABE LINCOLN BEARD   OLD DUTCH

The pictures on this page and pages 53 to 56 are from the "Modern Beards and Hair Styles" chart, published by the Associated Master Barbers and Beauticians of Colorado. The chart measures 18x24 inches, and can be ordered from The Master Barber & Beautician Magazine, 537 S. Dearborn St., Chicago 5, Ill., at $4 each. Send remittance with order. Allow 10 days for delivery.

CONNECTED SHORT BEARD

LIP GOATEE

FORMAL POINTED GOATEE

FORMAL GOATEE

SHORT MUTTON CHOP

ANCHOR BEARD

RING BEARD

FLAT BOTTOM GOATEE

LONG VAN DYKE WITH EXPOSED CHIN

CONNECTED MUTTON CHOP

TAILORED FRENCH FORK WITHOUT
MUSTACHE

LONG VAN DYKE

MODERN ABE LINCOLN

OLD SOUTHERN COLONEL

FULL BEARD

FRENCH OR ENGLISH FORK

OUTLINE OF SANITARY PROCEDURE

Personal Cleanliness and Attire

1. Bathe daily.
2. Keep freshly shaved. Have your hair trimmed each week.
3. Brush the teeth daily and keep breath clean at all times.
4. Keep nails clipped short, and hands and nails clean at all times.
5. Keep shoes shined.
6. Keep clothes clean and pressed at all times.
7. Wear clean uniform or smock while on duty.

Sanitary Procedure in Work

General

1. Seat patron facing workstand in order that he may view your procedure in the mirror.
2. Place chair cloth over patron (don't permit it to touch the skin).
3. Place all instruments to be used on the patron in the wet sterilizer. (Immerse razor, clipper blades, shears, comb, tweezers, etc., in the solution.)
4. Wash the hands with soap and water and dry them with a clean towel, in full view of the patron.

The Shave

1. Recline the patron and place the standard linen setup for the shave.
2. Lather the face and apply the first steam towel.
3. Strop the razor and re-immerse it in sterilizing solution. (The time that elapses while the face is being steamed and re-lathered is sufficient for completely sterilizing the razor.)
4. Relather and shave the face the first time over with the sterilized razor.
5. Strop the razor in preparation for the second time over and again immerse it in sterilizing solution.
6. Apply the second steam towel, sponging off the face.
7. Shave the second time over with the sterilized razor, and on finishing replace the razor in the sterilizing solution in preparation for further use. (Usually the patron's neck will need shaving.)

The Haircut

1. Place the standard linen setup for the haircut.
2. Using sterilized instruments, proceed to cut the hair. When

finished, clean and sterilize the instruments and place them in the sterilizing cabinet.

3. Remove the loose hairs, preferably with sterile towel, tissue or compressed air. *(Neck dusters are not recommended, for sanitary reasons.)*

The Neck Shave

1. Place the standard linen setup for the neck shave. Strop the razor and immerse it in the sterilizing solution.
2. Lather the neck and proceed to shave it with the freshly sterilized razor.
3. When all service is completed, clean and sterilize all instruments and place them in the dry sterilizer or sterilizing cabinet.

EACH HAIRCUT A CREATION

The barber should, before he begins work on a patron, create a picture in his mind of the kind of haircut that will be most becoming to the patron.

If the hair is cut to sculpture the lines of the head gracefully, it will prove that the work has been done by a barber who knows his business—one who is capable of emphasizing the proper contour lines and minimizing the bad ones.

Give the kind of haircut that will capitalize to best advantage the various features of each patron's head and face, and thus set him apart from other people as a distinctive individual.

Chapter 6

Haircutting

The Standard Linen Setup

THE FIRST factor that must be considered is a standard method of arranging the linen before the haircut is started, because it is important that no hairs fall on the patron's clothes. A *standard* method should be adopted for practical reasons, good form, and sanitation purposes.

During waits between patrons the chair cloth, which covers and protects the patron, should be neatly folded and placed over the left arm of the chair in such a way that the neckband is exposed to assure easy handling.

When the patron is seated in the chair, the chair cloth is picked up by its neckband and unfolded, the right and left hands of the operator grasping the ends of the U-shaped neck. With one smooth, graceful movement the chair cloth should be spread across the patron's shoulders from the front, being sure that the neckband of the chair cloth does not come in contact with the patron's skin.

The chair cloth should not be spread over the patron's head from the back. Once placed, it should entirely cover his clothing.

A clean towel or paper neckstrip should be placed around the patron's neck. If a towel is used, place one side-edge horizontally across the patron's back just high enough on the neck so that it can be tucked in about two inches under his collar. Then the two bottom corners are to be picked up, the towel folded so that the bottom edge is placed high up on the neck, the ends being brought forward around the neck, overlapped at the front of the neck, and held there momentarily with the left hand. With the right hand the operator then picks up the chair cloth. It is placed around the neck, overlapped at the back, and fastened with a pin or snap. Finally the towel is neatly folded down over the neckband of the chair cloth.

This setup must be smooth and snug-fitting for good protec-

tion, but never so tight that it may cause any discomfort to the patron. If a neckstrip is used it should also be neatly folded down over the neckband of the chair cloth.

Technique of Handling Instruments

THE CLIPPER. The student must first master the technique of handling the hand clipper before attempting to use electric clippers. The advantage in this lies in the fact that the hand clipper is a much slower-cutting instrument, and therefore the co-ordination of muscular movements involved can be perfected with less danger of overcutting while learning. Some artists prefer to use hand clippers exclusively.

In most instances the expert barber uses clippers to lay the foundation for shaping the haircut. For that reason clipper work should receive the thoughtful study of the student, for in his manipulation of this instrument lies the power of either perfecting or marring the finished job. A maximum of skill in the use of the clipper not only insures a better cut, but it also reduces the amount of time that must be spent on a haircut.

The most difficult phase of clipper work for the student to learn is to guide the clipper into the hair properly and at the right speed. The tension of the blades and spring on a hand clipper should be so adjusted that the handles may be manipulated easily, with the blades springing back to their normal position after each cut without undue friction.

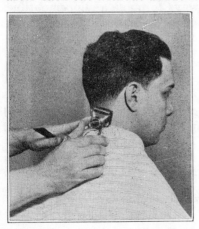

Fig. 53.

The proper method of holding a hand clipper is to place the entire thumb along the stationary handle, the thumb brace being in the recess between the thumb and first finger. Grasp the movable handle in such a manner that the small projecting guide on it lies between the first and second fingers, the fingers grasping the entire handle at about the first joint. To guide the clipper more steadily, place the index finger of the left hand on the clipper near the set screw. (Figs. 53 and 54.)

The purpose of holding the thumb along the clipper in this fashion is to give it firm stability, for it is very important, in the cutting process, that the blades pass straight through the hair, free from any side-to-side movement. Another important point in

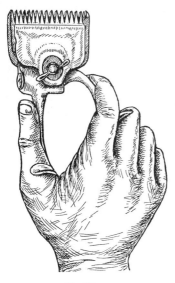

using the clipper is to take a full stroke with the moving handle so that the cutting blade moves the entire distance across the stationary blade. Do not move the clipper into the hair too rapidly, for then the clipper will pull.

The student should first take clipper exercises on a model head made of wood or some other kind of material until the movements become free and easy. In this way the arm and hand muscles involved will acquire necessary strength and dexterity.

One of the hardest knacks to acquire in the actual clipping technique is to make the proper taper instead of an abrupt, sharp clipper line. If a gradual, even taper is cut

Fig. 54.

with the clipper, the foundation for a well-shaped haircut is laid, and a great deal of shears and comb work is eliminated. (See necklines, page 68.)

Correct method of making clipper taper

Clipper Blades

Fig. 55.

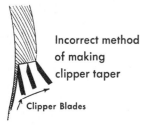

Incorrect method of making clipper taper

Clipper Blades

Fig. 56.

Figs. 55 and 56 show the right and wrong ways to make a clipper outline.

In order to make a gradual taper, tip the clipper blades down and start at the base of the neck. At the point where the taper is to begin, slowly and gradually tilt the clipper so that the still blade first becomes flat against the skin. Gradually continue to tilt it until the clipper rides on the heel of the still blade. Keep the cutting blade constantly in motion as it passes through the hair in order to avoid unevenness.

The Technique of Using the Electric Clipper

The use of the electric clipper is usually taught only after the student has become proficient in the use of the hand clipper. The electric clipper is an excellent time and labor saving device.

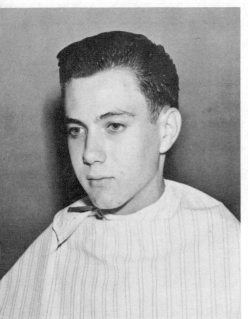

A

B

C

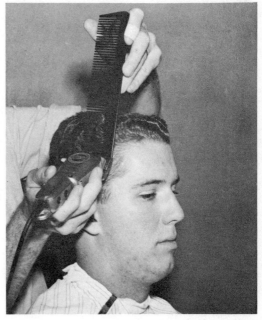

D

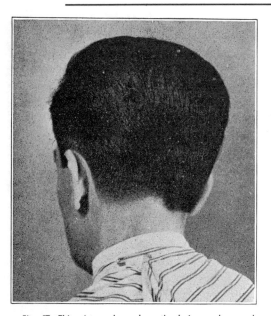

Fig. 57. This picture shows how the hair can be evenly tapered with the clipper, saving much shear and comb work. Taken when the neck was only half clipped, it illustrates the before-and-after appearance of the hair.

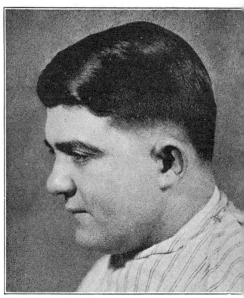

Fig. 58. This picture shows the haircut after the clipp shear and comb work have been done, but the finger wo not yet completed. Care must be taken to evenly blend shear and comb work with the clipper work.

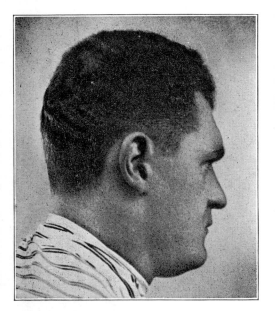

Fig. 59. In this haircut the 00 clipper was used on the back of the neck and the No. 1 clipper in front of and over the ears. This is a very popular haircut, especially with the patron with kinky or coarse, wavy hair.

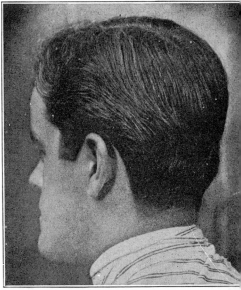

Fig. 60. The clipper was not used in this haircut, only shears and comb. Many patrons with very heavy, straight bushy hair desire this style and will patronize the barber w can trim hair with such finesse.

Fig. 61. The 00 clipper was used on the back of the neck, and the shears and comb in front of and over the ears. This style, with the hair combed back above the ears, is very becoming for the patron with dark, wavy hair.

Fig. 62. The long pompadour is an ever-popular style for men and boys. This style is becoming to the patron with the average-shaped head, and who has fine, silky or soft-looking hair.

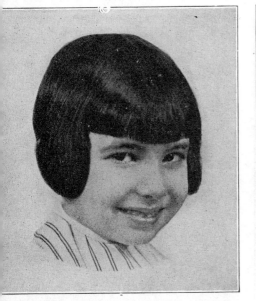

Fig. 63. Children's haircuts with bangs are becoming, and the operator who can cut bangs to the proper contour of the child's face will win many child patrons. Corrugated shears are excellent for trimming bangs.

Fig. 64. This style of ladies' hairdress requires both trimming and waving, which brings the patron to the shop more often. This means more revenue for the barber and beauty shop.

Figs. 65-66. In this long trim haircut the 000 was used on the neck and tapered out with the No. 1 clipper, comb and shee Shears and comb were used on the sides and top.

Fig. 67. In this haircut the 000 clipper was used on the neck and a coarser blade used on the sides, then tapered out short with the clipper, comb and shears.

Fig. 68. This is a medium pompadour. The 000 clipp was used on the neck, with No. 1 blades on the sid Shears and comb were used to taper the haircut.

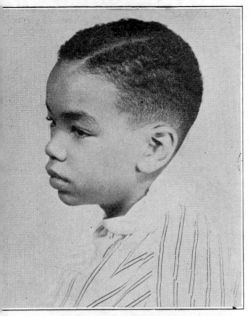 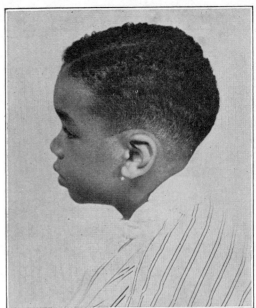

Figs. 69-70. The 000 clipper was used on the neck and the No. 1 on the sides about ¾-inch above the ears, and tapered out with comb and shears. Razor was used to make the outline.

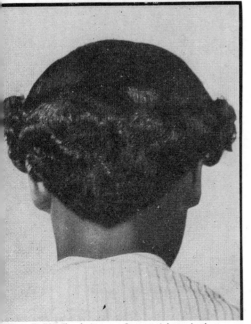 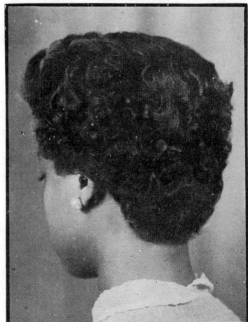

Figs. 71-72. The hair was first straightened, then permanent-waved and trimmed. The back may be cut either with a point or rounded, plus a variety of modifications to suit the patron. Photos through courtesy of T. N. Barnes Barber Supply, Co., Philadelphia, Pa.

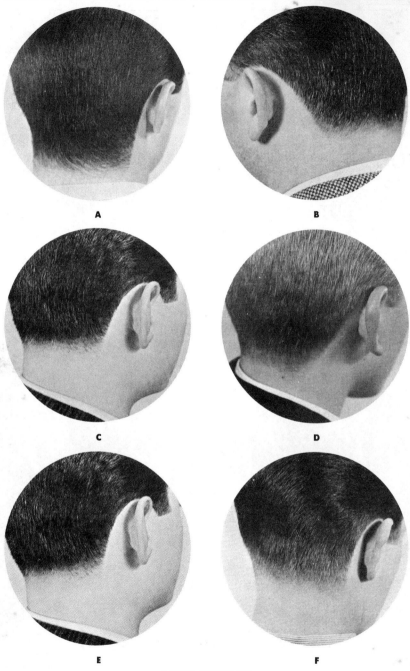

NECK OUTLINES

But it must always be remembered that, though it adds to the speed and ease of a barber's work, it is neither a substitute for artistry, nor does it add to a barber's artistic ability. (Fig. 6.)

The electric clipper is held lightly in the right hand and merely guided through the hair, since electric power moves the cutting blades.

The electric clipper work is started by placing the clipper lightly on the skin at the hairline, with the bottom plane of the teeth flat against the skin surface.

In this position it is guided slowly upward, with very little pressure on the skin, to the point where the clipper outline or taper begins. At this point the clipper is gradually tilted on its heel so that the teeth move gradually away from the skin to form a graduated length of hair. (See outlines, page 68.)

When the clipper work as described is completed, it is advisable to complete the haircut with the shears and comb.

For some types of cuts with high clippings, where one wishes to continue tapering with the clipper, there are two methods that may be followed, depending on the type of clipper used. When standard blades are used, the clipper work is continued by clipping over a comb. In this case the shaping is guided by the comb, as in shears and comb work. When adjustable blades are used, the work is continued merely by adjusting the cutting depth of the blades.

Some operators prefer to use a larger gauge hand clipper to complete the initial tapering. Others prefer starting the clipper work with a larger gauge clipper, then switching to the close-cutting clipper. Starting at the hairlines, the hair is removed up to the outline previously made by the larger gauge clipper.

Shears and Comb Work

The correct method of holding the shears is illustrated in

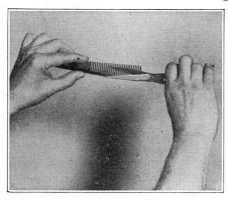

Fig. 73.

Fig. 73. The thumb and third finger lie in the grips, the small finger being on the finger brace and the first and second fingers bracing the shank. The comb is held in the left hand, the teeth pointing upward. The first finger is placed on the fine teeth near the center of the comb. The thumb is placed on the back of the comb just below the first finger. The other three fingers are bent over the fine part of the comb, holding it steady with the balls of the fingers. This position permits the comb to be turned easily in the left hand when the hair is to be combed downward. It is essential to practice turning the comb in the left hand, for, if the student becomes proficient in this, it will speed up his haircutting.

In practicing haircutting, grasp the comb in the left hand as shown in Fig 73, and, holding it parallel to the shear blades, begin working the shears; at the same time move slowly upward, as if cutting hair. This will develop perfect co-ordination of arm and hand movements. Always keep the shears and comb moving.

In cutting hair the barber should always stand slightly to the left of the point where the shear work is being done on the patron's hair. The right arm will then be extended, the shears pointing to the left. In this way he always commands an easy view of the exact point of contact with the hair.

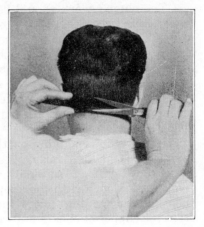

Fig. 74.

While working the shears, place the third finger and thumb in the grips at an angle. This will enable the barber, as he closes the shears, to exert a pressure that will bring the blades toward each other, thus maintaining a grip on the hair between the blades and insuring against any of it slipping. The finger should never be held straight, but should be bent slightly, as shown in Fig. 74.

Types of Haircuts

When instructing students or apprentices it is necessary to teach certain standardized types of haircuts which have been established among barbers through long usage. In order to give the student and teacher a basis to work on, six basic cuts or styles are designated. These are not proposed as specific standards, for each style may vary to suit the patron's individual choice and its suitability for his physical features.

The six styles are as follows: (1) The short cut, also called full crown; (2) the medium cut, also called half crown; (3) the long cut or trim (each of the three preceding styles may have a side or middle part); (4) the short pompadour, usually designated the "short pomp"; (5) the medium pompadour; (6) the long pompadour. The last two styles also may be parted. Butch, crew and flattop haircuts may be termed variations of the basic pompadours. (See pages 79, 80, 81.)

The Short Cut

In this cut the clipper is used on the sides and back of head. There is no absolute rule designating where the clipper taper should be, for this may vary with the patron's wish. This cut is very popular for small boys in the summertime. The average height of the clipper taper is about an inch or so below the crown in the back, and continues forward on both sides at the same height. A good example is the clipper work in Fig. 79.

The clipper work should begin at the right temple and continue around the head, to be finished at the left temple; in other words, clipping should be from right to left. Remember to tilt the clipper teeth outward at the point where the gradual taper begins. With shears and comb begin shearing at the right temple at the taper line. Continue the shears-and-comb work from right to left, finishing at the left temple. Some barbers reverse this technique and work from left to right. Either method is acceptable.

If the hair remaining on the head after the clipper work is completed is long and heavy, feed the hair through the coarse end of the comb, cutting from the top hair down, until the shears-and-comb work blends with the clipper work; then use the fine end of the comb for shading. There should not be any ridges left, either from the clipper or shears-and-comb work. An even, gradual taper, giving a smooth blended appearance, is desired.

Comb technique must be acquired, for if the hair is not picked up properly, and the comb is not held the proper distance from the head in certain cuts, unevenness will be the result. The comb should be tilted with the teeth slightly outward from the head. This will prevent the hair from slipping away from the comb, and in fine or close haircutting it avoids the likelihood of making ridges or niches.

Another fact that should be remembered by the operator is that *short* hair held in the comb should be cut with one cut of the shears. Do not make several cuts, as this may leave the hair uneven. It is also a waste of time.

In the extreme short cut, little or no finger work is necessary, for all hair above the clipper work may easily be cut over the comb.

The Medium Cut

The medium cut differs from the short cut, principally in length. In a medium cut the clipper is usually used all around the head, but not as high as in the short cut. It is used from a quarter of an inch to half an inch above the ears, and the clipper work in this case does not run horizontally around the head. Instead, it is gradually lowered from a quarter of an inch to an inch at the back of the head. (Fig. 58.)

The same care should be taken to develop a gradual taper with the clipper. Use shears-and-comb work at the taper line, for further blending, beginning at either temple. Trim the remaining hair carefully, shading it so that no pronounced ridges will show.

Sometimes in this haircut an upward cutting technique seems advisable. If the hair is *long* and it is desired to make two or three cuts on the section of hair held in the comb, hold the hair up with the comb after the first cut is made. Then bring the blades of the shears *underneath* the comb, holding the hair with the shears. Bring the comb underneath the shears again and lift the hair for the second cut. The teeth of the comb, as each cut is taken, should be tilted slightly outward from the head, keeping the comb in the lock of hair deep enough so that the cut will not be too close to the comb.

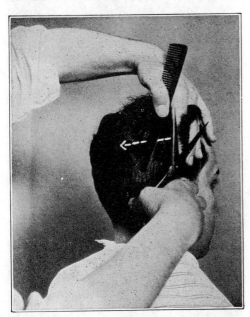

Fig. 75.

FINGER WORK. This phase of haircutting is very helpful in reducing any pronounced unevenness that may show after the basic shears-and-comb work has been completed.

In many instances the barber will find that finger work in a haircut is necessary, if the job is to be completed properly. And, since it is the barber's responsibility that each patron receive the haircut that best fits his particular personality, the skilled barber is one who is a master of this phase of haircutting technique. It is equally as necessary as the ability to properly handle clippers, or the ability to skillfully handle the shears and comb. The barber should master finger work if he is to create artistic medium and long types of haircuts.

The most important factor in doing this work correctly is the knack of properly picking up with the comb the hairs that are causing the unevenness. This is accomplished by first releasing the thumb from the thumb grip of the shears. Hold the shears firmly in the palm of the hand with the last two fingers, and grasp the fine end of the comb with the thumb and first two fingers of the same hand. Comb through the hair with the heavy end of the comb, holding the comb straight up and down.

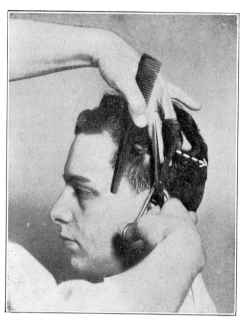

Fig. 76.

Start at either temple of the patron and comb the hair away from the forehead. Bring the portion of hair contained in the teeth of the comb outward as far as possible without permitting the hair to fall from the comb. Then reach over the top of the patron's head with the left arm, holding the fingers downward. When the first and second fingers of the left hand grasp the hair between the comb and the scalp. (Fig. 75.) Place the comb in the left hand between the thumb and first finger. Replace the thumb back in the thumb grip of the shears and cut the desired portion of hair with the shears.

After the first cut has been made, continue

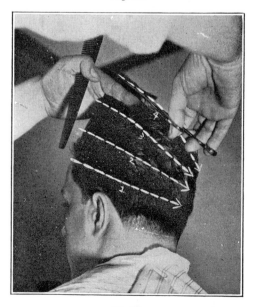

Fig. 77.

holding the lock of hair. Again grasp the comb between the first finger and thumb of the right hand and comb through the section of hair contained in the fingers of the left hand. At the same time gradually release the hair held in the fingers of the left hand, slide the comb beyond the cut just made, pick up the hair as was done before, and go through the same procedure. On the patron who combs his hair with a side part, work back to the middle of the head.

Then proceed to cut the other side and do the finger work, working toward the back of the head to meet the finger work already done. (Fig. 76.)

In doing the finger work on the left side, pick up the hair with the comb by taking a position at the left of the patron, and work the comb away from the forehead. On the right side the barber stands to the rear of the patron. Other than this the technique is the same.

If the patron desires to have the hair shortened all the way to the top, make the 1-2-3-4 cuts on each side. At the fourth cut the fingers are bent a little to conform to the shape of the head. When cutting hair over the fingers, upward cutting is preferred. (Fig. 77.)

The operator will note that if the hair is correctly picked up with the comb in the finger work, the hairs causing unevenness are clearly indicated, as they are longer than the other hairs.

Trims—Long and Medium

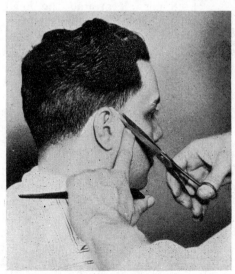

Fig. 78. (Only illustrates how to use shears in making outline around ears.)

The trim is different from the two former cuts, not only in length but also in outline.

The clipper work in the long trim extends only across the back of the neck, the taper coming out on a line even with the lobes of the ears.

The hairline in the front of and around the ear is outlined and "feathered" with the shears to the desired length. The outline is made around the ears by resting the shears on the first finger of the left hand and cutting with the points of the shears at the hair line. (Fig. 78.)

The shears-and-comb work is started in front of either ear, and the trimming is continued around the edges of the hairline of the head to the front of the other ear. In trimming back of the ears it will be necessary that the comb be held at an angle in order to give the proper shape to the haircut, and to avoid taking off too much hair. In doing the finger work on this haircut great care must be taken not to remove too much hair, especially over the crown.

The medium trim differs from the long trim only in the clipper work. The clipper may be used in front of and over the ears, but only about a quarter of an inch above the ears. In many instances the No. 1 clipper is recommended for this work. However, the No. 00 or No. 000 clipper should be used for the lower portion of the clipper work on the back of the neck. (Fig. 59.) In the long trim no clipper work should be done in front of or above the ears. (See Figs. 59 and 60 for long and medium trims.)

The Pompadour

A pompadour is a style of dressing the hair high over the forehead, either by combing long hair backward from the forehead to the crown of the head, or by brushing short hair back so that it stands erect.

The Short Pompadour

The short pompadour is done altogether differently than the medium and long pompadours. Begin the short pompadour by

cutting rather high with the clipper all around the head, similar to the clipping done in the short cut. Then comb the hair from front to back over the top of the head. The hair may be moistened if it does not stand up well. Then use shears-and-comb work to improve a long taper extending as high as possible above the clipper work.

When the taper around the head is finished, proceed to shape the top of the pompadour. (Fig. 79.) This requires a steady hand and a keen eye, for the short pompadour must have a smooth, almost flat surface across the top of the head. For visual study see pages 79, 80, 81.

Fig. 79.

In order to secure a good view of the shears-and-comb work, or top clipper work, stand in front of the patron. Pick up the hair in the heavy teeth of the comb at the front hairline, the teeth of the comb pointing toward the back of the head. Make the first cut according to the desired length (page 85, Fig. B), then continue cutting toward the crown of the head. Repeat this procedure until the entire top of the head has been covered.

The top of the haircut, when finished, should appear like a smooth brush. The length in front may vary from one to two inches, as desired by the patron. (Fig. 79.)

The Medium and Long Pompadours

These two haircuts follow in outline the medium and long side-part haircuts, except that the hair on top is somewhat longer in both cases. The hair in each case is combed straight back. In the medium pompadour the clipper is used all around the head, as in the medium side-part cut.

On the long pompadour the clipper is used only on the back of the neck. (Fig. 62.)

In doing the finger work on these two styles, some barbers part the hair in the center of the head, and then do the finger work, the same as on medium and long trims. Care must be taken in each case that too much hair is not removed, especially on the long pompadour, and particularly over the crown.

The long trim and the long pompadour are two of the most difficult haircuts to create. The student will come in contact with these styles very often in any barber shop, so he should get as much practice as possible on these two styles.

Butch, flat-top, crew and short pompadour haircutting offers no particular problem to the student. The instructor will explain and demonstrate the judicious use of clipper lengths in preparing the hair mass for the type of style desired by the patron. It then becomes a matter of shaping the hair mass to shortened or trimmed sides and rounded or flat tops. A short pompadour (or crew) allows for some length of hair on top with an almost flat effect, while a butch haircut is emphatically short. A pompadour is brushed up and back, while a butch is combed toward the front of the forehead. Flat-tops have a square effect where the sides join with the leveled flatness of the top. Flat-tops are also brushed up and back toward the crown of the head. (Pages 84, 85.)

Other variations of the short cuts are affected by the younger set, and some of these styles are illustrated on pages 79, 80, 81.

Shear-Point Tapering

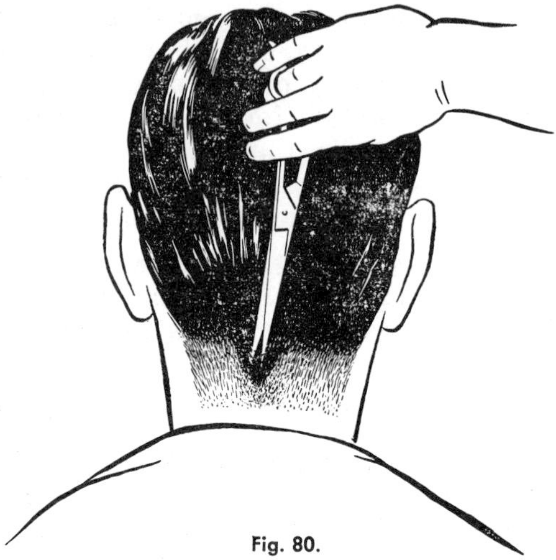

The barber will occasionally encounter a very difficult head of hair to cut, due to abnormal depressions (hollows) in the skull of the patron, areas where the grain of the hair forms whorls and instances where it seems almost impossible to blend longer hair in with shorter cut hair to bring about the desired evenness and smoothness necessary in a good haircut. Therefore the difficult technique of shear-point tapering should be mastered by the operator if he is to reach his goal of being a first-class barber.

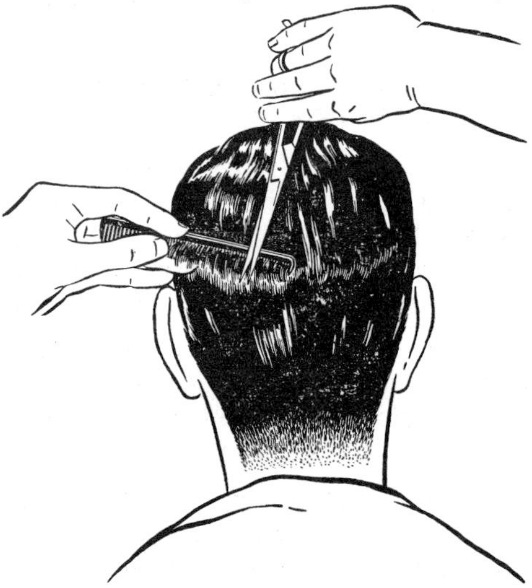

Shear-point tapering is done by inverting the hand holding the shears (Fig. 80) and thinning out dark areas and bunchy sections of hair, using only the cutting *points* of the shears. By *careful* thinning of the hair in the hollows, wrinkles and creases of the scalp, and dark hair patches caused by whorls, uniform shading can be achieved.

Fig. 80.

Fig. 81.

Ragged and choppy areas present in the longer portions of the hair may be corrected through shear-point tapering by thinning the hair into uneven lengths and blending the various lengths together into a smooth contour (Fig. 81). The operator is cautioned to sever only a *few hairs* at each cut, thus gradually developing the shaded outline or contour desired. Comb out the severed hairs after each cut is taken.

EXECUTIVE CONTOUR

BUTCH

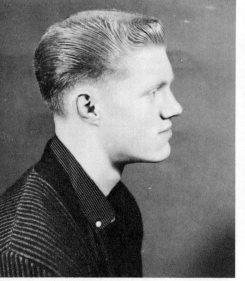

FLAT-TOP BOOGIE

IVY LEAGUE

The pictures on this page and pages 80 and 81 are from "Modern Hair Styling" chart, published by the Associated Master Barbers and Beauticians of California. The chart measures 16 x 21 inches, and can be ordered from the Master Barber & Beautician Magazine, 537 S. Dearborn St., Chicago 5, Ill., at $2 each. Send remittance with order. Allow 10 days for delivery.

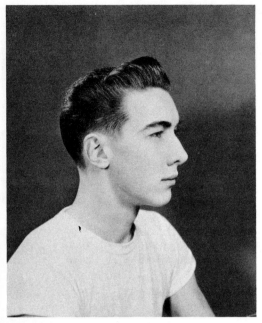

VANGUARD

FLAT-TOP

CREW

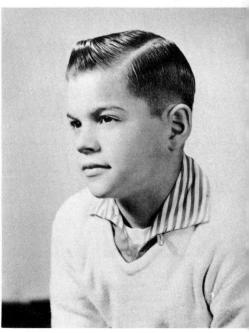

JUNIOR CONTOUR

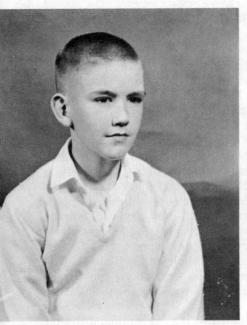

BUTCH

REGULAR CONTOUR

LITTLE LEAGUE

JUNIOR FLAT-TOP

Hair Styling for Men

This subject does not lend itself well to specification, and must not be limited by specified steps or rules.

Hair styling simply implies an artistic or professional haircut to fit the individual patron or to add beauty or character, or both, to a person's appearance. Thus there are almost as many styles as there are heads to wear them.

If two signs could be viewed, one painted by a butcher, baker or store clerk, and the other by a professional sign painter, the amateurishness of the one and the professionalism of the other could easily be discerned. The same is true of a haircut. It is either plain and stereotyped, or it will be marked by its artistry.

Professional haircutting offers the barber unlimited opportunity. A suggestion to a patron of a different style of haircut that is more becoming to him awakens respect for an operator's competency that would not otherwise be developed.

In order to create a professional hair style, one that is becoming to a patron and brings out his personality, the barber must acquire the ability to visualize in advance a mental picture of the finished style.

Rather than lay down specific rules it is recommended that an operator use his mind as well as his hands. The following principles may be the best guide:

1. Study the contour of the head and determine where fullness may be left or reduced in order to create a better contour through the artistic molding of the hair mass.

2. Study the general facial and head contours together, to determine what style arrangement or treatment may add some desirable characteristic or correct some unwanted feature.

3. Study parting the hair at different places and find the position, angle, or length of part that will add to the person's appearance.

4. Study the hair texture, cowlicks and other hair peculiarities for the purpose of determining the length or type of cut that will best favor the patron and will stay combed the longest.

5. Learn to shape the hair by the use of slithering, razor cutting, thinning and shear-point tapering.

Front Shingle

The front shingle haircut is accomplished by shingling the top hair so that it slopes slightly towards the front. The shingling begins at the posterior portion of the vertex, and is graduated so as to leave the hair heavier in front. The hair is usually clipped very close and very high all around the head. (Refer to explanation of short cut, page 72.)

This is a practical type of haircut, especially for those whose occupations expose them to dust and dirt. If the hair is very curly or kinky this cut can almost be completed with the clipper. Begin with the 000 blades and clip the hair rather high all around the head. Then with the No. 1 blades, continue upward to the crown and about one to 1½ inches up around the head. Then with No. 1 blades start at the posterior portion of the vertex and graduate the haircut as the clipper is moved forward to the front hair-line. No razor outline is made unless requested by the patron.

Pompadour

The Pompadour is a popular haircut. It lends itself to almost any shape of head. The ease with which it may be combed or brushed straight back makes it desirable. There are many variations of the Pompadour, but only four will be discussed.

Short Pompadour

This style of haircut is often referred to as a crew cut and vice versa. The clipper of the desired cutting length is used well up on the sides and back of the head, followed by the long tapering technique to produce a short rounded effect toward the crown and top of the head. The top hair is then shortened to the very short length desired, either by use of the shears and comb or the clipper and comb (page 85, Fig. C). (See pages 79 to 81 for pompadour and crew cuts.)

Low Pompadour

The Low Pompadour requires a very low clipper outline all around the head. The top is left long. A popular variation of this style is to cut the top hair fairly short, cutting from the front to the crown.

Medium Pompadour

The Medium Pompadour also has a clipper outline all around the head. The 000 blades are used on the neck. The No. 1 blades are used to continue up into the hair in back, and also to make the clipper outline on the sides. These coarse blades are moved upward about 1½ inches, but not higher than a point which corresponds to the level of the eye-brow.

Then a very important procedure is followed. Continue with the No. 1 blades, but invert the clipper so that the teeth of the blades point downward. With the clipper in this position, work from the top downward in narrow widths. It is in this way that the graduation or blend is accomplished.

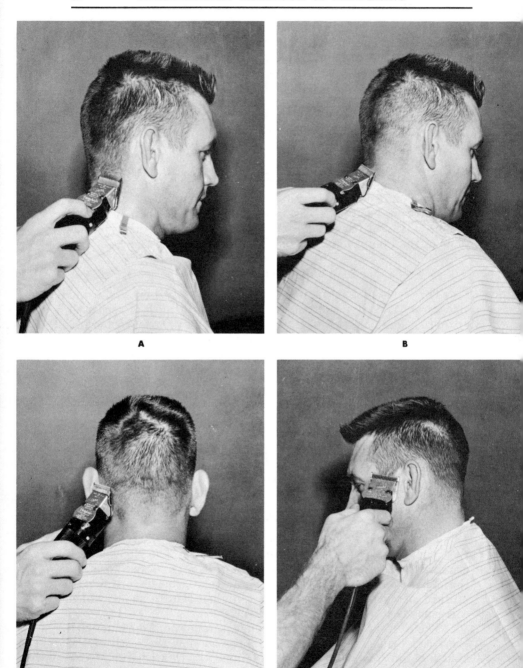

A

B

C

D

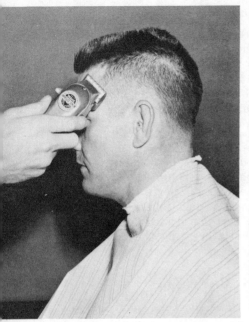

A

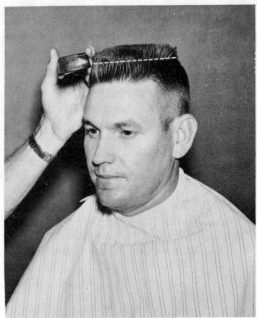

B

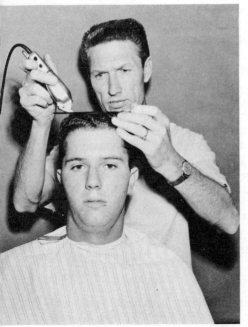

C

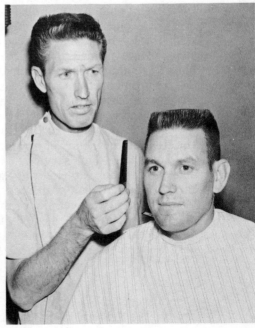

D

High Pompadour

The High Pompadour requires a very short and high clipper outline all around the head. The 000 blades are usually used. However, if a razor outline is to be given, use the coarser blades on the sides. The top hair is left very heavy, so that it may be combed back. This style gained considerable popularity among men in the armed services during World War II.

Flat-Top

Flat-tops are cut exactly like short pompadours, on top, except that a blocky effect is achieved through the technique of the long taper and shearing the hair off perfectly flat on top. This gives the haircut a blocky appearance where the sides and the flat top join. (Page 85, Fig. D.) The first top cut (page 85, Fig. B) is a guide for the barber in creating the length of the hair on top in the completed haircut.

Cutting Negro Men's Hair

A Negro's hair is characteristically very curly or kinky. Many of the established principles of cutting straight hair may be applied in cutting this type of hair. However, it is noteworthy that the techniques and implements used may differ. The graduation of the outline is accomplished largely by operating the clipper with downward strokes. Coarse blades ranging in size from 0, 0A, 1 and 2 are needed for finished blending. These same sizes of blades are almost indispensable for much of the general cutting.

It is important to note that outlining the haircut with the razor is not always done in cutting the hair of Negroes, but it is not incorrect to use the razor for this purpose.

Schools which primarily train Negro students should instruct the students in the art of straightening and dressing Negro men's and boys' hair. This service has become an important and profitable one in shops catering to Negroes. Students entering shops for further apprenticeship training where Negro patronage is catered to must know the techniques of this service. Instructions in the use of the materials used in this service are supplied by the manufacturers of the products, and the techniques suggested may be supplemented by the instructor.

Bald Heads

Cutting bald-headed men's hair is simply utilizing the principle of the light trim at the hair outline. Some bald men like the hair very short and desire that the clipper be used. In such

(Above photos courtesy of Modern Hairpieces, Inc., 1912 E. Colfax Ave., Denver 6, Colo.)

instances the clipper line marks the line from which the hair is tapered. Bald-headed men should be urged to consider wearing hair pieces. If the patron does wear a hair piece it is *always safe* to remove it before trimming the patron's hair, thus avoiding any possibility of cutting any hair from the hair piece. If additional trimming is required after the hair piece is refitted, then *extreme* care should be exercised not to cut into the hair piece.

The Barber and Hairpieces

Due to the rapidly increasing acceptance of modern, natural-looking hairpieces, barbers should make it a part of their training to know how to cut the hair of the patron wearing a modern hairpiece without damage to the thin blend hair around the edge of the hairpiece.

It is unnecessary for the patron to remove the hairpiece if the barber will comb the hair along the sides and around the back of the head with a back and upward stroke. This will separate the blend hair in the hairpiece from the growing hair while the haircut is performed, occasionally combing the blend hair down to insure that the natural hair blends with the hairpiece.

Never cut the hairpiece. No matter how tempting it may be to cut the uneven thin blend hair in the hairpiece, these irregular thin hairs are there to break the definite line where the hairpiece blends with the natural hair. This is important especially when the hair in the hairpiece gradually loses color. All hair, even growing hair, will fade as it is exposed to sunlight, as is the case when natural hair is allowed to grow long on top.

Designing Hairpieces

Designing hairpieces is a separate and distinct profession in itself and should not be attempted by a novice. It requires much training and experience. The amateurish attempt to design a hairpiece without scientific training will likely result in an error comparable to one that might be caused by an unskilled person who tries to cut hair without professional barber training. The outlook is even worse because the hairpiece will never grow so that the error can be corrected.

Delivering the Hairpiece

The delivering of a modern hairpiece cannot be done professionally by mail. The patron deserves careful fitting, precise instructions and actual training on the handling of the hairpiece, hence he should personally come to the shop.

A good quality hairpiece is costly to make, because it is all hand artistry, requiring a substantial investment by the one who buys it.

The benefits in appearance, personality, social acceptance and business success are definite to men in any walk of life, if the hairpiece is worn and serviced properly.

Servicing the Hairpiece

This is a phase of the profession that requires special training. The hairpiece must be dry-cleaned, blocked to reshape the foundation, the hair reset to its individual styling and the hair re-treated with the proper hair preservative.

The wearer should always purchase two hairpieces at the same time, and should replace them at the same time. By so doing, his hairpieces are identical, and a change is never detected when he substitutes one for the other. Also it is important for servicing that he change hairpieces at regular intervals, usually when he gets a haircut. Good, efficient service cannot be rendered on a "while-you-wait" basis.

Hairpiece Business and Barbering

The hairpiece business can be a part of barbering. Selling and servicing of hairpieces requires a booth properly arranged to deliver and service the patron in complete privacy.

Neck Shave

The neck shave is an essential part of a good haircut, for, no matter how well and neatly the hair may be trimmed, if the neck shave is not given artistically the appearance of the haircut may be entirely ruined. Hence the barber should use good judgment in shaping the neck outlines.

The neck shave, when giving a haircut, involves the outline in front of, above and back of the ears, and the sides and back of the neck, according to the style desired by the patron. The neckline may be round or oval on the back of the neck, or may be shaved straight down the sides of the neck. The latter style is most preferred.

Procedure

Apply warm lather at the hairline around the ears and on the back of the neck. Hold the razor in the freehand position. Hold the comb with the left hand and, with the fine teeth, straighten the hairs over the outline. Start shaving the outline on the right side of the patron's head, making a straight and even stroke in front of the ear, with the razor at the level desired by the patron, and continue shaving the outline above the ear. Make a graceful, evenly curved outline, but be careful not to shave too high around the ear. Follow as closely as possible the natural hairline. (Fig. 82.)

Shave down as far as the mastoid process, change position by holding the back of the ear gently forward with the left hand and continue to shave down the side of the neck, making a straight, even line. Transfer the lather from the razor to the side of the left hand near the base of the thumb or to the palm of the left hand.

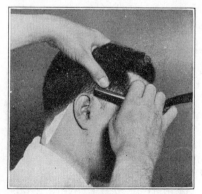
Fig. 82.

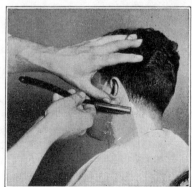
Fig. 83.

On the left side make the outline in the same way, using the reverse backhand stroke in front of the ear, then the freehand stroke over the ear and down to the mastoid process. Transfer the lather from the razor as before, change to the reverse backhand stroke, hold the back of the ear gently forward with the thumb of the left hand and shave down the side of the neck, making a straight, even line to match that on the right side. (Fig. 83.)

If, after shaving over the ears and down the sides of the neck, the neck is to be shaved round, take a position in back of the patron and shave the outline across the back of the neck that will give the best appearance to the haircut. This requires considerable study, and the student should give careful attention to this part of the work, as the neck shave does much toward giving that attractive appearance so much desired by the patron.

After the neck shave has been completed, remove the excess soap with a warm, moist towel. Dry the neck thoroughly. Replace the linen over the patron's clothing and proceed to comb the hair. (Note: The outliner, Fig. 14, may be used to shape the outline, instead of the razor.)

In combing the hair, hold the comb in the right hand and the hairbrush in the left hand. Begin by straightening out the hair with the coarse part of the comb. If the hair is to be parted, be sure to create a straight, even part, using the comb and hairbrush alternately, until the hair has been carefully, neatly and smoothly arranged in the fashion desired by the patron. (Fig. 50.)

In using the comb and hairbrush, be sure to not scratch the scalp with either instrument, as it is annoying to the patron to have the barber use too much pressure. As a result he may not come back to the same barber's chair. If the service is suitable to his personal liking, the patron will be glad to pay the price asked for the service, and will prefer coming back to the same shop and to the same barber. (Note: Many better class shops have eliminated the use of the hairbrush for sanitary reasons.)

Singeing

From a scientific standpoint, singeing the hair is a fallacy. One theory for its justification is based on the unfounded conception that hairs are hollow tubes, the ends of which, when cut, will allow some vital fluids to escape and deprive nature of some of its hair-growing substances, thereby causing alopecia.

Another false claim is that micro-organisms find easy access to the roots by the way of the imaginary hair tube, and cause diseases of the scalp. Some enthusiastic propounders of this viewpoint have gone so far as to claim that brain fevers, colds, sinus troubles and a score of other head maladies are caused by the invasion of germs through the hair tubes.

The hair contains no tube or vital fluid, and singeing it does neither good nor harm, except that singeing leaves an adherent coagulation on the ends of the hair, which is disagreeably noticeable.

A Becoming Hair Style Makes a Pretty Girl Even More Lovely

Women's Haircutting

Women's haircutting requires the use of different techniques, due to the fact that it must be cut to a certain design of hairdress, involving permanent waves, curls, flares, rolls and a multitude of arrangements and added adornments.

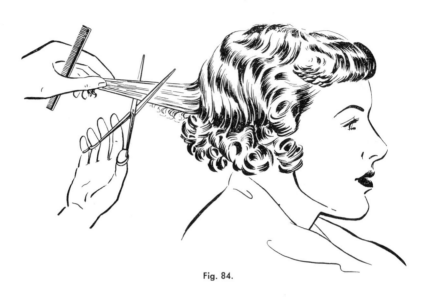

Fig. 84.

These techniques are: (1) Slithering; (2) Razor cutting; (3) Thinning shears method.

1. SLITHERING. This word simply means "sliding away," and has been adopted in haircutting to mean thinning the hair with standard shears by a cutting and sliding stroke.

Slithering is executed by picking up a strand of hair between the thumb and the first two fingers of the left hand, holding it away from the head and inserting the open blades of the shears underneath the strand as illustrated. (Fig. 84.) Make a first cut, *cutting a very, very small amount of hair,* and slide the shears along the strand, pushing the cut hairs toward the head.

Following this same procedure, take a similar cut about a half-inch away from the first cut, and again slide the cut hairs toward the head. Continue this technique until the entire strand is processed. The thinning process may be done from the scalp to the ends of the hair, or from the ends of the hair to the scalp, depending on the shaping desired.

In this way the shaping is accomplished by thinning the hair mass from within to any desired contour, and the hair is cut off to the desired length as each section is processed.

2. RAZOR CUTTING is a method of cutting the hair with a razor. This is done with a regular razor or a safety razor-like instrument known as a "hair shaper."

Razor cutting is done by picking up thin strands of hair between the first and second fingers of the left hand, presenting a wide surface for thinning the hair with the razor, as illustrated. (Fig. 85.)

Fig. 85.

Thinning with a razor is done by holding the razor flat, or almost flat, against the taut strand, and slicing along the surface from the scalp to the end of the hair strand. When the thinning is completed, the razor is tilted at a 45-degree angle, and the hair is sliced through at the desired length.

3. THE THINNING-SHEARS METHOD is the technique of shaping the hair with thinning shears. The single-serrated-edge shears are recommended for this work. (Fig. 86.)

In thinning the hair with the thinning shears the hair is picked up in strands similar to those for slithering, or razor cutting, depending on the results desired. The hair is thinned directly by cutting with the thinning shears according to the shaping design selected. The *length* is cut with *standard shears*. If the hair is to be shortened only a little, the length is cut *after* the thinning is completed. If the hair is to be cut to a considerably shorter style, it is cut *before* the thinning is done.

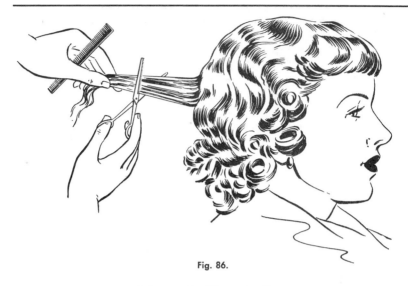

Fig. 86.

Women's Hair Styling

The same general rules apply here as outlined in hair styling for men (see page 82), except that in the case of women's work the styles vary in length from the short "three-inch," "little girl" and "feather" cuts, to medium lengths and long styles. Styles vary in combing arrangement, contour, thickness and hairdress designs.

Hairdress designs are innumerable. For the purpose of this book it suffices to advise that one must master haircutting techniques and thus enable himself to understand the art of hair shaping.

Types of Women's Haircuts

Styles in women's hairdressing change rapidly from year to year. What might have been old five years ago, or last year, might again be brand new this year. Basically, however, women's haircuts can be placed in three categories: short bobs, shingles and prepared hair masses for styling. We discuss all three because the student may find it necessary that he learn the techniques related to giving these services. Therefore, in addition to the explanations of preparation of the hair mass for styling, we also give mention to hair bobs and shingles.

The Straight Bob

A bob is a haircut in which the hair is cut straight off at the bottom of the lobe of the ear or at various lengths above or below that point. (Fig. 87.)

The straight bob is frequently the first cut for babies and toddlers, and in such cases the length extends about to the middle of the ear, especially in warm weather.

The straight bob with bangs, sometimes called the "Buster Brown cut" (Fig. 63, page 65), is one of the accepted styles for young girls.

If the hair is to be curled, the hair must be cut somewhat longer, especially in the back, to allow for shrinkage in length due to the curling process.

Fig. 87.

The Shingle Bob

The shingle bob is a haircut with the back shingled, and it may vary in length and style, with the sides bobbed and blended with the shingle.

Begin the shingle by combing the hair from the middle of the back of the head, and comb the top and side hair forward over each ear. Then shingle the hair from the hairline at the back of the neck to the desired shape, length, or style.

The Neck Line. There are three basic neck lines: (1) The natural or "feather-edge," the hair being tapered similar to a man's haircut; (2) the round neck line, a definite rounded outline produced with the clippers and shears, the round neck line varying

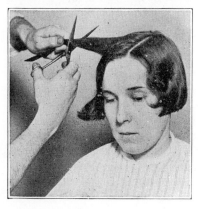

Fig. 88.

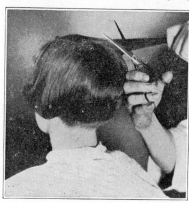

Fig. 89.

from a long oval to a short, flat, rounded outline; (3) the "V" neck line, a definite V-shaped outline of various lengths. This varies from a short, wide "V" to a long, narrow "V," depending on the style or effect desired. It is also formed with clippers and shears.

When the shingle and neck line are outlined, continue upward with the shingling, leaving the hair as long as possible for thinning. Then, with the hair properly parted, comb it down the sides and back and cut the length at the sides, allowing extra length for finishing (Fig. 88). Next, proceed to shape the side by thinning the hair masses by any of the three thinning methods, blending the sides with the shingle and reducing bulk in the shingle if necessary. (Fig. 89.)

When the hair has been shaped, work over the whole haircut for any smoothing or finishing.

The Tailored Bob

The tailored bob is a personally-styled cut of average ear lobe length, fitted in contour and hairdress to the individual. The

Fig. 90.

most important feature of this cut is that it is molded to bring out the most desirable contour.

The back may be left long for curling, bobbed or shingled, depending on how the hair is to be dressed. The neck line, when shingled, may be outlined round, oval, or V-shaped, depending on the individual's natural hairline and the thickness and length of the neck. The object is to bring out the most beautiful and most flattering mode. (Fig. 90.)

The sides must be shaped to blend in contour with the back, and be thinned and shortened to fit the eventual hairdress. If the dressing is a pompadour with waves, it is shaped as such, and enough length is allowed for wave shrinkage. If the hairdress is to be worn downward with end curls, or swept upward with rolls, then the hair should be shaped accordingly.

The frontal portion of the hair mass also is treated to fit the eventual hairdress, in order to achieve the best front-styling for whatever effect is desired. A variety of women's hair styles appears on pages 99 to 103.

Cutting for Waves

Certain types of haircuts have been developed, which have been variously named curly cuts, wave cuts and layer cuts.

Some false impressions exist among laymen relative to wave cutting. These are cuts to actually *facilitate* the *setting* of waves and curls, and are a means of causing sets to last longer, just like pin curls are a means to a hairdress but do not constitute a finished product. Hair cut in this manner does not automatically fall into curls or waves. The waves must be set in the hair by professional finger waving or artificial waving methods to achieve the wave formations.

Successful cutting for waves depends not only on the operator's skill but also on his scientific knowledge of hair and waving techniques.

Such factors as length, taper, whorls, elasticity and hardness of hair are to be taken into consideration. The haircutter must do this work with these factors in mind, always thinning and cutting as a particular hair mass may require. Too often failures come from processing the hair too much or not enough.

Technique

I. DESIGNING THE WAVES. The hair is combed straight back from the forehead. Some prefer to comb it wet, others dry; it is a matter of personal choice, depending on skill. Some are equally successful with either method.

When the hair is straightened out smoothly, the hair mass is "pushed up" or forward with the left hand while guiding the waves with the comb in the right hand. (Figs. 181, 182, 183.)

This will indicate the wave lines or natural wave tendencies. When the wave lines are found, proceed to set the hair in the most natural wave pattern.

If the hair is soft and one's waving technique is skillful, this may be done dry; otherwise it is best to set the hair while wet.

II. CUTTING. There are several methods of cutting. Some use shears and razor, others use the slithering method.

The hairs are picked up in strands along the wave crests and thinned out with shears or razor, thinning along the path of the wave trough or "dips." This reduces the bulk along the troughs and augments wave tendency in the hair at these lines, thus facilitating the eventual wave setting.

Another recognized method is the technique of cutting known as effiling.

In effiling the hair is further shortened and finely tapered along the wave lines, and the layers end in lines along successive wave crests. Most operators call this method "layer cutting."

III. WAVING. The final operation is setting the waves. The hair should be shampooed in order to get the best results, for oily hair will not hold a set.

Use a light solution of wave-set lotion for the average hair, or a heavier solution if the hair is coarse and hard textured. Use plain water in soft or permanent-waved hair. Proceed to set the hair according to instructions in finger waving. (See page 301.)

IT PAYS TO LOOK WELL

A correctly-fitted hairpiece is the only sure cure for a case of baldness.

A

B

C

D

A

B

C

D

A

B

C

D

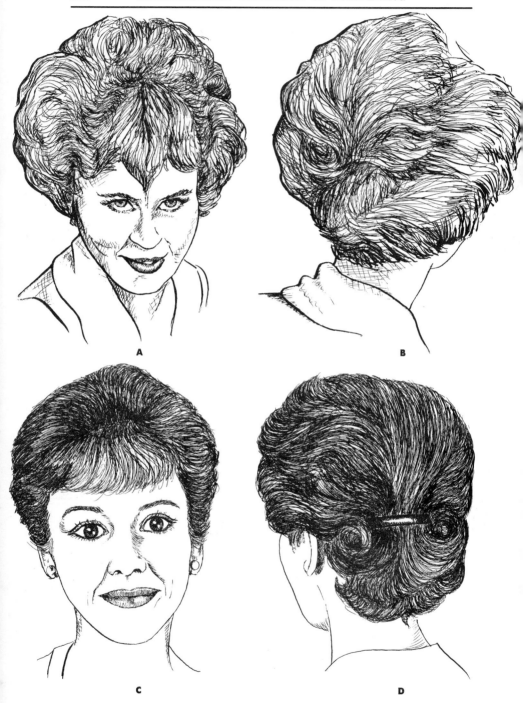

A

B

C

D

LOOK AT IT THIS WAY

To get a good idea of the kind of barber you are, and the kind of shop you are operating, there is a good way to go about it:

Think of yourself as a patron. You are the man in the chair. Such being the case, what are you doing to him that, if you were in his place, you would not like?

Are you, as the patron, being given hurried, careless service? Are you being handled roughly? Are the steam towels too hot or too cold? Following a shave, is your face being dried carefully and completely?

Is the barber's breath offensive? Are his hands and fingernails clean? Is his clothing immaculate, and of the type recommended for a professional barber?

Put yourself in the patron's place, and think as he is apt to be thinking. The result will be to your advantage—and to his liking.

Chapter 7

Basic Shampoo, Hair Tonic and Massage Services

S HAMPOOS, hair tonic applications and massages, combined with shaving and haircutting, make up the five basic services performed by barbers. The student must know the fundamental principles involved in giving these routine services. More detailed instructions are given on the various types of shampoos, tonic applications and massages in PART II—BARBER SCIENCE.

The Shampoo

An efficient shampoo has two major features in its favor. First, it imparts a decided feeling of stimulation to the patron. Second, it is a necessary measure for the healthy preservation of the hair and scalp. True, the patron may give himself a shampoo (so-called) at home, but such an inferior substitute for the same service in a barber shop will not bear comparison. Done by the patron at home, it is a laborious process, and it is physically impossible for him to cleanse the hair and scalp with the same degree of thoroughness as can the barber. Furthermore, at home he will inevitably leave a residue from the shampoo lather in his hair, and this residue is injurious to the hair.

Learn to give a shampoo worthy of the name. To do this requires training and observation, together with the use of high grade materials and proper equipment. A patron receiving service of the quality indicated soon learns the superiority of the barber shop method over his own inefficient home efforts, and he becomes a regular shampoo buyer in the barber shop.

When preparing to give a shampoo, see that everything is in readiness, for no time should be wasted in looking for supplies or needed equipment after the work is started. During the winter months the shop must be comfortably warm, as it will be more difficult to relax the scalp of the patron if he is chilled.

The operator should be sure that his fingers are warm, so wash the hands with plenty of warm water. Warm fingers are more pliable and will be more soothing to the patron. Arrange the chair cloth and make every effort to see that the patron is fully relaxed.

Linen Setup

The linen setup for a shampoo is the same as that used for haircutting, except that the towel is left slightly loose so that a second towel can be tucked inside of it around the neck.

After the first towel is arranged as above-mentioned, a second clean towel is folded in half, lengthwise, and the folded edge is tucked inside of the first towel all around the neck from back to front. However, this standard procedure may be modified. Some shops use three towels for the shampoo linen setup.

After the linens have been neatly arranged, briefly massage the scalp. This loosens up the epidermic scales, debris and the scalp tissues.

The shampoo preparation should be carefully applied to all parts of the scalp by spreading portions of the hair apart with the second finger and thumb of the left hand, and the shampoo applied directly on the scalp. After sufficient shampoo has been applied, the scalp should be thoroughly massaged. Using a water dispenser, gradually apply enough warm water in the hair to make an abundant, creamy lather over the entire scalp.

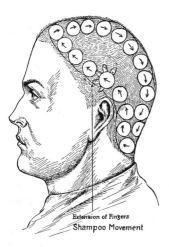

Extension of Fingers
Shampoo Movement

Fig. 91.

Now stand back of the patron. Place the finger tips of both hands at the back of the head, just below the ears, and with continuous rotary manipulations move up back of the ears to the temples, then up to the center of the forehead. From there continue back along the center of the head on top, then over the crown, down over the back center of the head to the neck, then to the first position again, as indicated in Fig. 91.

Care must be taken when applying the water and shampoo, and also when manipulating, that the shampoo lather does not run on the forehead, or into the eyes or ears of the patron.

Repeat this movement for a

couple of minutes, then, pressing firmly on the head, remove the excess lather or suds with a front-to-back sweep with the palm of the right hand and transfer it to the left hand each time until you have gone all over the scalp. Carry this lather to the lavatory and rinse both hands.

Add more shampoo and water and repeat the rubbing again. If the scalp is very dirty, the lathering may be repeated a third time. Prepare for rinsing by tempering the water in the spray to the temperature desired by the patron. If the water is either too hot or too cold, the patron is uncomfortable.

Rinsing

The Inclined Method

Request the patron to take a seat at the lavatory on a stool provided for that purpose and proceed to rinse, with the patron's head dipped forward in the lavatory basin. Be sure that the water is comfortably warm, and be careful not to get any water on the towels, or on the clothes, or in the ears of the patron. Nothing aggravates a patron so much as to find himself suddenly wet due to the barber's carelessness.

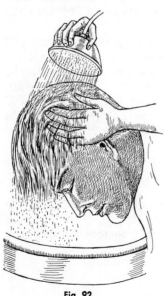

Fig. 92.

This method of rinsing (Fig. 92) is the standard method used for generations.

If the scalp and hair have been extremely oily or dirty, repeat the lathering at the lavatory after rinsing. This procedure is now practiced in most shops. Rinse the hair *thoroughly*, running the fingers through it as you do so. When this has been done, turn off the spray and press out the dripping water with the hands, being careful not to pull the hair. Using the towel previously tucked around the patron's neck, blot the water from the patron's face and ears, then the excess water from the hair.

Discard this towel, and have the patron take his position in the chair again. Now, taking a fresh towel, thoroughly dry the face and ears, and dry the hair as much as possible.

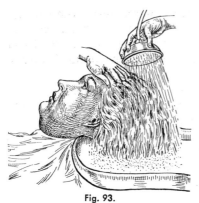

Fig. 93.

Tuck another fresh towel around the back of the neck, and complete the hair drying either with drumming movements of the fingers or with an electric hair dryer. The latter is preferable if the hair is somewhat long.

If the patron wishes to have his or her hair thoroughly dried with a towel, do this with a third towel. In most cases two towels are sufficient to complete the drying.

This method of giving a rinse is not entirely ideal, since the water runs over the face, and the position is somewhat uncomfortable. However, this method must necessarily be used in shops that do not have individual lavatories at each chair.

The Reclined Method

In the reclined method (Fig. 93) the entire shampoo is given at the lavatory. Without individual lavatories the latter method would be quite inconvenient or impossible, since the chair must be close enough to the lavatory to permit water to flow into the basin by means of a shampoo board.

The reclined method has become very popular, because it affords greater comfort to the patron and is a faster service.

To prepare the patron, turn the chair with the back to the lavatory. Place the linens as before, substitute a shampoo board for the head rest, and incline the patron so that the board will drain into the basin. Make sure that the patron's neck rests comfortably by placing a folded towel in the groove of the board as a pad for the neck.

Rinse the hair by holding the spray close to the hair. Care should be taken that water does not run into the eyes and ears of the patron.

The hair should always be *thoroughly* rinsed after the shampoo.

Dry the hair with a fresh towel, as previously explained, being sure to include the face, eyes and ears.

Hair Tonics

Through common usage the term "hair tonic" has come to signify many types of lotions or proprietary preparations for the hair and scalp.

Hair tonics are manufactured for many purposes. Some are devised specifically for the prevention of dandruff conditions; others for the removal of dandruff once it has appeared; others are manufactured for the sole purpose of dressing the hair. The latter may be classified as the oily types and the non-oily types.

There are still others to be used on white hair only, and some to be used on all *but* white hair, since they contain ingredients that may discolor the hair.

In other words, there are many types of hair tonics for many purposes and uses. Therefore it is of primary importance that the barber become familiar with each type of tonic before recommending or dispensing it, for, unless he is able to choose the right lotion for a particular condition, he runs the chance of diminishing the patron's respect for him.

It may be found that, after careful choice and application, results may be found wanting on a patron, after proving successful with several others. This is due to some variation from normal in the patron's condition, or allergy of his scalp to a particular mixture. Thus one can never afford to neglect his study of hair preparations.

Next to knowledge of the purposes and uses of these products, the operator should carefully study and record his results, and as time goes on his recommendations will be more certain, and results will be almost assured. This makes for professional expertness. It is recommended that a reference card system, giving the clinical results of preparations used, be made a part of a barber's professional equipment.

In spite of the complexity of this subject, there are standards that should be followed in all cases. For instance, the barber who says: "How about a tonic today?" and then slops a tonic on a patron with no scientific purpose, gives a fifteen-second, indifferent rub, and then rakes the scalp with this comb, does no justice to the tonic, the patron or himself, to say nothing of the damage he does to the profession.

If the tonic is to do some good to the scalp, that scalp must be briefly manipulated first to increase its blood supply. The movements should be firm, but not rough. Heavy, harsh, scrubbing manipulations are not only injurious, but also are very discomforting to the patron. The cushion tips of the fingers should be used, and they should be applied by working them through the hair, reaching the surface of the scalp. Work on the scalp with scientific manipulations which move the skin of the scalp.

Apply two or more hot towels to prepare the scalp for better reception of the liquid. The skin cells have absorptive qualities, and steam towels have a tendency to soften them. With the cells in this softened condition, hair tonics will penetrate them more readily.

Apply the tonic carefully, using only the needed amount and working it in thoroughly with correct manipulations. In short, always give an adequate service with a tonic application.

Scalp Steam Procedure—Towel Method

Prepare a moderately hot steam towel. Carry it folded to the back of the chair. Grasp both ends, unfold it and lay the center portion against the back of the head. Bring the right end forward and lay it over the right side of the head, being careful not to cover the ear and forehead. Then bring the left end forward to overlap the right end. If free ends are protruding over the forehead, tuck them under the towel at the hair line in front. Press the towel snugly over the entire head, and proceed to heat a second towel.

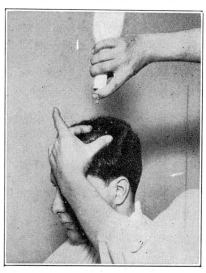

Fig. 94.

To change the steam towels, carry the second towel to the same position at the back of the chair. Hold it in the right hand. Remove the towel on the scalp by grasping the two ends together between the palm and last two fingers of the left hand. Using the free thumb and first two fingers of the left hand, grasp the left end of the towel held in the right hand, unfold it, and apply it to the scalp. The towel held in the left hand may now be placed over the towel on the scalp, to help retain heat in the latter.

Leave the towels on the scalp a minute or two, then remove and fold them neatly and place them on a sterile paper towel, either on the workstand or the lavatory. Two steam towels are sufficient, preceding the tonic application.

Some prefer to apply the steam towel to the scalp by starting from the right side of the head, and overlapped on the left side. Either method has enough acceptance to be considered standard practice. Also, the mechanical scalp steamer may be used.

The tonic is applied by grasping the tonic bottle with three fingers and the thumb of the right hand, the forefinger bracing

Fig. 95.

the nozzle of the bottle. (Fig. 94.) With the second finger and thumb of the left hand spread the hair apart so that the tonic may be applied directly to the scalp. Proceed in this manner all over the scalp. (Avoid over-saturating the hair and scalp with tonic, as this is unnecessary and wasteful.) After the tonic is applied, the scalp is thoroughly manipulated, either by hand manipulations or with a stimulax machine. (Fig. 95.) Tonic applications facilitate combing the hair of the patron.

Tonic applied in this manner is effective and will result in much benefit to the patron, therefore the barber should request a sufficient fee for this type of service.

Manufacturers, especially of the standard products, have, through experience and study, evolved the most efficient method of using their products. In most cases special instructions are printed on the containers, or instructive pamphlets are procurable from them and their agents.

It is advisable to study these informative pamphlets in order to become thoroughly acquainted with the nature, purpose and particular mode of administering each product. Manufacturers and dealers are eager to assist you.

Massages

Rolling Cream and Combination Massage

For many years the rolling cream massage was the only type of facial offered in the barber shop. With the advent of Barber Science, however, this form of facial has been slowly fading into disuse, and is gradually being replaced by more specialized types of facials, devised for specific purposes, such as the rest facial and facial packs.

The rolling cream massage consists chiefly of steaming the face, applying the preparation and rubbing it until it rolls off the skin. This procedure is followed either with a plain or witch-hazel steam.

The purpose of this treatment is to cleanse and massage the skin. However, it has been proven that a rolling cream massage is less efficient as a cleanser than ordinary cleansing cream, and, on scientific grounds, the old method of using rough manipulations is now taboo among the experts.

An outline for giving the rolling cream massage is given below, because there is a minor demand for this service. It has been modified to conform as much as possible to the modern principles of face massaging and facials.

Procedure

Make sure that the clothing of the patron is well covered by the chair cloth and towels.

Steam the face with several evenly-tempered, warm towels, and apply the soft rolling cream. Manipulate the face with rhythmic, rotary, stroking, rubbing movements, executed with the cushion tips of the fingers on the portion of the face above the lower jaw, and using the hand on the neck in a cupping fashion, until most of the cream has been rolled off. Care should be taken not to roughen the skin, and avoid permitting particles of the cream to roll into the eyes or down the neck of the patron.

Apply a small portion of cold cream and cleanse the skin with lighter manipulations. (See rest facial movements, page 258.)

Remove all the cream with a warm towel and follow with a mild witch-hazel steam, using three or more moderately hot towels. Finish with one or two cool towels, apply toilet lotion, dry the face and powder it.

If the patron should desire what is termed a "combination" or "double massage," which means giving a rolling cream massage followed by use of the stimulax technique, it should be used after application of a cold cream base, as this will tend to further cleanse the rolling cream from the pores of the skin, and the cold cream will act as a lubricant. The second part of the "double massage" is utilization of stimulax massage techniques.

The Stimulax Massage

The vibrator facial is one of the original forms of vibratory face massages. Its purpose is comparable to the amplified facial, the more modern method. It is now given with the aid of the stimulax machine. (Fig. 95.) It has a disadvantage in being somewhat mechanical in nature, but it is quite beneficial if given properly.

The fundamental principles in its use are these:

1. The vibrations must never be too rapid. The mechanism should be equipped with a speed regulator to reduce the rate of vibrations to a minimum.

2. The vibrator should be handled with slow, rotary or stroking movements, rather than hurried, zig-zag movements over the face, thereby insuring the effectiveness of the treatment.

3. The stimulax is snugly clamped to the back of the right hand. Around the eyes and nostrils it is best to administer the vibrations indirectly, by stroking the finger tips of the left hand over these regions and applying the vibrating right hand gently to the back of the left hand. This is referred to as "indirect vibrations."

4. The movements must conform to the muscles underlying the skin. When rotary movements are given, vary the pressure of the vibrations so that the effect will be given in the desired direction.

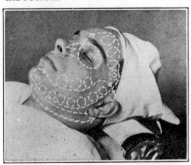

Fig. 96.

Movements

Since the movements are executed similarly on both sides of the face, it is sufficient to describe only those of the left side. A series of movements has been chosen that will cover all portions of the face and neck without breaking contact. This insures a smoother and more pleasant facial.

Place the finger tips of the left hand on the left nostril and place the vibrating right hand fingers over them. Vibrate through the left hand, moving the fingers lightly up and down on the left side of the nose. Continue around the orbit. (Fig. 96.)

Now place the vibrating right hand directly onto the skin, and with rotary movements work over the forehead, moving from the center to the left temple, as indicated. The pressure of the movement should be on the upward and outward portion of the movement. Pause a moment at the left temple. Continue these rotary movements down along the jaw bone to the tip of the chin, then move back and upward on the cheeks with wider movements to cover the entire cheek, with the pressure on the upward portion of the movement.

When the temples are approached again, continue with a slow stroke around the left ear, and with a lighter stroke pass over the jaw bone again to the center of the neck beneath the chin, as indicated in Fig. 96. Rotate back along the neck to behind the ear, then up to the temple, and thence on up to the forehead, stopping at the middle of the forehead.

Place the right hand on the left fingers again, and continue the massage over the right side of nose and the right side of the face. The same movements are used on the right side of the face as on the left.

In case the combination massage is given, the finish is applied at this time. The method to be followed is described under the heading "Procedure," on page 112.

BE MORE PROFESSIONAL

To make a strong bid for notice, try to arouse curiosity. You can do this by combining something new with that which is already familiar to your patrons. Haircutting offers you this opportunity. A suggestion to the patron for a different style of haircut that is more suitable to his facial contours and personality will many times awaken a respect for the operator's competency that would otherwise not come to life.

PART II

Barber Science

BARBER SHOP SALESMANSHIP

Barber shop salesmanship is a mental process. You cannot use force on a patron. You can neither hypnotize nor coax him to buy against his will. Conviction of the advantages of an offer is the basis of every sale. Only after conviction is established—first, in the mind of the barber, and second, in the mind of the patron—will an agreement be reached, and the patron sold.

To convince yourself you must have a thorough scientific knowledge of your service and the technical facts of the barber business, supported by confidence in the value of your offer, whether it relates to a shave, haircut or a scientific face or scalp treatment.

Every practicing barber and barber student should memorize the above definition of barber shop salesmanship.

FOREWORD TO

BARBER SCIENCE

B ARBERING, to be a profession, must consist of more than a mere manual training in the use of instruments, and procedures of haircutting, shaving, and other services rendered. It must also include the knowledge of the elements of science pertinent to the profession.

The first part of this book deals with mechanical training in the art of barbering, often referred to as the practical phase of barbering.

Barber Science deals more with the theoretical foundation that gives intelligent purpose to the practical work.

The degree of the barber's perfection in performing his services necessarily depends on the extent of his knowledge of that part of the human body on which he works.

In order to understand the skin of the face or scalp, it is necessary that he have considerable knowledge of the whole body mechanism.

Digestion, circulation and neurology must be studied, because these body systems are intimately related to the skin of those parts upon which the barber works. Knowledge of cells, bones, muscles, skin and hair is necessary in the modern barber's education. He must understand the use of modern electrical devices which are now standard equipment in the modern barber shop.

In possessing scientific knowledge of our work we are professional practitioners; without it we remain mere mechanics.

In the last forty years, the trend of legislation governing the practice of barbering bears witness to the refinement that is taking place in the barber profession, and among its personnel. The public welfare demands that the barber be an individual who is worthy of the trust imposed in him, in his personal contacts with humanity. He must have an acute awareness of the results of his ministrations, either helpful or detrimental, and it is to the end that he may live up to his responsibilities that knowledge of Barber Science is made available to him in this Textbook.

Chapter 8

Hygiene, Sanitation and Bacteriology

AN important phase of the barber profession is the practice of sanitation and hygiene. Combined, these terms may be defined as the science of the preservation of health. Sanitation is a more restricted term, referring to environment, while hygiene is a broader term, including its application to the individual. For instance, cleanliness of food and eating implements, and the preservation of food, require attention to sanitary measures. These things, plus the consideration of diet and personal cleanliness, are hygienic in character.

Due to the nature of the barber profession, which emphasizes personal service, barber practitioners are in constant personal contact with people. They use instruments and preparations on person after person. They are always in danger of contracting communicable diseases from their patrons and transmitting diseases to them, or spreading infection from patron to patron. The paramount duty of barbers, both to themselves and to their fellowmen, is to practice constantly the rules of sanitation and hygiene and gauge their conduct on these premises, that:

1. They will not spread disease from practitioner to patron.
2. They will not infect themselves.
3. They will not spread disease from patron to patron.

Barbers must be free from communicable diseases. As professional practitioners they should favor and promote legislation that tends to minimize the spread of infection.

Through knowledge they must recognize the general conditions that may endanger themselves and their patrons, and by sanitary practices safeguard public health.

Bacteriology

Infection is the communication of a disease or the disease-producing agent (generally called bacteria) from one organism

119

to another. Bacteria are a low class of microscopic organisms which have the power to produce profound changes in man, animal and plant life.

In general, disease-producing organisms or bacteria are called *pathogenic bacteria*. Bacteria or germs which do not produce diseases (for example, lactic acid bacilli) are called *non-pathogenic bacteria*.

Bacteriology is the science or study of bacteria. It is the purpose of this chapter to reveal enough of the practical fundamentals of this science to make available to the student an intelligent understanding of the relations and principles of sanitation, and a clear understanding of how to put these principles to work in the barber profession.

In the year 1683, in Delft, Holland, there lived a lens-grinder by the name of Leeuwenhoek. One day he scraped some tartar from his teeth and examined it under his lenses. To his surprise he found tiny living organisms. He was the first man to see bacteria, but no immediate progress resulted from his discovery.

It was not until the middle of the 19th century that bacteriology was brought to the front through the studies of Louis Pasteur, who clearly demonstrated that these microscopic bodies, like larger animals and plants, come into existence by methods of reproduction, and not by any process of spontaneous generation. He was perhaps the first to succeed in demonstrating that certain species of these microscopic organisms were the direct cause of certain diseases.

Fig. 97.

Although the shapes of bacteria have been determined, they are so small that knowledge of their anatomy is unknown. There are hundreds of different species, and they have three general forms, namely: round-shaped, called *coccus;* rod-shaped, called *bacillus;* and cork-screw shaped, called *spirillum.* (Fig. 97.)

These tiny forms group themselves in various types of bunches and chains, which is one method of identifying them. They are all extremely minute and never visible to the naked eye. They are the smallest living organisms which microscopes have revealed. They range from 1/100,000 of an inch to 1/400th of an inch in size.

Staphylococci are common pus-forming bacteria, which grow in bunches or clusters. They are the cause of pimples, boils, carbuncles and many other skin diseases. (Fig. 98.)

Another type of bacteria is the streptococci, which reproduce to form a chain-like structure. Usually this germ is also pus-producing. Streptococci are the causes of tonsilitis, appendicitis, erysipelas, lung diseases, throat diseases and many other ailments. (Fig. 98.)

Reproduction of Bacteria

In their method of reproduction bacteria multiply by each individual organism lengthening and dividing in the middle into two halves. Each half soon becomes a new organism, which in turn divides in the same manner.

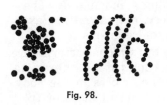

Fig. 98.

It is this power of rapid reproduction by simple division that makes disease-producing bacteria such a great menace. Their minute size would make them harmless enough, if it were not for their extraordinary power of multiplication. Some forms of bacteria, under favorable conditions, grow so rapidly they divide every half hour or less. This rate of growth would, within 24 hours, produce millions of new bacteria. This power of growth is augmented by the fact that bacteria feed on food which is already in condition for their absorption. They are not obliged to produce any of their own food, as most plants do, or even search for it, as do animals—they live in the midst of it.

The foods in which bacteria live are endless in variety. As they feed on the materials which serve them as food, chemical changes take place in the materials, resulting in numerous ingredients which did not previously exist in the food mass.

Substances created by the action of pathogenic bacteria are called toxins, or poisons, and these contaminated foods become a menace to health. On the other hand, there are types of bacteria that produce chemical changes beneficial to mankind. Such bacteria are utilized in the manufacture of foods, beverages and materials, such as cheese, vinegar, alcoholic liquors, leather, tobacco, etc.

Bacteria and Infection

There is no other form of life so universally found in nature as are bacteria. Bacteria exist wherever there is life. They do not exist at great depths in the soil, but at the surface of the earth they are abundant, especially if the soil is moist and full of organic material. They exist in all bodies of water, including the great depths in the oceans, and they are found at high altitudes.

They exist in excessive abundance in decaying matter, wherever it may be. They are carried and spread by every animal and insect. They are ever-present on the surface of the body, on our clothing and on everything we touch. They are present in every crevice and pore of the skin, in the secretions of the body openings, and under the nails.

Many types of bacteria have the ability to exist through periods of cold or famine by adoption of a special form of spore. This spore withstands the drying effects of the air, and can withstand high as well as low temperatures. In such an inactive state they require no food and can live almost indefinitely. These spores abound everywhere in great variety, only awaiting favorable conditions to emerge as active micro-organisms.

There are three principal routes by which bacteria are admitted into our bodies: (1) By penetration through abrasions of the skin, or entry by way of any of the orifices in the body, (2) by being swallowed into the digestive tract in foods or from anything placed in the mouth, (3) by breathing.

Milk, for example, may be spoiled by lactic acid bacteria, which feed on the sugars in milk and produce lactic acid, causing the milk to sour. Meat, fruit and other foods, spoiled because of the action of bacteria, are unfit for consumption, owing to the formation in them of poisonous by-products, known as "ptomaines." These ptomaines are of uncertain chemical compositions which are poisons that taint foods, and when taken internally may cause great distress and even death.

It must never be forgotten that bacteria are living cells, and as such are subject to the conditions that govern all living things. As a rule, in animals and humans they are most active at blood heat.

The conditions necessary for bacterial growth are heat, moisture and food. The condition that favors infection in humans is lowered resistance of the body, because bacteria appear to be rather powerless to produce disease unless the condition of the person is favorable for their reception and activity.

When any of the tissues become inflamed, either as a result of injury or infection, the first effect is irritation, followed by increased supply of blood to the part. If this irritation continues, or is severe, the flow of blood slackens and a condition of congestion results.

Should harmful bacteria get into the blood via a sweat gland opening in the skin, or if the barber pricks the skin with a contaminated instrument, their toxins soon destroy many of the cells immediately surrounding that point of entry. (Fig. 99.) The capillaries in the area at once become distended.

The leucocytes (white corpuscles) then collect in the capillaries and pass through their walls, moving to all sides of the infected part. They form a wall around the infected area, and

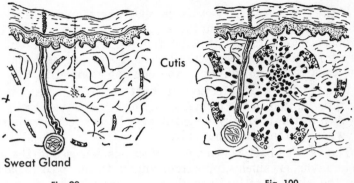

Cutis

Sweat Gland

Fig. 99.   Fig. 100.

a death struggle takes place between the bacteria and the leucocytes. (Fig. 100.) Under the microscope the leucocytes may be seen to move toward the germs, swallow them into their substances and digest them. This procedure is illustrated in Fig. 101.

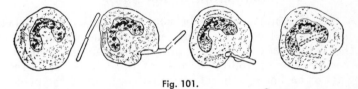

Fig. 101.

As a result of this death struggle a large number of leucocytes, bacteria and tissue cells are destroyed, causing redness, swelling, pain, and the formation of pus. In the skin a pimple or boil may appear, or a carbuncle may develop. (Fig. 102.)

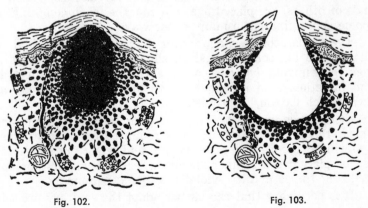

Fig. 102.   Fig. 103.

Pus consists of dead and living corpuscles, decayed tissue cells, dead and living bacteria, and substances thrown off by the blood.

If the leucocytes are victorious, the infected area will become localized. This area soon ruptures and the pus drains out. Then if properly cared for so that no further infection sets in, the cavity formed from the destruction of tissue will heal and new tissue cells will form, filling in the opening typified in Fig. 103.

In a condition of infection, it must not be inferred that its activity is limited to the primary part affected. It can easily find its way into the blood, by which it may be carried anywhere or everywhere throughout the body.

The various bacteria causing infectious diseases of the skin, such as favus, erysipelas, impetigo, ringworm and sycosis barbae, enter the skin directly through some break or opening, such as a pimple, cut, scratch or irritation.

The bacteria that cause diseases of the lungs, such as tuberculosis, pneumonia, influenza, bronchitis, etc., are for the most part inhaled.

Sanitation in the Shop

A fact that must always be kept in mind by the barber is that infection and contagious diseases are due to the entrance into the living body of specific organisms that grow on it and cause sickness or disability because of the toxins they produce. Every act of barbering, therefore, must conform to the principles of sanitation.

There is no worse offender than the human hand in the transmission of disease-producing bacteria from man to man. Our hands touch every conceivable thing. They come in contact with door knobs, handle money, touch our clothes, grasp the hands of others, are placed over our mouths when coughing, and become contaminated in many other ways.

Every operator should wash his hands with germicidal soap and sterilize his combs, brushes, clippers, razors, tweezers and other instruments *before* serving each patron, to protect him from infection. And he should wash his hands with soap *after* serving each patron, to protect himself.

Clean linen must be used on each patron and discarded immediately after use. State laws require that all instruments be sterilized before and after usage, and when not in use that they be placed in a cabinet sterilizer serviced with either vapor sterilizing fumes or ultra-violet sterilizing equipment.

It is necessary that the barber adopt the sanitary procedure of sterilizing his instruments by either cold or hot immersion *immediately* before usage, *in all instances.*

Considering sanitation in connection with shaving, it is not advisable to give a close shave unless the patron insists, and he should be warned that a close shave makes his skin more subject to infection. When a close shave is given, the cuticle, which acts as a protector to the underlying, sensitive tissues, has been partly scraped off, leaving the skin at the mercy of pathogenic bacteria. Moreover, if the patron should rub or scratch his face with his fingers after a close shave he is apt to infect himself, and the barber would probably be charged with causing the infection.

The shop owner must see to it that the entire shop is kept clean at all times—that sanitary procedures include a systematic cleaning of walls, chair equipment and floors at regular and frequent intervals.

Sanitation in the barber shop involves sterilization, disinfection and antiseptics.

Sterilization is the destruction of all organic life, whether infectious or not.

Disinfection is the destruction of *infectious* germs.

Antiseptics are agents which check the growth of germs. *Antisepsis* means the exclusion of germs.

Sterile means free from germs.

The methods of sterilization are:

1. **Dry heat** (not applicable for barber shop use).

2. **Moist heat.** This involves boiling in water, or steaming under pressure in an apparatus such as an autoclave. Boiling is a convenient and effective method for shop use, and acceptable equipment is available for this purpose.

3. **Vapors.** This method is universally used, and is recommended by many state authorities to keep instruments sterile. The vapor method is used in a closed cabinet by placing a piece of cotton or blotting paper (to further vaporization) in a small dish of vapor-producing solution. One such solution is a teaspoonful of borax to one tablespoonful of formaldehyde. The vapors thrown off by this solution *keep* the cleaned instruments sterile.

4. **Rays.** Recently, germicidal lamps have been developed which utilize certain of the ultra-violet radiation bands found to be high in bactericidal action. These lamps are incorporated in fixture cabinets and maintain sterile air in them. These rays will not effectively sterilize instruments, but will keep previously cleaned and sterilized instruments in an antiseptic condition while not in use.

5. **Chemicals.** The method of sterilization most commonly used in barber shops is to place all instruments in a germicidal

Fig. 104.

solution for a brief period before and after using. Such solutions are kept in enameled sterilizing trays (Fig. 104), glass jars or manufactured sterilizers containing special designed trays to accommodate the various types of instruments (Fig. 105).

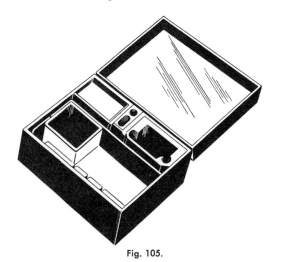

Fig. 105.

Chemicals for Disinfecting

Many chemical compounds in the form of liquids or tablets are recommended by State Departments of Health and are available at supply dealers. The barber should use preparations which are designed specifically for sterilization purposes and which do not damage or corrode the metal of his instruments. There are also preparations for disinfecting the hands, which should be used as a further sanitary precaution.

The following is a list of chemical disinfectants and their strength of solution which are accepted by some State Boards of Barber Examiners:

		To prepare	
(1)	Formalin (25% solution)	Formalin	2 parts
	(Formaldehyde)	Water	5 parts
		Glycerine	1 part
(2)	Liquor Cresolis Compound (4% solution)	L. C. Comp.	1 part
		Water	24 parts
(3)	Phenol (5% solution)	Phenol	1 part
	(Carbolic acid)	Water	19 parts

Some proprietary disinfectants, such as quatenary ammonium compounds, are approved by the medical and dental associations and state authorities.

Antiseptics that may safely be used on the skin are:

1. Iodine—a mild 2% solution is recommended in preference to the regular 7% tincture of iodine.
2. Alcohol 50% (don't use on inflamed areas).
3. Boric acid (full strength water solution).
4. Hydrogen peroxide (antiseptic and cleansing agent).

There are many effective skin antiseptics procurable in drug stores under various trade names, such as mercurochrome, mercresin, metophen, mercarbolic, merthiolate and others.

Cosmetic antiseptic lotions are now sold by supply dealers.

Keeping a sanitary shop and following sanitary procedures are not only a barber's obligations, but they are also fine business principles, with satisfied patrons as the rewards.

Personal Hygiene

Personal hygiene is not confined to freshly washed hands. The barber must be the exemplar of personal cleanliness. He must take his daily bath in order to be free of offensive body odors.

Mouth hygiene is especially important. Keep the teeth clean. Watch the diet during working hours. Avoid strong-flavored foods. If for some reason the breath is foul, visit a physician in an effort to eliminate its cause.

Shave daily. Keep the hair trimmed weekly.

Keep shoes shined and uniform spotless.

Cultivate morality and maintain a clean mind.

Finally, include a wholesome attitude while at work.

THIS DAY I WILL BEGIN

"A thing well begun is half done." So goes the old saying. The hard part is to begin.

It has been said that some men are born lazy and others energetic. This is not true. Almost all of us are born with an aptitude for laziness. It is easier to lie in the shade than to walk along a hot, dusty road.

We all have about the same capacity for getting tired, but those who get into the habit of work and study, and keep cultivating the habit, will in time develop energy, both physical and mental, that will go far toward helping them along the way.

Beginning a thing—that is where the pull comes. Don't wait for the more convenient day that never comes. Many people think of success as they think of a four-leaf clover. If they are chosen favorites of fortune, they think they will find it, but success is not luck. Success is playing the game.

Good advice is that which the poet gives:

"Are you in earnest? Seize this very minute!
What you can do, or think you can, begin it!
Only engage, and the mind grows heated;
Begin it—and the work will be completed."

This much is certain: If one is not preparing for a job higher up, he is making every preparation for one lower down. There is no standing still in this busy world.

Chapter 9

Anatomy and Physiology of Cells

I T is not sufficient just to *know how* to do the various services that constitute the practice of barbering; we must also be intelligent in our work by *knowing why* we do them. For that reason we have devoted several chapters to anatomy and physiology of the body.

A cell is a minute portion of living substance or protoplasm. Cells are the structural units of the body.

A cell contains a central, granular body termed the nucleus. The nucleus is the functional center of the cell. It is the primary, active portion of the cell, essential for nutrition, growth, secretion and reproduction.

Surrounding the nucleus is a less granular mass, a passive portion of protoplasm, called cytoplasm. This in turn is surrounded by a membrane defined as the cell wall.

Every part of the body is made up of organized groups of cells collectively performing complex, specialized activities in the living processes, and each cell, individually, carries on a specific function.

Metabolism is the building-up and breaking-down processes within the cell. In other words, metabolism is the constructive and destructive chemical changes continuously going on in the living cell.

Anabolism is the building-up process of the cell, whereby the cell absorbs food stuffs and transforms them into tissue elements.

Catabolism is the breaking-down process, whereby the cells convert complex chemical substances into simple ones, in the production of energy. For example, muscle cells burn up body sugars to release energy for their work in producing movement for the body. The waste products created because of these chemical changes are eliminated by the body.

It is well to note here that all these chemical changes of the living cell may be increased or somewhat decreased in the patron by the things we do in our services. We can decrease over-activities by relaxing ministrations, or we increase cellular activities by stimulating treatments.

Cells may be stimulated by:

1, Heat; 2, Massage; 3, Electricity (vibrations, high-frequency, ultra-violet and infra-red applications); 4, Drugs.

All the processes of life are dependent on individual cells, which are affected by respiration, elimination, motion, irritability, growth and reproduction.

Cell Respiration. Each cell, in a sense, breathes oxygen, and uses it in the production of heat and energy. In this process, while absorbing oxygen, it also accumulates carbon dioxide, which is eliminated through the lungs. Tissue respiration is carried on by the exchange of gases through the cell walls.

Growth and Reproduction. Each cell assimilates food stuffs from the surrounding tissue fluid or lymph and converts them into living substances for its growth, and when the individual cell reaches its maturity it reproduces another like cell.

All living cells, plant or animal, reproduce by dividing into two cells; thus the common phrase, "Cells multiply by division."

Cells of plants and lower forms of animals divide by simply splitting into two "daughter" cells. This process is known as direct cell division (amitosis).

Human cells divide by a more complex method referred to as indirect cell division (karyokinesis or mitosis).

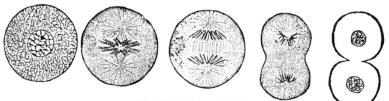

Fig. 106. Division of Cell.

Division of a Cell. (Fig. 106.) This illustrates various steps in the mitosis of a cell. The nuclear substance forms itself into two groups of chromosomes, each of which has all of the traits of the individual cell nuclei. These groups then migrate apart from each other. The chromosomes rearrange themselves into two separate nuclei, which in turn become the centers of new cells as the cytoplasm splits in two, forming two daughter cells.

Tissues, Organs and Systems. Tissues are masses of similar cells united together to form organs.

An organ is a part of the body, having a definite function to perform, or it may be considered as a group of tissues performing a specialized function.

A system is a group of organs performing a unified series of functions.

Cells and Tissues

Cell

Definition	A minute structure of living protoplasm, measuring from 1/300 to 1/3000 of an inch in diameter.
Protoplasm	Cytoplasm—portion of cell exclusive of nucleus. Nucleus—the functional center of the cell.
Respiration	Furnishes oxygen. Produces heat and energy. Removes carbon dioxide.
Metabolism	Anabolism—building-up process. Catabolism—breaking-down process.
Reproduction	Nucleus divides, cytoplasm arranges itself around each new nucleus.
Elements body is composed of	Carbon, hydrogen, oxygen, nitrogen, sulphur, phosphorus, chlorine, sodium, potassium, calcium, magnesium, iron, silicon and fluorine. Traces of iodine and manganese.

Tissues

1. Epithelial	1. Inner and outer body covering. 2. Linings, heart, respiratory, digestive. 3. Forms glands.
2. Connective	1. Ligaments, joints, tendons. 2. Fibrous, elastic. 3. Adipose. 4. Cartilage, bone, blood tissue.

3. Vascular—vessels.

4. Muscular.

5. Nervous.

The Body Systems

1. Skeletal.

2. Muscular.

3. Nervous.

4. Circulatory (vascular).

5. Respiratory.

6. Digestive (alimentary).

7. Excretory.

8. Endocrine.

9. Urogenital.

KNOWLEDGE FOLLOWS A MENTAL APPETITE

Have you ever noticed a hungry man? He thinks more about eating than anything else. Once his appetite is excited, his chief desire is to satisfy it.

A man who is not hungry can sit at a table and content himself with tasting a bit here and there. No matter how costly or how dainty the food, he will eat but little. For the time being his appetite is forgotten.

He is in the same class with many who do not care to learn more. Mental food is as necessary as other food, but one must create an appetite for it. What we all need to do is to build an appetite for knowledge, and the possession of that knowledge will come in a matter of time and will be a source of cultural enrichment.

Chapter 10

Digestion

AS the process of learning is continued, a greater awareness of the value of education is revealed to the barber. The more he learns, the more he knows. The more conscious he becomes of his obligations to the public he serves, the more certain he becomes that he should know considerable about all functions of the body. Good digestion is a requirement for a healthy body. Reasonable knowledge of the digestive processes, therefore, is an aid to his becoming a true professional barber.

We now understand that all the living cells of the body need a constant supply of fresh food. The body is composed of sixteen elements: carbon, hydrogen, oxygen, nitrogen, sulphur, phosphorus, chlorine, sodium, potassium, calcium, magnesium, iron, silicon, fluorine, small quantities of iodine and traces of manganese. Various combinations of these elements give us a great variety of substances which we call foods. Technically speaking, a food is anything which, when taken into the body, is capable of building up tissue or supplying heat to the body.

All foods are divided into six constituents, namely, (1) fats, (2) carbohydrates, (3) proteins, (4) mineral salts, (5) water, and (6) vitamins.

1. Fats are composed of carbon, hydrogen and oxygen, and are familiar to us in such forms as butter, lard, vegetable oils and the fats of meat and milk. Most of the fatty substances are liquefied at the temperature of the body, and are not soluble in water.

2. Carbohydrates are the sugars and starches. They are compounds of carbon, hydrogen and oxygen. Carbohydrates are found for the most part in three closely related food groups— grape sugars; milk, cane and malt sugars; and starches found in wheat, corn, potatoes, etc.

3. Proteins contain carbon, hydrogen, oxygen, nitrogen, a minute portion of sulphur and traces of phosphorus. They are the only food stuffs that contain nitrogen in any appreciable quantity. The foods that are most rich in the various forms of proteins are lean meat, eggs, milk, cheese, fish, wheat, beans and oatmeal.

133

4. Mineral salts are formed from the elements iron, calcium, sodium, potassium, magnesium, phosphorus, sulphur, chlorine, iodine, fluorine and silicon. These salts are found in the tissues and fluids of all living things, and they rank third in quantity among the constituents of the body. They are essential ingredients of nearly all substances used for food, but a diet that does not contain vegetables and fruits is quite certain to be lacking in some of these salts, calcium and iron especially. They help to maintain the acid-base equilibrium of the tissues, and iron is the chief constituent of hemoglobin, the oxygen-carrying material of the blood.

5. Water (H_2O) is a compound of two parts hydrogen and one part oxygen. Next to air, it is the most vital necessity in sustaining life. It supplies fluid for glandular secretions, for the chemical actions occurring during the digestive processes, and for balanced metabolism. It is an important factor in body heat regulation. It constitutes two-thirds of the body weight, and through food and drink it will usually constitute five-sixths of the daily body intake.

6. Vitamins are specific food substances necessary, in small amounts, for the proper functions of the body organisms. These substances are found in varying quantities in every sort of vegetable and animal foodstuffs. A well-planned diet assures that an individual will assimilate all vitamins required for good health.

Before the discovery of vitamins, about 1904, many people suffered vitamin deficiency diseases like beriberi, pellagra, rickets and scurvy.

Research studies devoted to vitamins are tremendous, and developments in this field are being reported daily. Diseases stemming from vitamin deficiencies are gradually disappearing. The average man is now aware of the general rule that has evolved from this new science, namely, that a *healthy diet* is a *balanced diet*. If a person includes all classes of foodstuffs in his meals from day to day, he is assured an adequate supply of the necessary vitamins needed to maintain a healthy body.

The Classification of Vitamins

Vitamin A—Substances classified chemically as carotenoids, related to plant pigments.

Deficiency of Vitamin A causes: (1) Night blindness, (2) abnormalities of epithelial tissues, skin dryness, scaling, and atrophy.

Source—Leafy vegetables; alfalfa; green stalks like asparagus, broccoli and celery; peas and beans, carrots, sweet potatoes, peppers, egg yolks, butter, cream.

Vitamin B Complex is a group of several vitamins, namely:

1. Thiamine, formerly B_1, destroyed by heat (cooking); a factor in carbohydrate metabolism; necessary for growth. Its deficiency is responsible for beriberi.

2. Riboflavin, formerly B_2. Antipellagric.

Others of the B Complex vitamins are: Niacin, pyridoxine, choline, folic acid, biolin, inositol, pantothenic acid, and para-amino benzoic acid. It is well to note here that the last two named factors are found to be associated with hair color in animals, but to date there is no evidence of their efficacy in restoring color in human hair.

Sources of Vitamin B Complex group—Peas, beans, spinach, whole grain, nuts, lean meat, eggs, milk and fruits.

Ascorbic Acid, formerly Vitamin C, is effective against scurvy. Its deficiency causes hemorrhages in the skin and mucous membranes. Source—Citrus fruits, uncooked tomatoes and peas, and raw vegetables.

Vitamin D is a group of some ten compounds, of which the two important ones are ergosterol D_2 and calciferol D_3. These are the anti-ricketic factors found in raw milk, eggs, fresh and canned fish.

Vitamin E—Alpha tocopherol, antisterility factor, found in raw wheat.

Vitamin K—The antihemorrhagic factor. Source—Alfalfa, spinach, kale, fish meal, liver, tomatoes and egg yolk.

When the barber is aware of the importance of vitamins in the maintenance of health, he is in a position to advise his patrons by recommending that they seek the advice of a physician who will aid in correcting hair, skin and scalp conditions. Of the Vitamins listed, it is most important that the barber thoroughly understand vitamins A, B, C and D.

The Digestive Process

Each move we make, the winking of the eyelids, each thought that passes through the brain, each beat of the heart, each breath we draw, awake or asleep, requires energy, which destroys some of the body cells. If this waste goes on without repair, the body soon wears out and life ceases.

Nutrition is the process by which the tissues are built up to replace those that are wasting away.

Before food can nourish the body it must undergo physical and chemical changes. It must be broken up and the useful parts of it must be dissolved and liquefied. Foods must be mixed with each other, and the useful ingredients must be separated from those which are worthless. All foods, including bread, butter, milk, eggs, beef, pork, vegetables and fruits, must be changed into substances that can be absorbed into the blood stream, to be carried to all the cells of the body and absorbed into them. This process is called digestion.

It is important for the barber to understand the process of digestion, as he will come to subjects later on in the Textbook that will necessitate his having this knowledge. Much of the barber's services consist of massaging the scalp and face to stimulate the parts under manipulation. If he has knowledge of what body nourishment really is, and how it is prepared through digestion, it will help him to understand the value of services that, through stimulation, help nourish those parts of the body on which he works.

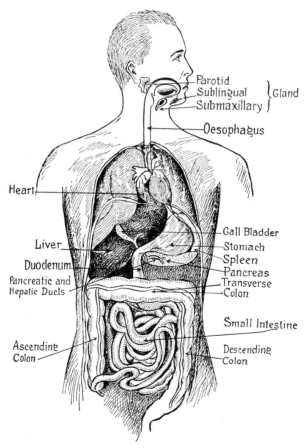

Fig. 107. The Digestive System.

One must appreciate the value of a service himself, before he can successfully sell it to others.

The digestive system consists of the alimentary canal and its appendages, *viz.*, lips, tongue, teeth, salivary glands, pharynx, oesophagus or gullet, stomach, liver, pancreas and intestines. (Fig. 107.)

The process of digestion is divided into different stages, *viz.*, prehension, mastication, swallowing, gastric digestion (stomach), intestinal digestion, and defecation.

Prehension is the act of conveying the food to the mouth. Once in the mouth the process of mastication begins, which consists of grinding and chewing the food by the teeth. At the same time the salivary glands pass their secretions, called saliva, into the mouth, to be mixed with the food.

There are three pairs of these glands. The largest pair, known as the parotid glands, is situated, one on either side of the face, below and in front of the ears. They secrete a fluid that empties into the mouth through a duct just opposite the second molar tooth of the upper jaw. This liquid helps to moisten the food. The second pair, called the submaxillary, is located beneath the lower jaw toward the back, one on either side of the face, and are the size and shape of a walnut. The third pair, called the sublingual, is located underneath the tongue and are almond-shaped. The latter two pairs secrete a ropy, thick saliva which packs the food and makes swallowing easy.

A fact to remember in connection with all these glands is that their secretion (saliva), by virtue of the enzyme (ptyalin) which it contains, acts on starchy foods (white bread, corn, potatoes, etc.), transforming the starch into a variety of sugar called glucose. It is necessary that starchy foods be masticated well for the proper starch-to-glucose process, in order that the blood stream will absorb it. A few seconds after bread has been under mastication, glucose will turn it sweet in the mouth. Ptyalin has very little effect on fats and proteins, except to render them softer and better prepare them for the action of the other digestive juices in the stomach.

After the food has been chewed, moistened and packed together (in this form it is called bolus), the tongue draws it back into the pharynx.

The pharynx is a striped, muscular, somewhat cone-shaped tube. When the act of swallowing is about to be performed, the pharynx muscles draw it upward and dilate it to receive the food. As the muscles relax, the pharynx sinks, and the muscles then contract upon the food, which is pressed downward and onward into the oesophagus or gullet.

The oesophagus is a tube extending from the pharynx to the stomach. This tube has muscles extending around it, and when the food enters it they contract, one after the other, the upper one first and the next in order, thus gradually forcing the food into the stomach. The opening of the stomach which connects with the oesophagus is called the cardiac orifice.

The food is now in the stomach, which serves as a reservoir for enough food to supply the body with nourishment for several hours. The stomach will hold from one to two quarts.

The muscular arrangement of the stomach, which is controlled by the sympathetic nervous system, is constructed to facilitate the peristaltic action of the stomach, during which it presses upon the food and moves it back and forth.

The cavity of the stomach is always the size of its contents, which means that when there is no food in it, it is contracted. When food enters, it expands just enough to hold it.

The walls of the stomach are lined with a multitude of gastric glands which secrete a fluid known as gastric juice. This juice is a definite chemical substance manufactured within the glands, and is a thin, nearly colorless liquid with a mild acid reaction. The essential constituents are hydrochloric acid and two enzymes, pepsin and rennin.

Combined with hydrochloric acid, pepsin is the chief active principle of gastric juice for digesting proteins, such as lean meats, eggs, etc., changing them into a substance called peptone. The hydrochloric acid acts also as an agent in the destruction of some forms of bacteria that enter the stomach. The rennin changes casein, the protein of milk, into a curd.

The fats undergo no true digestive change in the stomach. They are set free from their mixture with other foodstuffs by the dissolving action of the gastric fluid. They are liquefied by the heat of the body, and are scattered through the mixture in emulsion by the movements of the stomach.

Within a few minutes after the entrance of food into the stomach, small contractions start in the middle region of the organ and run toward the pylorus (the orifice or opening into the duodenum). Some foods pass through the pylorus into the duodenum twenty minutes after entry into the stomach. Other foods are churned in the stomach for as long as six hours.

Rolling from side to side like an electric washer, the food is rubbed down into smaller and smaller masses, while the gastric glands constantly pour their secretions on the foods, helping to break up and dissolve the food substances, until ultimately the mixture consists of a mass having the consistency of moderately thick pea soup. This mixture is called "chyme." During the process of digestion, at varied intervals, portions of this chyme are discharged through the pylorus into the duodenum.

The duodenum is part of and continuous with the small intestine, which is a convoluted tube about twenty-three feet in length, extending from the pylorus to the beginning of the large intestine.

In the duodenum, the chyme, which consists of broken-up and dissolved proteins; peptones derived from the proteins; sugars from the carbohydrates; fatty acids from the fats; portions of all foods not yet digested; hydrochloric acid from the gastric fluid, and lactic acid produced by fermentation, receives its final chemical preparation to complete the digestion through addition of juices from the intestines, pancreas and liver.

The small intestine has a peristaltic worm-like movement, which churns the contents about and mixes them with intestinal juice, important juices from the pancreas and another from the liver (bile). The latter two organs pour their juices through ducts called the pancreas and bile ducts. These two ducts join with a tube that opens into the duodenum, called the ampulla of Vater.

The pancreatic fluid has the power of acting on all the foodstuffs, proteins, carbohydrates and fats. This action is due to the enzymes, trypsin, amylase and lipase.

Trypsin, like the pepsin in the stomach, acts on proteins, and the final completion of protein digestion takes place from addition of the enzymes of the intestinal juice, erepsin, when the proteins are transformed into a substance called amino-acid. The amylase action is similar to the action of ptyalin, the enzyme of the salivary gland. The starchy foods that escape digestion in the mouth are digested by this enzyme. Lipase splits up some of the fats into fatty acids and glycerine.

The pancreatic juice is a strongly alkaline liquid, consequently when mixed with the chyme it neutralizes most, if not all, of the hydrochloric acid of the latter.

The bile is an alkaline liquid, and serves as a digestive secretion by accelerating the action of the lipase of the pancreatic fluid in transforming fats into glycerine and fatty acids.

After the juice from the pancreas, the bile from the liver and the intestinal juice have accomplished their part in altering the proteins into amino acids, fats into fatty acids and glycerine, and carbohydrates into simple sugar, these nutriments are absorbed into the blood.

In the lining of the small intestine there are thousands of finger-like projections that are called villi. (Fig. 108.) Their purpose is to draw the digested nutriments into the blood. They act

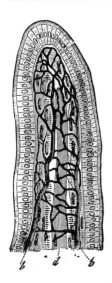

Fig. 108. An Intestinal Villus. b, b, capillary network; d, lacteal vessel.

as pumpers that suck or absorb the liquefied substances into the blood for the body to use as fuel and building material.

In the structure of the villi there are vessels called the lacteals, which absorb the fatty acids and glycerine. These processed materials are then carried to the great thoracic duct, which empties into the subclavian vein, thence into the superior vena cava to the heart and to the capillaries. The capillaries absorb the other substances, carrying them into the portal vein to the liver, through the liver into the hepatic vein, which in turn carries these nutriments through the inferior vena cava to the heart. (Fig. 109.) From here the nutriments are sent to all parts of the body, which will be explained in the chapter on Circulation. All material that the gastric, pancreas, bile and intestinal juices fail to transform into a soluble and absorbable nutriment is gradually worked downward by the peristaltic contraction of the intestines, and is eliminated as waste matter via the colon.

The subject of digestion is one that should be given much thought and study. Imperfect digestion, or improper functioning of the digestive organs, has a direct effect on the skin. The skin, it must be remembered, is also an eliminative organ of the body, and whenever the digestive organs fail in their duty, that much more work is thrown on the skin.

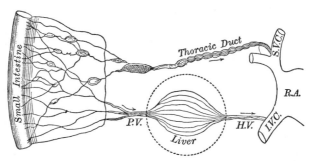

Fig. 109. The paths by which the products of digestion enter the general circulation. (P.V.: Portal Vein; H.V.: Hepatic Vein; S.V.C.: Superior Vena Cava; I.V.C.: Inferior Vena Cava; R.A.: Right Auricle.)

Another important fact to be remembered in connection with this subject is that the action of the gastric glands is hindered by stimulation of the sympathetic nervous system, and the emotions of anger, pain, worry, etc., may retard digestion.

The barber should be careful in his actions neither to aggravate the patron, nor render any service that is unpleasant, painful or irritating.

Digestion following a meal is also retarded by excess mental or muscular activity. The barber should be an advocate of relaxation and take advantage of every occasion to impress on his patrons the high value of scientific barber service for the alleviation of mental and physical strain or fatigue.

YOUR REAL COMPETITOR

In the majority of cases your competitor is not the fellow across the street, but, instead, your own carelessness in rendering services to the patron. Pay particular attention to the little things; in their sum total they weigh up either for or against you.

KEEP IN TUNE WITH THE TIMES

Nowadays the barber must handle his patrons with tact, and must constantly be on the alert, seeking newer things, for we are coming into a new era. We must introduce something different than the old cut-and-dried come-and-get-it attitude that has been at the root of many a business failure.

Chapter 11

The
Circulatory System

THE study of cells and tissues has shown that they must have a constant supply of food, air and water, and a means of constantly eliminating waste materials.

The study of digestion has shown how all foods are digested or prepared in such a way that they are transformed into liquid food substances, available to and usable by the cells.

The circulatory system may be called the transportation system of the body. It is the system of tubes or channels that carries air, water and foods to all parts of the body, and transports all waste products from the tissues to points of elimination.

The circulatory system is composed of a blood and a lymph system.

The blood vascular system is composed of the heart, arteries, capillaries and the veins. The arteries are tubes that carry the blood from the heart. Arterial branches extend to all parts of the body, the final extensions of which are called capillaries. The arteries are usually deeply situated, which affords them natural protection from possible accidental injury. In places where they are located close to the surface the pulse can be felt, as in the wrists, on the temples and at the sides of the neck.

The pulse results from the alternate dilation and contraction of the artery, reflecting the dilations and contractions of the heart. As each expansion of an artery is produced by a contraction of the heart, the pulse, as felt in any superficial artery, is a convenient guide for ascertaining the character of the heart's action.

The arteries are somewhat elastic and are capable of being slightly extended, which adapts them for receiving the additional amount of blood pumped into them at each contraction of the heart. This elasticity changes with the age of the individual, and with advanced years arterial walls grow stiffer and more rigid in an individual, tending to cause higher blood pressure.

The capillaries, as stated, are exceedingly minute vessels which receive the blood from the arteries and carry it to the veins. All cells and tissues, with the exception of the cartilages, hair, nails and cuticle, are transversed by these networks of capillary vessels. The capillaries are by far the most important vessels, as they have permeable walls, and it is through their thin walls that all the exchange between the blood and tissue fluids takes place.

In the glands the capillaries supply the substances requisite for secretion; in the alimentary canal they take up some of the elements of digested food; in the lungs they absorb oxygen and give up carbon dioxide; in the kidneys they discharge a portion of waste products collected from other parts; constantly, through their walls, the interchange is going on which is essential to the renovation and life of the whole body.

The veins are tubes that carry blood from the body to the heart. Their walls are much thinner and contain less elastic tissue. The veins are provided with valves whose function it is to prevent the backward flow of the blood.

The blood circulates constantly, visiting every portion of the body. It cannot go astray, as it circulates in closed channels. The central powerhouse or pump that forces the blood through the body is the heart.

The blood is of a bright red color in the arteries (except in the pulmonary artery between the heart and the lungs), and is known as "arterial blood." In the veins (except in the pulmonary veins between the lungs and the heart), the blood is a dark, purplish red in color, and is known as "venous blood."

The pulmonary artery transports *venous* blood from the heart to the lung for purification. The pulmonary vein returns *purified* blood from the lungs to the heart, which then pumps it through the *arteries* to all parts of the body.

Blood is salty in taste and has a reaction that is slightly alkaline. It is a somewhat sticky fluid, a little heavier than water, has a peculiar odor, and has an average normal temperature of about 98.6 degrees Fahrenheit.

It is estimated that about one-twentieth of the body weight of an adult is blood. For instance, in a body weighing 160 pounds, eight pounds are blood, or four quarts by measure. The blood consists of an enormous number of minute cells or corpuscles floating in a transparent, slightly yellowish fluid known as "plasma." More than eight-tenths of the plasma content is water. The blood serves the cells as a carrier of nutriments such as fats, salts, amino acid derived from the proteins, and glucose derived from carbohydrates. It also serves as a medium to carry away the waste thrown off by the cells, such as carbon dioxide gas, dead cells, uric acid, etc.

The corpuscles are formed in the bone marrow, and are of two kinds, red and white. (Fig. 110.) The red corpuscles (erythrocytes) are coin-shaped cells, and their function is to carry oxygen to the tissues, and carbon dioxide from the tissues to the lungs. They do this by means of hemoglobin, an iron-containing compound, and a most important chemical constituent of the corpuscle. Because of this iron, hemoglobin has an attraction for oxygen, and when hemoglobin and oxygen are brought together they unite, turning the corpuscle bright red in color (arterial blood). But this combination is very weak, and the corpuscle readily gives up its oxygen to surrounding fluids which contain less oxygen. In this process the blood turns to a purplish red (venous blood).

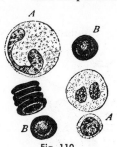

Fig. 110.
A. White corpuscles.
B. Red corpuscles.

These minute red corpuscles float in the blood stream, taking on oxygen in the lungs, and carrying it to and unloading it at the tissues. From the tissues the red corpuscles absorb carbon dioxide, and carry it to and unload it in the lungs, where it is eliminated as the breath is exhaled.

The white corpuscles, or leucocytes, less numerous than the red, perform a different duty. They are called the policemen of the body. Their work is to destroy disease germs. They approach a germ, collect around it and attempt to devour it. If they are victorious the germ is destroyed, and body health is restored. But if the germs are too numerous, and too powerful, the corpuscles are destroyed and the disease is in control. (This action is explained further under the subject of sanitation.)

The Heart

The heart is a strong, hollow, muscular organ situated behind the breast bone, with the greater portion to the left of it. It is about the size of a closed fist and shaped like a blunt cone.

It is divided into four rooms or cavities. The two upper cavities are called respectively the right and left atrium, and the lower cavities, right and left ventricle. (Fig. 111.)

The right atrium is connected with the superior vena cava, the large vein that drains the venous blood from the upper half of the body, and with the inferior vena cava, the vein that returns to the heart the venous blood from the parts below the diaphragm. An important fact to remember is that the proteins, carbohydrates and salts absorbed from the small intestines are emptied into the right atrium through the inferior vena cava, and the fats are transported to the right atrium through the superior vena cava. (Fig. 111.)

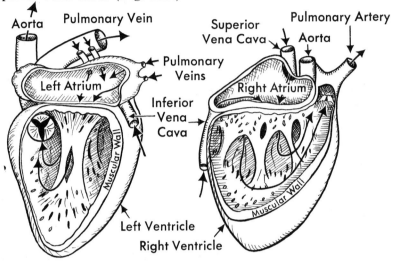

LEFT CHAMBERS OF HEART   RIGHT CHAMBERS OF HEART

Fig. 111.

Between the right atrium and right ventricle is a valve called the "tricuspid valve." After the blood enters and fills the right atrium, a contraction of this cavity opens the valve, forcing the blood into the right ventricle. After the ventricle is filled the tricuspid valve closes. This prevents the blood from flowing back into the atrium. At nearly the same instant, by a strong contraction of the ventricle, a valve (pulmonary valve) opens into the pulmonary artery. The blood is thus forced through this artery to the lungs. Its return to the ventricle is prevented by the closure of the pulmonary valve. The blood is reoxygenated (purified) in the lungs.

Oxygenation

The air we breathe is received into the trachea or windpipe, and from there it passes into the bronchial tubes. At the termination of these tubes is a great number of small air sac projections known as alveoli. The walls of these tiny air sacs consist of an elastic, thin and delicate tissue. Lodged in this tissue is a very close network of capillaries. The walls of the capillaries are also very thin and delicate. The air reaching the alveoli is separated from the blood in the capillaries by these thin membranous walls. (Fig. 112.)

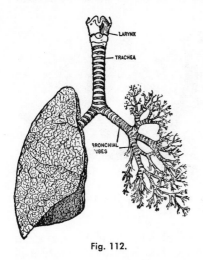

Fig. 112.

These thin membranous walls are of such construction that the oxygen in the alveoli and the carbon dioxide in the blood within the capillaries can easily pass through it.

The passage of oxygen to the blood and of carbon dioxide from the blood to the air is controlled by the laws of diffusion of gases. There is more oxygen in the alveoli than in the venous blood in the capillaries, hence the oxygen pressure is higher in the alveoli, with the result that some of the oxygen passes from the alveoli into the blood in the capillaries. The same principle applies to the passage of carbon dioxide from the blood within the capillaries, where the carbon dioxide gas pressure is higher, to the air in the alveoli, where the gas pressure is lower. The result is an exchange of gases through the capillary and sac walls and also a change in the color of blood. The aerated blood is changed from purplish red dioxygenated blood to bright red oxygenated blood.

The aerated blood, which now contains oxygen, is returned from the lungs to the heart through the pulmonary vein, which empties into and fills the left atrium. There is a valve between the left atrium and left ventricle, known as the bicuspid valve. This valve opens, permitting the blood to pass from the left atrium into the left ventricle. After the left ventricle is filled the bicuspid valve closes. Another valve (aorta valve) opens into the aorta, and the blood is pumped into it from the left ventricle. Return of the blood to the ventricle is prevented by the closure of the aortic valve.

The aorta is a large artery that receives the arterial blood from the heart. Other arteries branch from the aorta and extend to all parts of the body. These branches divide into smaller and smaller branches and finally become the capillary system.

The blood entering the capillaries from the arteries contains the nutriment and oxygen to be delivered to the cells.

Between the walls of the capillaries and the cells are lymph spaces filled with tissue fluid or lymph. The thin walls of the capillaries are permeable, and the blood plasma, carrying with it nutriment as well as oxygen, filters through these walls and becomes lymph. (Fig. 113.)

The tissue cells take from the lymph the nutriment and oxygen they need to maintain their functional activity and return to the blood the waste-products of this activity.

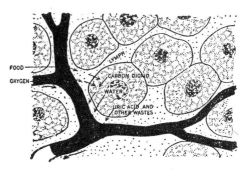

Fig. 113. The lymph acts as a middleman between the cells and the blood.

The surplus food material, together with other waste products (carbon dioxide), arising from the catabolism of the tissue cells is carried away from the tissues and back to the blood stream by a system of absorbent vessels called lymphatics. The lymphatic system is an extensive network of vessels and glands which filter tissue fluid and set up defenses against the spread of infection. These vessels are very minute in the lymph spaces, but connect to form larger vessels which unite with the veins and finally empty their contents into the blood stream through the inferior vena cava.

The capillaries, as described before, are very minute in size. They are so abundantly distributed throughout the body that a pin point cannot enter the tissues anywhere without breaking them and causing the blood to escape.

The summary of circulation is as follows: The blood coming from all parts of the body through the venous system enters the right atrium of the heart through the superior vena cava and inferior vena cava; from the right atrium it passes into the right ventricle; from the right ventricle into the pulmonary artery to the lungs, where it is changed to arterial blood; through the pulmonary veins to the left atrium of the heart; from the left atrium to the left ventricle; from the left ventricle to the aorta; to all parts of the body; into the venous system and back to the heart again.

The circulation from the heart to the lungs and back to the heart is called the *pulmonary circulation,* and the circulation from the heart throughout the body and back again is called the *general circulation.*

We have now completed another very important subject in Barber Science that should be kept in mind constantly, while studying the rest of the subjects, as the blood supply has everything to do with the life of the body. Lack of proper blood supply means lack of nourishment, which results in poor growth (hair) and lack of tone (muscles, skin).

Patrons should be made aware of these facts, attention especially being called to the value of increasing the blood supply through face and scalp manipulations, as, ordinarily, the face and scalp get the least amount of exercise of any part of the body. Besides, the blood has more difficulty circulating to the head, as it is the highest portion of the body.

Blood Supply of Face and Scalp

Other than a superficial knowledge of the circulatory system, the barber's function is to stimulate blood supply to the areas of the body to be nourished, principally the head, neck and face. Emphasis is therefore placed on the heart, arteries and capillaries which supply oxygenated and nourishing blood.

It must be understood that the hair itself contains no blood vessels. In the study of anatomy of the hair it is known that the bulb is the lower extremity of the root and grows from the papilla at the bottom of the hair follicle. The papilla has the physiological power to produce hair cells by cell division.

It has been further learned that the bulb is hollowed out and fits over the cone-shaped papilla that rises from the pit of the follicle.

The papilla is supplied with capillaries derived from the deeper circulation of the skin. It is from the papilla that the bulb receives its nourishment. A sufficient blood supply is indispensable for the best condition of the hair.

The growing power of the hair, its length and duration of existence, its nourishment, its glossiness and its entire formation all depend on an adequate blood supply.

Although the human scalp has a profuse network of capillaries, blood circulation in it is not as efficient as in many other parts of the body. It has less actual blood pressure than almost any other body area, due to the fact that it is the highest point from the heart.

Moreover, the lack of natural muscular activity lessens circulation in it. Muscular activity is a considerable factor in the facilitation of both blood and lymph circulation. Another factor is that the scalp is probably neglected from early childhood. It receives little or no stimulative exercises, whereas all other parts of the body are exercised daily. Combing the hair once or twice a day and a shampoo once a month is the ordinary stimulation the scalp receives.

The scalp adheres quite tightly to the skull, and the flow of blood through the capillaries of the scalp is somewhat retarded. When pressure is applied, such as would result from wearing a hard or tight hat band, a retardation of blood circulation occurs, causing the hair to become undernourished and stunted.

When sub-normal circulation cuts off the blood supply to the capillaries which nourish the papilla, the cell-producing power of the papilla suffers and it fulfills its functions sluggishly. If this condition prevails over a long period, the hair will fall out.

It is equally apparent that everything that facilitates the circulation and increases the quantity of blood in the capillaries of the papilla will further its maintenance and lengthen the life of the hair.

By studying Fig. 114 the exact location of the arteries and

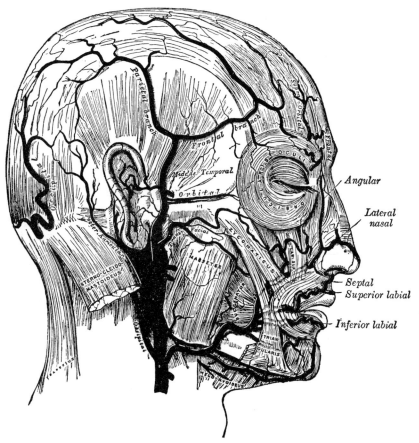

Fig. 114. Arteries of the face and scalp.

the sites of their superficial emergence on the face and scalp may be seen.

The principal arteries which supply the head are the common carotids. They arise directly from the arch of the aorta above the heart, and ascend in the neck behind the sternocleidomastoid muscle to the level of the thyroid cartilage (Adam's apple), where they divide into the external and internal carotid arteries. The internal carotid artery and its branches supply the inner skull. The external carotid and its branches supply the scalp and face.

The third branch of the external carotid is the origin of the facial artery which supplies the pharynx and face. Its branches are known as the inferior palatine, tonsillar, glandular, muscular, submental, masseteris, buccal, inferior labial, inferior and superior coronary, lateralis nasi and angular. The transverse facial originates from the temporal artery and supplies the parotid glands, masseter muscle and the skin of the face.

The external carotid begins at the middle of the sternocleidomastoid muscle and ascends just behind the ramus of the lower jaw in front of the ear. At a point beginning in the substance of the parotid gland, its name changes to superficial temporal. It ascends upward over the temporal muscle, where its pulsations may be easily felt. At a point about two inches in front of the top of the ear, the superficial temporal divides into the frontal and parietal branches.

The frontal branch runs tortuously upward and forward to the forehead, supplying the muscles and skin in this region, and all of the anterior part of the scalp, except the extreme frontal portion, which is supplied by the supra-orbital arteries. The parietal, larger than the frontal, curves upward and backward on the sides of the head. It lies superficially over the temporal fascia, and its branches overlap with branches of its fellow of the opposite side, and with branches of the posterior auricular and occipital arteries. This parietal branch supplies the anterior (front) part of the posterior (back) half of the scalp.

The extreme posterior portion of the scalp is supplied by the occipital and posterior auricular branches of the external carotid. The former emerges from behind the mastoid process, which serves as the insertion for the sternocleidomastoid muscle, and ascends up into the scalp, dividing into numerous branches which reach the vertex (top) of the skull. Its branches also overlap those of its fellow of the opposite side and with branches of the posterior auricular. The posterior auricular emerges in front of the mastoid process just behind the ear, extending backward and upward, and, with the occipital branch, supplies the area behind the ear.

The supra-orbital branch of the internal carotid emerges from the supra-orbital foramen, which is a small opening in the skull just above the orbit, which permits the artery and nerves to pass through. This notch can be felt above the eyes. This artery ascends and supplies the extreme frontal portion of the scalp. All arteries in the scalp dwindle into a profuse network of capillaries which nourish the hair, all of the scalp and the muscles and skin of the forehead.

Circulation

Circulation

Arteries
- Carry blood from the heart.
- Divide into capillaries.
- Possess elastic walls.

Veins
- Carry blood to the heart.
- Begin where capillaries end.
- Walls thinner than arteries; less elastic.
- Contain valves.

Capillaries
- Network of minute tubes.
- Connecting link of arteries and veins.
- Through their thin walls, exchange between blood and tissue fluids takes place.

Blood
- Bright red in arteries (except pulmonary artery).
- Dark red in veins (except pulmonary veins).
- Sticky fluid, salty to taste.
- Temperature 98.6 degrees F.
- 1/20 of body weight.

Function
- Carries nutriment and oxygen for the cells.
- Carries away waste thrown off by cells.

Composition
- Red corpuscles—carry oxygen.
- White corpuscles—protect the body from bacteria.
- Plasma—fluid about 8/10 water. Carries nutriment to cells, carbon dioxide from cells.

Lymph
- Acts as middleman between the blood and tissues.
- Carries nourishment from blood to tissues.
- Carries waste from tissues to the blood.

Heart
{

Right atrium { Receives blood from superior and inferior vena cava.

Right ventricle { Receives blood from right atrium, drives it to lungs through pulmonary artery.

Left atrium { Receives blood from lungs through pulmonary veins.

Left ventricle { Receives blood from left atrium, and drives it through aorta to all parts of body.

Pulmonary System—Blood circulating from the heart to the lungs and back to the heart.

General System—Blood circulating from heart through body and back to the heart.

1. Kidneys—Urea is filtered from the blood brought to each kidney by a branch of the Renal artery.

2. Liver—Portal circulation: Passage of blood from the gastro-intestinal tract and spleen through the liver and exit by the hepatic vein.

Chapter 12

The Bones
of the Head

THE skeletal system is the supporting structure of the body. The skeleton is made up of bones, cartilages and ligaments. The number of bones in the human skeleton is usually given as 200. This figure excludes the tiny ear bones, which would raise the total to 206. It must be understood, too, that tall individuals sometimes have an extra pair of ribs, so, the number is not absolutely fixed.

Classification of bones is made according to shape:

Long bones, like those of the legs.

Short bones, like those of the fingers.

Flat bones, like those of the cranium.

Irregular bones, like those of the spine.

The functions of the bones are as follows:

1. They give shape and strength to the body and keep the organs in position.

2. They protect the organs from injury.

3. They afford a solid place for the attachment of muscles by means of which motion is given to various parts of the body.

Chemically bones consist of about one-third organic matter and two-thirds inorganic matter. The organic part of bones consists of bone cells, blood vessels, connective tissue and marrow. The inorganic part consists of calcium carbonate, calcium phosphate and other inorganic salts.

The bones receive their nourishment through blood vessels which enter the hard substance by way of a network of tubes or canals.

The bones are covered with a tough, fibrous membrane (periosteum) except at the joints, where they are covered with cartilage. If the fibrous membrane is removed the bones die. When a bone has been burned for a sufficient length of time it will be so brittle that it may be easily broken. If it be soaked in muriatic acid, it will entirely lose its stiffness, and if the bone is of sufficient length it can be tied into a knot. Through these experiments it is understood that the bones contain a mineral substance which makes them stiff and hard, and a certain amount of animal substance or gelatin which binds them together and gives them a slight degree of elasticity. The mineral substance is mostly lime, and composes about two-thirds the weight of the bone.

The bones in a human being do not reach their full development before the age of 25.

The Skull

The skull is an oval, bony case which gives shape to the head and protects the brain. It is formed by the union of the eight cranial bones neatly dovetailed together, and fourteen facial bones.

A very important fact to understand is that the bones of the skull serve as fixed attachments for the muscles of the head, face and neck.

BONES OF CRANIUM: Occipital, 1; parietal, 2; frontal, 1; temporal, 2; ethmoid, 1; sphenoid, 1; total, 8. (Fig. 115.)

The Occipital Bone. This bone is situated at the back and base of the skull. It serves as attachment for the trapezius and occipital muscles and for insertion of the sternocleidomastoid muscle. The bottom of this bone is pierced by an oval opening called the foramen magnum. This opening permits the spinal cord to pass through to the medulla oblongata, a posterior part of the brain, which is continuous with the spinal cord.

Parietal Bones. By their union the greater portion of the left and right sides of the roof of the skull is formed.

Frontal Bone. This bone resembles a cockleshell, and not only forms the forehead but also enters into the formation of the roof of the orbits (eye sockets) and of the nasal cavity.

The hollow spaces of the arch formed by part of the frontal bone over the eyes are known as the frontal sinuses, which are filled with air and open into the nose. Just above the orbit a slight distance from the nose is the supra-orbital notch or foramen, through which blood vessels and nerves pass. They may be felt if pressure is applied in the proper places.

Temporal Bones. They are situated on the right and left sides and at the base of the skull. The upper or squama portion is the thinnest portion of this bone, and affords attachment for the temporal muscle.

The lower part forms the mastoid portion and gives attachment to the posterior auricular muscle, and the mastoid process serves as an insertion for the sternocleidomastoid muscle.

The Ethmoid Bone. This bone is an exceedingly light, spongy bone placed between the two orbits and at the root of the nose. A portion of it is pierced with numerous openings which permit the passage of nerves from the olfactory or first cranial nerve to the mucous membrane of the nose. The olfactory nerve governs the sense of smell.

The Sphenoid Bone. It articulates with and binds the other cranial bones together. It helps form the cavities of the orbits and nose. In form it resembles a bat with wings extended.

BONES OF THE FACE: Nasal, 2; vomer, 1; inferior turbinated, 2; lacrimal, 2; zygomatic or malar, 2; palatine, 2; superior maxillary (upper jaw), 2; inferior maxillary (lower jaw), 1; total, 14. (Fig. 115.)

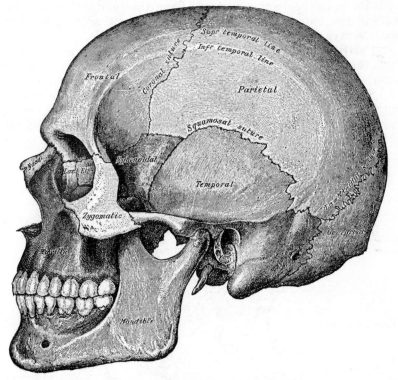

Fig. 115. Side view of the skull.

Nasal Bones. They are two small, oblong bones placed side by side at the middle and upper parts of the face, forming by their junction the bridge of the nose.

Vomer. A single bone placed at the lower and back part of the central septum (wall or partition) of the nasal cavity.

Inferior Turbinated. They are situated in the nostrils, on the outer wall of each side. Each consists of a layer of thin, spongy bone, curled upon itself like a scroll.

Lacrimal Bones. These are the smallest and most fragile bones of the face. They are situated at the front of the inner wall of the orbits, and resemble a finger nail in form, thinness and size. They are named lacrimal because they contain a portion of the canal through which the tear ducts run.

Zygomatic or Malar Bones. These bones form the prominence of the cheeks and part of the outer walls and floors of the orbits. They are commonly known as the cheek bones.

A prominent spine of the bone projects backward from the body of the zygomatic and articulates by the free extremity, with the spine projecting forward from the temporal bone, thus making the two members form the zygomatic arch. The zygomatic serves as the origin for the masseter muscle.

Palatine Bones. They are shaped like an "L" and help to form the back part of the roof of the mouth, part of the floor and outer wall of the nose, and a small portion of the floor of the orbits.

Superior Maxillary or Upper Jaw Bones. These are two in number, right and left. They form part of the floor of the orbits, the floor and part of the outer walls of the nasal cavities and the greater part of the roof of the mouth. They contain the upper

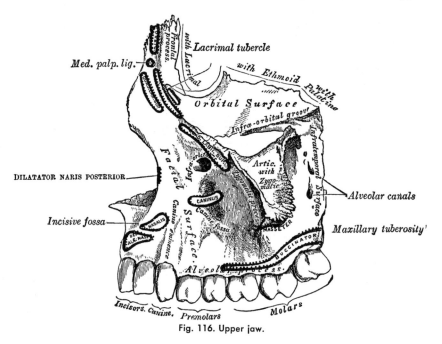

Fig. 116. Upper jaw.

teeth. Just above the incisor (front, cutting) teeth is a depression, the incisive fossa, which gives origin to the depressor alae nasi muscles. Just above and a little to the side of the fossa, the nasalis (compressor naris) muscle has its origin. (Fig. 116.)

A depression just above the canine teeth, called the canine fossa, gives origin to the levator anguli oris muscle. Above the canine fossa and just below the orbit is the infra-orbital foramen. It serves as a passageway for the infra-orbital blood vessels and infra-orbital nerves. The part of the upper jaw bone that contains the sockets for the teeth is called the alveolar process.

Inferior Maxillary or Lower Jaw, also known as **Mandible.** This single bone is the largest and strongest bone of the face, and consists of a curved horizontal portion, the body, and two perpendicular portions, the rami. (Fig. 117.)

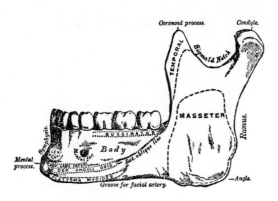

Fig. 117. Lower jaw.

It serves for the reception of the lower teeth. Just below the incisor teeth is a depression, the incisive fossa, which gives origin to the mentalis (levator menti) muscle. Below the premolar tooth, on either side, midway between the upper and lower borders of the body portion, is the mental foramen, which serves as a passageway for the mental blood vessels and mental nerves.

Running backward and upward from the chin on the lower jaw is a faint ridge known as the oblique line. It affords attachments for the quadratus labii inferioris (depressor labii inferioris) muscle and the triangularis (depressor anguli oris) muscle. The platysma is inserted below this line.

The ramus (branch) or the perpendicular portion has two processes, the coronoid and condyle. The coronoid process affords insertion to the temporal muscle. The condyle process articulates with the sockets in the temporal bones, which allows free movements in mastication.

The ramus serves as insertion throughout nearly the whole

extent for the masseter muscle. Along the alveolar border, as far forward as the first molar tooth, the buccinator muscle is attached.

The Hyoid Bone. This is an isolated U-shaped bone lying in front of the throat, just above the laryngeal prominence (Adam's apple). It supports the tongue. The omohyoid muscle is inserted into this bone. (Fig. 118.)

Fig. 118.

Principal Bones of the Head and Face

CRANIUM		FACE	
Occipital	1	Nasal	2
Parietal	2	Vomer	1
Frontal	1	Inferior Turbinated	2
Temporal	2	Lacrimal	2
Sphenoid	1	Zygomatic (Malar)	2
Ethmoid	1	Palatine (Palate)	2
	—	Superior Maxillary	2
	8	Inferior Maxillary	1
			—
			14

Principal bones of entire head.. 22
Hyoid bone in the neck.. 1

Chapter 13

The Muscles

THE study of muscles is known as myology. The greater part of what is known as flesh is collected into bands and so fastened to the various parts of the skeletal system of the body as to pull them in the different directions required. These fleshy bands are called muscles. They are about 500 in number, have many different sizes, shapes and lengths. Besides their use in producing body motion, they are so arranged as to give form and symmetry to the body.

Fig. 119. Muscle fibers.

A muscle is an organic bundle of contractile fibers, all extending in the same general direction. The fibers are separated from one another by a delicate membrane of connective tissue. (Fig. 119.)

The muscles are nourished by the food elements and supplied with oxygen in the blood, as are the other parts of the body. Muscles are well supplied with capillaries which are supported by the connective tissue. The capillaries do not penetrate the cells, but each cell is bathed in lymph which comes through the thin walls of the capillaries. The lymph supplies the cells with nutriment and oxygen, and carries away the waste.

The muscle tissue is also well supplied with nerves. Certain nerves convey impulses from the nervous system to the muscles, and control contractions. These are the motor nerves. Certain other nerves have sensory ends in the muscles. These convey to the central nervous system the state of contraction of the muscles, and telegraph muscular pain to the brain.

There is a circuit of nerves between the brain and the muscles. One nerve (sensory) conveys to the brain the sense of the condition of the muscle, and another (motor) carries impulses from the brain to the muscles, giving control of the action of the muscles.

Muscles are attached to the bones, cartilage, ligaments, tendons, skin, and sometimes to each other.

The attachments of the opposite ends of muscles are known as "Origin" and "Insertion." The first term, "Origin," is applied to the more fixed attachment, such as the bone, or some other muscle. The second term, "Insertion," is applied to the more movable attachment, or the part of the skin or muscle which it moves.

Hence it can be understood that, through the contraction of the facial muscles, the features of the face are altered into different expressions under the influence of emotion.

A muscle has power to contract and change its shape, or to become shorter and thicker. Technical terms and words will be avoided and a simple explanation will be given as to how the voluntary muscle contracts. (Fig. 120.)

There are three types of muscles— voluntary, involuntary and cardiac. The barber's services have to do almost entirely with voluntary muscles, those muscles which can be controlled by the brain "willing" them to move. The voluntary muscles are therefore dealt with in this Textbook.

The voluntary muscle fiber is found to be marked by alternate light and dark bands, which pass transversely across the fiber. According to Schaffer, the dark portion, called sarcous element, is made up of longitudinal tubes. When the muscular fiber is contracted, the clear portion is driven into these channels or tubes, and is caused to shorten and broaden (contract).

Fig. 120. Wave of contraction passing over a muscular fiber.

Muscles of the Head, Neck and Face

The muscles of the head, with a few exceptions, occupy the anterior portion of the head and serve to give characteristic form to the face. The muscles of the head are divided into:

1. Muscles of Expression.
2. Muscles of Mastication.

The following are the names and locations, as well as the actions, of the important muscles of the head. It is essential that the barber understand them, for in applying facial manipulations these muscles are affected. (Fig. 121.)

Epicranius (Occipito Frontalis). This muscle covers the whole vertex (top) of the skull, extending from the base of the

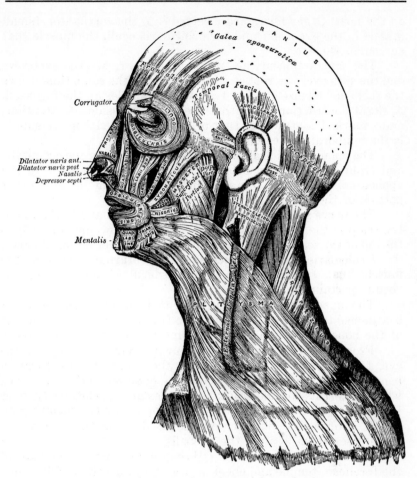

Fig. 121. Voluntary muscles of the head, face and neck.

back portion of the skull to the eyebrows. It consists of two portions, the occipitalis and the frontalis, connected by an intervening tendinous aponeurosis.

The occipitalis arises from the occipital bone and the mastoid part of the temporal bone, and is composed of two muscular strips about 1½ inches in length, which are directed upward and are joined with the aponeurosis. Its function is to draw the scalp backward. Its nerve supply is the posterior auricular branch of the facial nerve.

The frontalis portion is the muscle that covers the forehead. It has no bone attachment. It has its origin in the aponeurosis. Its fibers in the middle blend with the procerus, a muscle located on the nose. Other fibers are inserted into the corrugator (small muscle in the eyebrow) and the orbicularis oculi, the muscle that surrounds the eye.

The contraction of the frontalis muscle raises the eyebrows and the skin over the root of the nose, and at the same time draws the scalp downward, causing transverse wrinkles on the forehead. A slight contraction gives the face the expression of attention; and a marked contraction, that of astonishment. Its nerve supply is the temporal branch of the facial nerve.

The aponeurosis is a thin fibrous sheet between the occipitalis and frontalis. The skin of the scalp is closely adherent to the aponeurosis, and the skin is thicker here than on any other portion of the body.

The nerve supply to the skin of the forehead and to the top of the scalp is the supra-orbital nerve. From the occiput in back to the top of the scalp, the nerve supply is the greater occipital nerve.

Orbicularis Oculi (Orbicularis Palpebrarum). This is the muscle that surrounds the eye. "Orbicular" means circular, "oculi" pertains to the eye.

The muscle arises from the inner margin of the orbit, where it is attached to the nasal portion of the frontal bone, and to the part of the bone of the upper jaw that meets with the frontal bone.

From its origin its fibers sweep with gentle curves over the eye, forming a thin flat layer over the eyelid. It also forms a heavier layer that extends up into the eyebrow, where it blends with the corrugator and frontalis muscles and spreads partly over the temple and cheek. This muscle is supplied by the facial nerve.

It is termed a sphincter muscle, as it closes the eyelids and compresses them against the eyeballs.

When this entire muscle is brought into action the skin of the forehead, temple and cheek is drawn toward the middle angle of the orbit (eye socket), causing wrinkles at the outer corners of the eyes. These wrinkles are sometimes called "crowsfeet." During the summer months, sharp sunlight causes a great deal of "squinting" of the eyes, and crowsfeet become more prominent.

In massaging this muscle, one should use light pressure, as it may irritate the eye. Care should be taken that creams are not worked into the eyes, as this causes smarting.

Corrugator (Corrugator Supercilii). This is a small, narrow, pyramidal muscle located in the eyebrow underneath the orbicularis oculi and frontalis muscles. It arises from the nasal portion of the frontalis bone, and from this attachment its fibers extend upward and outward and terminate in the deep surface of the skin about the middle of the eyebrow. It blends with the orbicularis oculi and frontalis muscles.

The fibers of this muscle draw the eyebrows downward and inward, and throw the skin of the central part of the forehead into vertical wrinkles, producing an expression of frowning. It also contracts when one shows an expression of suffering or pain. It is termed the frowning muscle.

Procerus (Pyramidalis Nasi). This is a small pyramidal muscle on the nose. Its fibers arise from the deep tissue of the skin covering the lower portion of the nasal bone.

From this attachment its fibers extend upward and are inserted into the skin over the lower part of the forehead between the eyebrows. Its fibers also blend with fibers of the lower and middle portion of the frontalis muscle. The action of this muscle is to draw the eyebrows downward, producing wrinkles across the bridge of the nose.

The contraction of this muscle produces a stern threatening expression, or one of severe anger.

Nasalis (Compressor Naris). This is a transverse muscle of the nose which arises above and to the side of the incisive fossa of the upper jaw. The incisive fossa is the depression above the incisor or front teeth of the upper jaw. From its origin the fibers pass upward, blending into the skin across the bridge of the nose. Its function is to compress the nostrils.

Dilator Naris, Posterior and Anterior. These are small muscles situated at the nostrils. The posterior arises from the margin of the nasal opening of the upper jaw, and is inserted into the skin near the outer edge of the nostril. The anterior is a delicate muscle situated just in front of the posterior. It is attached to the cartilage of the nose, and inserted into the skin of the nostril. These muscles blend with the quadratus labii superioris, which will be described later. They help to dilate the nostrils in difficult breathing and in some emotions, such as anger.

Depressor Septi (Depressor Ala Nasi). This muscle arises from the incisive fossa of the upper jaw, its fibers extending upward and inserting into the septum and ala (wing) of the nose. The septum is the partition of the nose. The function of this muscle is to draw the ala (wing) of the nose downward, thereby contracting the nostril.

Quadratus Labii Superioris. This muscle is a broad sheet, the origin of which extends from the side of the nose to the zygomatic bone. Some of its fibers form the angular head, which arises from the upper part of the frontal process of the upper jaw. It broadens as it descends, and part of it is inserted into the ala (wing) of the nose, and part of it into the orbicularis oris (the muscle which surrounds the mouth).

The fibers of the middle portion form the infra-orbital head, which is attached just above the infraorbital foramen. From this origin the fibers descend and are inserted into the muscular substance of the upper lip. The lateral fibers form the zygomatic head, and are attached to the malar surface of the zygomatic bone. From this origin its fibers extend obliquely downward to be inserted in the upper lip.

The contraction of the infraorbital and zygomatic heads gives the face the expression of sadness. The entire muscle acts to lift the upper lip.

Caninus (Levator Anguli Oris). This muscle is concealed by the lower part of the orbicularis oculi and the quadratus labii superioris. It arises immediately below the infraorbital foramen. From this origin its fibers pass downward and are inserted into the angle of the mouth, where it blends with the orbicularis oris, and some of its fibers pass into the lower lip. The function of this muscle may be understood by the name *levator*, meaning lifter, and *anguli*, pertaining to the angle of the mouth—lifter of the angle of the mouth.

Zygomaticus (Zygomaticus Major). This muscle arises from the zygomatic bone. From this origin its fibers pass obliquely downward to be inserted into the angle of the mouth, where it blends with the fibers of the orbicularis oris, caninus and triangularis.

The contraction of this muscle draws the angle of the mouth upward and outward, giving the face the expression of laughing.

Mentalis (Levator Menti). This muscle arises from the incisive fossa of the lower jaw. (The incisive fossa is the slight depression just below the cutting or front teeth of the lower jaw.) From its origin it descends and is inserted into the skin of the chin.

The word *levator*, means "lifter," and the word *menti* pertains to the chin; hence we understand its function is to lift the skin of the chin. Its action wrinkles the skin on the chin and causes the lower lip to protrude, giving the face an expression of doubt and dislike.

Quadratus Labii Inferioris (Depressor Labii Inferioris). This muscle arises from the oblique line of the lower jaw, just inside of the mental foramen, and its fibers pass upward and are inserted into the skin of the lower lip and blend with the orbicularis oris muscle. At its origin its fibers blend with the fibers of the platysma muscle (a muscle situated on the side of the neck). The oblique line mentioned in the description of this muscle is a faint ridge that runs backward and upward on the lower jaw from the chin.

The mental foramen (also mentioned) is an opening in the lower jaw just below the second premolar tooth, which permits passage of blood vessels and the mental nerve.

The name *depressor* means to draw down, *labii* pertains to lip, and *inferioris* means lower; hence the function of the muscle is to draw the lower lip downward and slightly sideward, developing an expression of ridicule or sarcasm. This muscle is thin and fan-shaped.

Triangularis (Depressor Anguli Oris). This is a triangular-shaped muscle also arising from the oblique line of the lower jaw. Its fibers converge as they pass upward. They insert principally into the orbicularis oris, but a few insert into the risorius. Some of the fibers are continuous with those of the levator anguli oris muscle. At its origin it blends with the platysma muscle. Its function is to depress the angle of the mouth, giving the face an expression of contempt.

Buccinator. This muscle is an important part of the substance of the cheek. It arises from the alveolar borders of the upper and lower jaws in the region of the molar teeth. (The alveoli are the bony sockets in which the teeth are rooted.)

From the muscle's origin its fibers extend toward the angle of the mouth, where they converge and blend with the orbicularis oris. The central fibers cross each other here, the lower fibers entering the upper lip, while those from above enter the lower lip.

Although the buccinator muscle is not classified as a muscle of mastication, it acts during mastication to prevent food accumulation between the cheek and the teeth. The contraction of this muscle forces the food back between the teeth into the cavity of the mouth. It is also used for blowing and whistling. Musicians, when playing wind instruments, use this muscle.

The Stenson's duct of the parotid gland (one of the salivary glands) pierces the muscle just opposite the second molar tooth of the upper jaw.

Risorius. This muscle arises from the masseter muscle. Its fibers extend forward to the angle of the mouth, blending with the orbicularis oris.

It is a narrow bundle of fibers, broadest at its origin. It retracts the angle of the mouth and produces an expression of grinning.

Orbicularis Oris. This is the muscle that surrounds the mouth. *Orbicularis* means circular or rounding, and *oris* pertains to the mouth. It lies in the substance of the lip, and its fibers are arranged in oval rings.

The last eight muscles named above, with the exception of the mentalis, are all inserted into and blend with this muscle, and with their assistance cause either a direct closure of the lips or protrudes them forward. It is a rather fleshy muscle.

The fifteen muscles so far described and the frontalis are supplied by the facial nerve and its branches.

Masseter. This muscle is arranged in two sets, the deep and the superficial. The superficial portion, the larger, arises from the cheek bone. Its fibers extend downward and backward, and are inserted into the angle of the lower jaw. The deep portion is much smaller. It also arises from the cheekbone and passes downward and more forward. It is inserted into the lower jaw.

This muscle helps to fill out the back portion of the cheek. It is one of the muscles of mastication, as it assists in raising the lower jaw against the upper jaw. One can see the prominence of this muscle when food is being chewed. It is supplied by the mandibular branch of the trigeminal or fifth cranial nerve.

Temporal Muscle. This is a fan-shaped muscle situated at the side of the head. It covers the whole temporal fossa. Its fibers converge as they descend, and end in a tendon which passes downward and is inserted into the coronoid process of the lower jaw.

This is one of the muscles of mastication, as it assists in raising the lower jaw and retracting it. It is supplied by the mandibular branch of the trigeminal or fifth cranial nerve.

The coronoid process spoken of in the description of this muscle is a projecting bone in the lower jaw on the inner side and above the last molar tooth of the lower jaw.

Omohyoid. This muscle consists of two fleshy bellies united by a tendon. It arises from the shoulder blade, and from this origin it inclines forward and slightly upward across the lower part of the neck. It passes under the sternocleidomastoid muscle, becomes tendinous, changes its direction almost vertically upward, and is inserted into the hyoid bone. Its purpose is to assist in swallowing by depressing the hyoid bone. It is supplied by the cervical branch of the facial nerve.

Platysma. This is a broad sheet of muscle on the side of the neck. It arises from the pectoral (chest muscle) and deltoid (shoulder muscle). Its fibers extend upward and middleward along the neck and blend with skin and muscle at the angle and lower part of the mouth. Some of its fibers are inserted into the bone beneath the oblique line of the lower jaw. It helps to depress the lower jaw and is supplied by the cervical branch of the facial nerve.

When this entire muscle is brought into action it depresses the angle of the mouth and also produces wrinkles on the side of the neck, giving the face a melancholy expression.

Sternocleidomastoid. This is the most prominent muscle of the neck. It receives its name from its two origins and insertion. It arises from the sternum (chest bone) and clavicle (collar bone), passes obliquely upward across the side of the neck, and inserts principally into the mastoid process of the temporal bone (portion back of the ear) and partly to the occipital bone. It is thick and narrow in the center, and thinner and broader on each end.

When the muscle at one side of the head acts, the head is drawn downwards to that side, and the face is turned to the opposite side and tilted upward. If the muscles on each side act simultaneously, they bend the head in a forward direction. This muscle is easily recognized in thin persons by its forming a cord-like prominence obliquely situated along each side of the neck. It is supplied by the accessory nerve and by the second cervical nerve.

Superior Auricular. This is a small, thin, fan-shaped muscle. It arises from the skin of the scalp above the ear. Its fibers converge as they pass downward and insert into the ear. Its function is to elevate the tip of the ear.

Posterior Auricular. This consists of two strips of muscle that arise from the mastoid process of the temporal bone and insert into the back part of the ear. Its function is to retract the ear.

Anterior Auricular. This is a fan-shaped muscle arising from the skin of the scalp at the temple. Its fibers converge and insert into the front part of the ear.

The last three named muscles are all supplied by the temporal branch of the facial nerve.

Trapezius. This is a flat, triangular muscle covering the upper and back part of the neck and shoulders, extending from the superior curved line of the occipital bone to the twelfth dorsal vertebra. It has attachments to all dorsal vertebras. Its action is to draw the head directly backward and sideways. The origins of the muscle are the superior curved line of the occipital, spinous processes of the last cervical and all dorsal vertebras. It inserts into the clavicle and spine of the scapula, and the acromion (triangular-shaped process at the summit of the scapula). It is supplied by the accessory nerve and branches of the cervical plexus.

Outline Summary of Muscles

(Names in *italic* are the old terminology.)

NAME	ORIGIN	INSERTION	FUNCTION	INNERVATION
		Scalp		
1. Occipitalis } 2. Frontalis } Epicranius (*Occipito frontalis*)	Superior ridge of occipital anterior margin of galea aponeurotica	Posterior margin of galea aponeurotica Blends with procerus, corrugator, orbicularis oculi muscles	Draws scalp backwards Pulls scalp forward and causes transverse wrinkles on forehead	Occipital Facial
		Eyelids		
3. Orbicularis oculi (*Orbicularis palpebrarum*)	Inner margin of orbit	Near origin encircling orbit	Compresses eyelids and draws skin of forehead, temple and cheek medially	Facial
4. Corrugator (*Corrugator supercilii*)	Inner margin of orbit	Skin of eyebrow	Draws eyebrows inward and downward, and causes vertical wrinkles at root of nose	Facial
		Nose		
5. Procerus (*Pyramidalis nasi*)	Tissues at bridge of nose	Into fibers of the frontalis	Draws down inner angle of eyebrows and causes vertical wrinkles at root of nose	Facial
6. Nasalis (*Compressor naris*)	Upper jaw near wing of nose	Skin at lower bridge of nose	Compresses the nostrils	Facial
7. Depressor septi (*Depressor alae nasi*)	Incisive fossa of maxilla	Septum and ala of the nose	Contracts the nostril	Facial
8. Dilator naris posterior	Upper jaw near wing of nose	Skin at margin of nostrils	Enlarges aperture of nose	Facial
9. Dilator naris anterior	Cartilage of the nose	Near tip of nose	Enlarges aperture of nose	Facial
		Mouth		
10. Quadratus labii superioris				
A. Angular head	A. Frontal process of maxilla	Middle of upper lip and wing of nose	Raises middle of upper lip and dilates nostrils	Facial
B. Infra-orbital head	B. Maxilla, just above infra-orbital foramen	Upper lip	Raises upper lip	Facial
C. Zygomatic head	C. Malar surface of zygomatic bone	Upper lip	Raises upper lip near angle of mouth	Facial

170

(Names in *italic* are the old terminology.)

NAME	ORIGIN	INSERTION	FUNCTION	INNERVATION
11. Caninus (*Levator anguli oris*)	Just below infra-orbital of foramen	Angle of the mouth	Raises angle of mouth	Facial
12. Zygomaticus (*Zygomatic major*)	Zygomatic bone	Angle of the mouth	Raises angle of mouth upward and outward	Facial
13. Mentalis (*Levator menti*)	Incisive fossa of mandible	Skin of chin	Raises and wrinkles skin of chin and pushes up lower lip	Facial
14. Quadratus labii inferioris (*Depressor labii inferioris*)	Oblique line of lower jaw	Orbicularis oris and skin of lower lip	Depresses lower lip	Facial
15. Triangularis (*Depressor anguli oris*)	Oblique line of lower jaw	At the angle of the mouth	Pulls down the corners of the mouth	Facial
16. Buccinator	Alveolar borders of upper and lower jaw near molar teeth	Orbicularis oris at angle of mouth	Flattens cheeks; used in inflating cheeks	Facial
17. Orbicularis oris	From fibers of other muscles	Acts as insertion for other muscles	Opens and closes mouth and protrudes lips	Facial
18. Risorius	Fascia of masseter	Orbicularis oris and skin at angle of mouth	Draws out angle of mouth	Facial
		Mastication		
19. Masseter	Zygomatic bone	Ramus of mandible	Closes jaw	Branch of Mandibular
20. Temporalis	Temporal bone	Coronoid process of mandible	Closes jaw	Branch of Mandibular
21. Pterygoideus externus (*Exterior pterygoid*)	Wing of the sphenoid	Condyle of the mandible	Chewing	5th
22. Pterygoideus internus (*Interior pterygoid*)	Fossa of the sphenoid	Angle of mandible	Chewing	5th

(Names in *italic* are the old terminology.)

NAME	ORIGIN	INSERTION	FUNCTION	INNERVATION
Neck				
23. Platysma	Clavicle and fascia of pectoral region	Mandible and corner of mouth	Wrinkles skin of neck	Cervical branch of facial
24. Trapesius	Occiput and vertebral spines	Posterior surface of clavicle and shoulder	Draws head backward and sideways	Accessory and 3rd & 4th cervicles
25. Sternocleidomastoid	Sternum and clavicle	Mastoid process of temporal bone	Turns head obliquely and pulls it forward	Spinal accessory
26. Digastricus anterior	Inner surface of inferior maxillary	Hyoid bone	Elevates the hyoid and the tongue	Inferior dental
27. Digastricus posterior	Digastricus groove of mastoid process	Hyoid bone	Elevates hyoid and tongue	Facial
28. Stylohyoideus	Styloid process	Body of the hyoid bone	Draws hyoid up and back	Facial
29. Sternohyoideus	Sternum and clavicle	Hyoid bone	Draws hyoid down	Cervical
30. Omohyoideus	Upper border of shoulder blade	Hyoid bone	Depresses hyoid bone in swallowing	Cervical
Ear				
31. Auricularis superioris	Skin of scalp	At ear	Raises ear slightly	Facial
32. Auricularis posterioris	Temporal bone	At ear	Pulls ear backward	Facial
33. Auricularis anterioris	Front of ear	At ear	Pulls ear forward and backward	Facial

Chapter 14

The
Nervous System

IN treating the subject of the nerves, it is necessary only to show their ordinary function. There is nothing simple about the nervous system, but so long as its functions are kept in mind, some progress can be made in understanding it.

The nerves in the human body vary in size from the tiny tendrils that enter the dental structure to the largest individual nerve, the sciatic, which is often half an inch or more in diameter. The spinal cord is not an individual nerve, but a *bundle* of nerves.

Life is sustained only by the various organs acting together in harmony. Without nervous action, the body and its organs would be as quiet and useless as a factory with machinery and fuel, but without a superintendent and workmen to operate it.

In order that growth or repair may go on in the body, and that the brain may rule the movements of the body, an organization must exist in the body to keep all the parts working together properly. This organization is the nervous system.

There are two distinct divisions of the nervous system:

I. The cerebrospinal nervous system consists of the brain, spinal cord, spinal nerves and cranial nerves, and it controls speech, taste, and sight, in addition to governing the voluntary muscles.

II. The sympathetic nervous system is a system of ganglia which controls the action of the stomach, bowels, circulation, digestion, glands and the involuntary muscles.

The principal nerve center is the brain. It occupies the main cavity of the head and is carefully protected from injury by the skull. The front and upper part of the brain, about three-fourths of the organ, is known as the cerebrum; the back and lower portion is the cerebellum.

The cerebrum is the seat of all intelligence. Without it all sensations—light, sound, taste, smell, touch, heat, hunger—are lost. When it fails to function, all power of moving the *voluntary* muscles is gone. The cerebrum is the part of the brain that gives one the power to think and feel. It is the part that enables one to remember, to love, to hate, to be glad and to be sad. The cerebrum decides what one shall do; it sends out messages to the muscles when one wishes to move them.

The cerebellum lies under the back portion of the lobes of the cerebrum. The cerebellum assists in maintaing muscular tone and co-ordination. Injury to the cerebellum may result in muscular weakness, loss of muscle tone, and inability to direct the involuntary movements of the muscles that support the body and move the limbs, hence causing one to stagger.

From the brain a mass of nerves known as the spinal cord extends downward through the spinal column to the lower extremity of the body's trunk. An enlarged part of this cord, which lies next to the cerebellum and within the skull, is known as the medulla oblongata. Thirty-one pairs of nerves issue from the spinal cord and extend to the different parts of the trunk and limbs. These are called the spinal nerves. Each of these nerves issues from the spinal cord in two parts or roots, one coming out of a groove on the back portion of the spinal cord and the other from a similar groove in the front.

The posterior root is sensory and the anterior root is motor.

Motor and Sensory Nerves

It is the special business of the nerves to carry messages to and from the nervous centers. Of the threads which make up these nerve cords, some report to the nerve centers as fully as possible all that is going on in the parts of the body where they are placed. Because they are able to do this work only by the sense of feeling or through some special senses, these are known as nerves of feeling, or *sensory nerves.*

It is the business of another set of nerves to carry impulses from the nerve centers to the muscles whenever the nerve centers decide that muscles ought to make certain motions. Since the muscles move in obedience to the messages carried to them by these nerves, they are known as *motor nerves.* Some nerves contain both motor and sensory tendrils, but some are exclusively one or the other.

Motor and sensory nerves are also called efferent and afferent nerves, respectively—efferent (carrying impulses *from* the brain) ; afferent (carrying impulses *to* the brain).

Much of the governing of the body by the nervous system is done without conscious thought. For instance, if a finger touches a hot stove the heat starts an impulse up the sensory

nerves. The impulse passes into the spinal cord, then into the
motor nerve, and travels down to the muscles of the arm, causing
them to contract and jerk the hand away. An impulse also goes
to the brain and registers pain, but the hand is moved before the
pain is felt consciously. Actions of this kind are called *reflex
actions*. They are different from the voluntary actions that are
caused by impulses which start in the brain and pass out to the
muscles, ordering some part of the body to move.

Whatever one does purposely, the mind, through the brain,
directs. But when actions are repeated a sufficient number of
times, the muscles become accustomed to the movement and the
acts are performed with ease and almost without thinking. This
unconscious repetition of an action is *habit*. The precision and
rapidity of action which come from habit constitute *skill*, and
the method by which skill is obtained is *training*. The training
which converts acts into habits relieves the mind and the brain
and permits them to study new things and to perform new acts.

One learning to play the piano is obliged to fix his entire
attention upon the position of his hands and fingers and upon the
keys they are to strike. When training has given him skill, he
strikes the keys correctly without conscious effort, and he is able
to give his mental attention to the music. In like manner, skill
enables the barber to cut hair with the least conscious attention
on the shears and comb, and with all his attention directed toward
doing artistic work.

The nerves are greatly affected by emotion. A joyous and
happy mood increases nervous action. The vital organs do their
work well, and a glow of health pervades the whole body. Grief
and worry diminish nervous action. Sudden, bad news sometimes
so paralyzes the nerves that the heart ceases for a time to beat,
and faintness or even death may result. Ill temper, envy, sulkiness
and all kinds of selfishness and meanness diminish nerve force
and tend to derange the actions of the vital organs.

Blushing is a condition in which the dermal blood vessels
are suddenly dilated and the face is reddened and heated, as a
result of an embarrassing emotion. The condition develops from
the action of a special set of nerves called vaso-dilators. Fear
causes a reduction of blood supply, which leaves the skin white
or pale. The condition develops from the action of a special set
of nerves called the vaso-constrictors. The vaso-dilator and
vaso-constrictor nerves are a part of the sympathetic nervous
system.

High Nerve Tension

Nerve cells, like other cells, store up energy in the form of
foodstuffs during the sleeping and resting periods.

During the course of daily activity these energy substances are used up and the nerves get tired. Under average conditions normal nerve fatigue results, and the nerves are refreshed by adequate rest, during which time the used-up energy is rebuilt to its proper level each day.

If the body is overworked physically and mentally the nerve cells are depleted to an excessive degree, and there is an abnormal breaking down of the cells. The toxic substances often reach a dangerously high level, causing excessive fatigue and nervous strain.

Prolonged nervous fatigue brings on digestive and circulatory disturbances, as well as poor complexion, dull eyes, lusterless and falling hair, and the body becomes chronically tired.

Nerve fatigue is induced by muscular and mental work. High nerve tension is induced by overwork and mental strain.

In this modern age of keen competition, faster living tempo, worry, and complex economic, political, social and psychological adjustments, the average person is subject to constant nerve strain and fatigue.

For this reason it is recognized in the barber profession that many services have been created for the person who feels fatigued, and who could patronize the barber and be relaxed by his ministrations.

Cranial Nerves

There are twelve cranial nerves on each side of the head. They rise from the brain and pass through openings in the base of the skull.

The first, or olfactory nerve, is the nerve of smell. It has numerous fibers distributed in the mucous lining of the nasal chamber.

The second, or optic nerve, is the nerve of sight. Its cells are situated in the innermost or rear portion of the eye.

The third, or motor oculi nerve, is a motor nerve. It acts on most of the muscles that move the eye.

The fourth, or trochlear nerve, is the smallest of the cranial nerves. It acts on the muscles that raise the eye and rotate it downward and inward.

The fifth, the trigeminus or trifacial, is the largest cranial nerve. It is the sensory nerve of the head and face, and the motor nerve of the muscles of mastication. The sensory fibers arise from the semi-lunar ganglion (nerve center) and are subdivided into three branches, as follows (Fig. 122):

(1) The ophthalmic branch, the smallest, is a sensory nerve. It supplies the eyeball, the lachrymal gland (tear gland), the

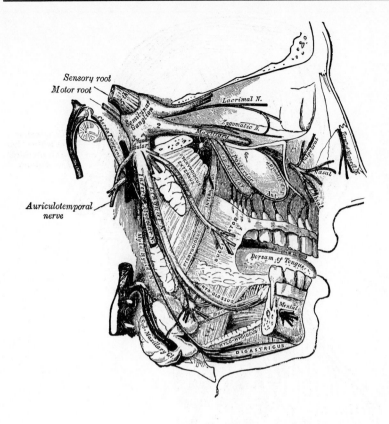

Fig. 122. Trigeminus or fifth cranial nerve, and its branches.

mucous lining of the nose and eye, and the skin and muscles of the eyebrow, forehead and nose.

(2) The superior maxillary, the middle branch, is a sensory nerve which spreads out to the sides of the nose, the lower eyelid, the upper lip and the upper teeth.

(3) The inferior maxillary, or mandibular branch, is the largest of the three. It is both sensory and motor. It sends branches to the temple, external ear, lower lip, teeth, gums, and the muscles of mastication.

The sixth cranial, or abducens nerve, is a motor nerve. It supplies one of the muscles known as the external rectus, which moves the eyeball outward.

The seventh cranial, or facial, nerve consists of both motor and sensory fibers (Fig. 123). It supplies motor fibers to all muscles of expression in the face and to some of the muscles of

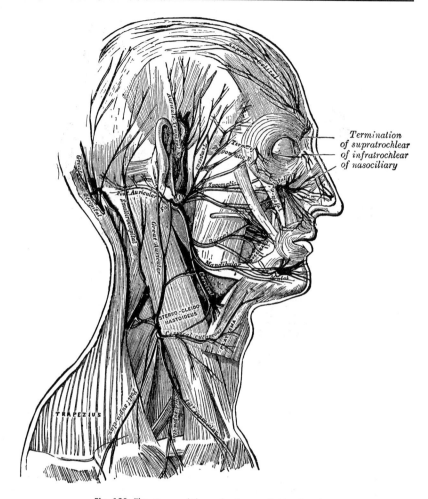

Termination
of supratrochlear
of infratrochlear
of nasociliary

Fig. 123. The nerves of the scalp, face and side of neck.

the neck and ear. The sensory fibers supply the submaxillary and sublingual glands. (These are salivary glands spoken of in chapter 10 on digestion.)

The eighth cranial, or auditory, nerve is the nerve of hearing.

The ninth, or glossopharyngeal, nerve contains both sensory and motor fibers supplying the pharynx, tongue, tonsils and parotid gland (salivary gland).

The tenth cranial, the vagus or pneumogastric nerve, contains both sensory and motor fibers. It passes through the neck to the upper part of the abdomen. It supplies the larynx, a portion of the respiratory organs, the pharynx, oesophagus, stomach and heart.

The eleventh, or spinal accessory, nerve supplies the sterno-cleidomastoid and trapezius muscles, the two principal muscles in the back portion of the neck.

The twelfth, or hypoglossal, nerve is the motor nerve of the tongue.

The trigeminus (fifth cranial nerve), the facial (seventh cranial nerve) and the spinal accessory are the most important nerves for the barber to understand, as these nerves and their branches are affected when giving facials by hand or with mechanical appliances; also when using electric current devices.

Nerve Points of the Face

The principal nerve points for the barber to keep in mind when giving shaves or scientific facials are (Fig. 124):

1. The supraorbital nerves, located just above the orbits.
2. The infraorbital nerves, located just below the orbits.
3. The mental nerves, located just below the premolar teeth on either side of the lower jaw.
4. The cervical nerves, located on the sides of the neck.
5. The seventh cranial or facial nerve, located just below and slightly in front of the ears. They pass through the substance of the parotid glands.
6. The semilunar ganglions of the fifth cranial or trigeminus nerves, located on either side of the head just above and slightly in front of the ears on the temples.

The principal nerves for the barber to keep in mind when working on the scalp are (Fig. 123):

Greater occipital, located in back of head; supplies back part of scalp and extends as far forward as vertex of the skull.

Posterior auricular, located back of ears; supplies skin back of ears.

Superficial temporal, located on sides of head; supplies the skin of the temporal region.

Supraorbital, passes through supraorbital foramen and ascends on the forehead into the scalp; supplies the skin on the front and top portions of the scalp.

On the subject of facials much has been said regarding relaxation, and in order that the barber may help the fatigued patron relax the following suggestions are offered.

First, suggest that the patron will be more comfortable with his coat removed and collar loosened. When giving the shave, attention should be given to adjusting the chair to an angle that will be comfortable for the patron. Adjust the head

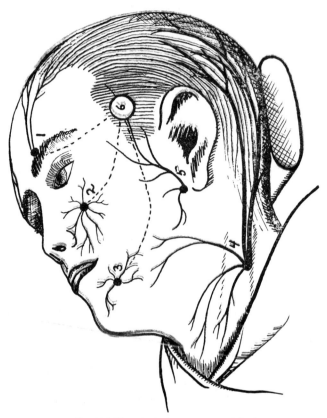

Fig. 124. The principal nerve points of the face.

rest so that the lower portion is at the same level with the shoulders of the patron. Recline the chair enough so he will not stretch his neck to keep his head in place on the head rest. Persuade him to rest his arms on the arm rests of the chair. Make sure that his feet are resting on the flat side of the foot rest.

After the beard has been shaved and after the second steam towel has been placed over the patron's face, the barber should gently press down on the nerve sites indicated in Fig. 124, which are the principal sensory and motor nerve sites in the face and neck. Three or four of these spots may be pressed at the same time. When removing the towel, grasp it in the usual manner with each hand and use a soothing, stroking movement over each nerve site. This will feel restful to the patron and he will unconsciously relax. At this point the barber may suggest to the patron that he treat himself to the luxury of a rest facial or other facial service.

The Nervous System

Functions of Nervous System
{
Ruler of the body.
Controls all visible and invisible activities.
Controls human thought and conduct.
Governs all internal and external movements of the body.
Gives power to see, to hear, to move, to talk, to feel, to think and to remember.
}

Nervous System
{

Brain— Principal Nerve Center
{
Controls sensations of light, sound, taste, smell, touch, heat, hunger and sight.
Controls voluntary muscles.
Gives power to think and feel.
}

Spinal Cord
{
Thirty-one pairs spinal nerves.
Nerves (sensory) from back grooves bring feeling to cord.
Nerves (motor) from front grooves carry orders to muscles.
}

Cerebro-spinal Nervous System
{
Consists of brain, spinal cord, spinal nerves and cranial nerves.
Controls speech, taste and sight; also governs voluntary muscles.
}

Sympathetic Nervous System
{
Acts on the stomach, bowels, circulation, digestion, glands and skin.
Controls involuntary muscles.
}
}

Kinds of Nerves
{

Sensory (Afferent)
{
Receive sensations of touch, cold, heat, sight, hearing, taste and pain.
Convey sense of relaxation to body.
}

Motor (Efferent)
{
Carry impulses from nervous center to muscles for certain motions.
}
}

Fatigue of Nerves
{
Toxins found in body.
Step slows up.
Body becomes tired.
Eyes dull, complexion poor.
Digestion disturbed.
Loss of hair.
}

Table of the Cranial Nerves and Branches

Name	Function	Branch	Sub-branches
1. Olfactory	Smell		
2. Optic	Sight		
3. Motor Oculi	Motion (of eye muscles)		
4. Trochlear	Motion (of eye muscles)		
		1. Ophthalmic	Lacrimal Frontal Nasociliary
5. Trigeminus	Sensation and motion (taste)	2. Maxillary	Zygomatic Superior alveolar Nasal
		3. Mandibular	Buccinator Lingual Inferior alveolar Mylohyoid
6. Abducens	Motion (of eye muscles)		
7. Facial	Motion		1. Supraorbital 2. Infraorbital 3. Buccal 4. Greater occipital 5. Lesser occipital 6. Temporal 7. Mandibular 8. Superficial cervical 9. Posterior auricular 10. Infra-trochlear 11. Mental 12. Malar 13. Zygomatic 14. Nasal
8. Auditory	Hearing		
9. Glosso-pharyngeal	Sensation and motion (taste)		
10. Pneumo-gastric	Sensation and motion		
11. Spinal accessory	Motion (speech)		
12. Hypo-glossal	Motion (muscles of tongue, thyroid, sterno-hyoid and omohyoid)		

Chapter 15

The Skin
And Its Appendages

THE skin is the term applied to the outer covering of the body. It is more than a blanket for the underlying structures; it is the living envelope of the human body, and is an organ of the body, with definite physiological functions.

The general structure of the skin varies in the different areas of the body. In the scalp, and where it is exposed to wear, as on the soles of the feet and palms of the hands, it is thicker than on other parts of the body. In less exposed areas it is thinner and more tender.

There are three main divisions of the skin. The outermost division is the *epidermis*. Under it is the second division, the corium or *dermis*. The second division is also known as the true skin. Under the corium is the third division, the subcutaneous tissue or *subdermis*.

The epidermis comes in contact with all the outside influences—air, water, dirt, germs, drugs, clothing, heat, cold, etc. It is the outside bulwark of the defense mechanism of the body. The epidermis is a specialized structure. A human being can live but a short time if the epidermis is destroyed.

The epidermis is composed of five layers of cells and is without blood vessels. (Fig. 125.)

The bottom layer of the epidermis, known as the germinating layer, is the growing layer. The cells that make up this layer have the power of reproduction, and it is the only layer of the epidermis that grows. The cells are constantly dividing. The older ones are pushed toward the surface by reproduction of new cells from below. On their passage from the germinating layer to the outer surface the cells age and change their shape and their chemical consistency until they have finally formed into flat, horny scales.

The layer above the germinating layer is known as the mucous or Malpighian layer.

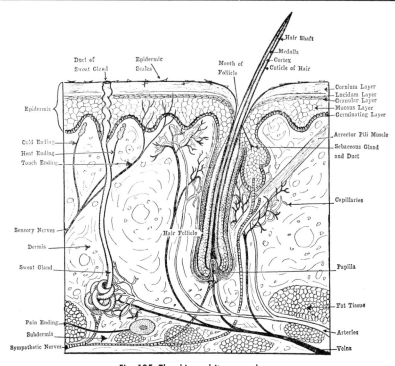

Fig. 125. The skin and its appendages.

The layer of cells above the mucous layer is the granular layer. This layer consists of the same cells which were produced in the germinating layer. At this stage the cells become filled with specks, like grains; hence the term "granular layer." This is a step in the process of cornification of the epidermis. The granules are now keratohyalin.

The next layer of cells is known as the lucidum layer. It is a semi-transparent layer, and is composed of closely-packed cells in which traces of flattened nuclei may be found.

The outermost layer of the epidermis is called the corneum or cuticle layer, and is composed of horny, flat cells that form into squames (scales). The cells that make up this layer are the same cells that originated in the germinating layer, and which have undergone physical and chemical changes in their progress to the surface of the skin.

The cuticle or corneum layer is composed of keratin, which is highly resistant to the entrance of germs, toxins, chemicals, gases, water and other foreign substances and poisons.

Keratin is the chemical constituent of horn. It is indigestible in pepsin and hydrochloric acid, and can withstand a fifty per cent solution of mineral acids for a prolonged period. It is readily broken up or dissolved by alkalies. It is a protein material, containing a considerable amount of sulphur and silicates.

These keratinous cells are constantly being shed from the body. They are removed in bathing, shampooing, washing the face and hands and in shaving. They are rubbed off with every motion. For the most part, loss of these cells is rarely noticed, yet they are being shed constantly.

The corium (dermis or true skin), lying between the epidermis and subdermis, is a highly sensitive and vascular layer of connective tissue. It is composed of bundles of white fibrous and elastic tissue arranged in a network, in the meshes of which are fat tissue, blood vessels, lymphatics, sebaceous glands, sweat glands and hair follicles. It supports numerous blood vessels, lymph vessels, nerves, glands, hair follicles and papillae.

The papillae project into the epidermis, which is moulded over them. These papillae elevations contain blood vessels and nerve endings, giving the skin a keen sense of touch. (Fig. 125.)

The elasticity of the skin is dependent upon the fibers of the dermis, which are elastic by nature.

The subcutaneous (subdermis) tissue may be regarded as a continuation of the dermis, except that it contains more fatty tissue.

The subdermis contains blood vessels, nerves, lymphatics, sudoriferous (sweat) glands and parts of the hair follicle of deeply-seated hairs. It is from the subdermis that the main blood vessels of the dermis ascend to branch off in all directions, supplying the oil and sweat glands and the hair follicles.

Capillaries are present in each papilla structure in the dermis as fine threads which are rather tortuous, as if they were longer than the length of the papilla and had to curve in order to fit the limitations of space. Each capillary loop has an arterial branch and a venous branch; that is, the system is a closed one.

The skin, exclusive of the epidermis, which contains no blood vessels, is capable of holding from one-half to two-thirds of all the blood in the body. Hence a general hot application to the body, by dilating the surface blood vessels, withdraws a large amount of blood from the internal circulation.

Cold has the opposite effect, causing a contraction of the blood vessels on the surface of the skin and forcing the blood out of the skin into the deeper blood vessels. (Fig. 126.)

The Sweat (Sudoriferous) Glands

The sweat glands are convoluted, tubular glands, with the deeper portions coiled into tiny balls which are lodged in the

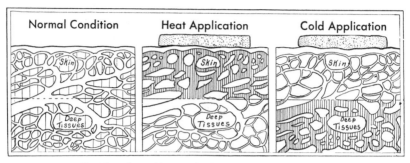

Fig. 126. Effects of heat and cold on the skin (shaded areas
represent concentration of blood).

subcutaneous tissue. Extending from the coil the tube is straight
or slightly tortuous, but upon entering the epidermis it assumes
a spiral course, terminating in a funnel-shaped opening, the
sweat pore. (Fig. 125.)

The coil is closely invested by a meshwork of capillaries,
and the blood in the capillaries is separated from the cavity of
the glandular tubes only by the membranes which form their
respective walls. (Figs. 125 and 127.)

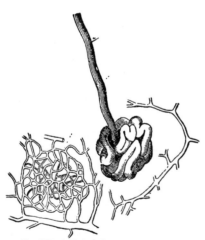

Fig. 127. Coiled end of a sweat gland.

Sweat glands are abundant everywhere in the skin, but they are largest and most numerous at the arm pits, the palms of the hands, soles of the feet and the forehead.

Functions of the Sweat Glands. Sweat is an excretion, and its value lies in the elimination of waste matter and in the loss of body heat by the evaporation of water (perspiration). When the kidneys are not functioning properly, and the blood contains an excessive amount of waste matter, the sweat glands, in addition to their normal function, will excrete some of the wastes ordinarily excreted by the kidneys.

The chief normal constituents of perspiration are about
two per cent organic substances and 98 per cent water. The
organic substances consist of salts, fatty acids, a small quantity
of carbon dioxide and a slight amount of urea.

Quantity. Under ordinary circumstances the perspiration that the body is continually throwing off *evaporates* from the surface of the body. This is known as insensible perspiration. When more sweat is excreted upon the surface of the body than is removed at once by evaporation, it appears on the skin in the form of drops. This is known as sensible perspiration.

The sweat glands are richly supplied with secretory nerve fibers. The activity of these glands may be influenced by external heat (hot towels), muscular exercise, strong emotions and the action of various drugs. In all such cases the effect is the result either of direct stimulation of the nerve-endings in the glands, or indirect stimulation through the sensory nerves of the skin. The common causes of profuse sweating are high external temperature and muscular exercise.

Sebaceous Glands

Associated with the hair follicles are the sebaceous glands, which secrete sebum. From one to six sebaceous glands are attached to each follicle. Sebum is a semi-solid, oily substance containing various fats, fatty acids, cholesterol, salts, albuminous material and water mixed with epidermic debris. The sebum passes through a duct from the gland into the sides of the follicle. Many of the ducts from these glands also open directly upon the surface of the skin, supplying sebum to the scalp and skin. (Fig. 125.)

The sebaceous gland is provided with a network of capillaries, and the output of sebum is stimulated by an increased blood supply to the gland and a rise in skin temperature. Alteration in the quantity and quality of fat in the food also affects the activity of the sebaceous glands. Unlike the sweat glands, sebaceous glands are not under direct nervous influence. The chief function of sebum is to lubricate the hair and prevent

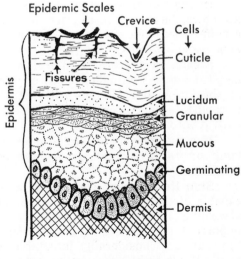

Fig. 128.

it from becoming dry and brittle, or injuriously affected by water. Also, it lubricates the skin, making it soft and pliable, and protecting it from sunburn and chapping from wind or cold.

Absorption

In the chapter on Cells, the life processes as they are carried on within the cells were outlined. It was shown how the balance of life is maintained by the co-ordinated interchange of substances through the cell walls.

When a fatty substance, such as cream, oil or ointment, is applied to the surface of the skin, it penetrates into the tiny fissures at the surface of the cuticle, and over a period of several hours slowly seeps through the spaces between the superficial, sloughing cells. (Fig. 128.)

This process of penetration is increased in proportion to the thinness of the fat. Warm oil is thin, consequently it has greater penetrability.

The rays from red dermal lights have the effect both of increasing the penetrability of the superficial cells by its relaxing action on them, and of thinning the oils. Radiation with a red dermal lamp for five minutes will develop a penetration of oils which would otherwise require several hours were the radiation not used.

Use of the red dermal and the infra-red lamps is advised where a greater and more rapid absorption of oil, creams or ointments is desired.

In the use of water or alcoholic solutions of any type, such as tonics, bleaches, antiseptics, astringents or soothing lotions, a lamp is less efficient because its heat tends to evaporate these aqueous substances.

Steam, preferably from well-wrung hot towels, is recommended for its high efficiency in increasing both the penetration of the lotion and adding to its activity. Steam has the ability to penetrate the epidermal cells, and carries substances in solution with it into the cells.

If a rule may be deduced, use red dermal light or infra-red lamp on fatty substances, and steam for water or alcoholic solutions.

Skin Respiration. The skin is a respiratory organ which is capable of eliminating watery vapor and carbonic acid gas, and absorbing minute amounts of oxygen. These functions are important to understand, because the functions of the skin of the scalp are considerably interfered with and loss of hair may result if air-tight constricting hats are worn.

Sensation. The skin contains nerves of special sensibility, such as heat, cold, pain, touch and pressure. These nerves are called sensory nerves. Fig. 125 reveals the several sensory nerve endings of the skin, each having its own special duty to perform. The nerve endings that register the sensation of pain are deeper in the skin tissue than the others.

These five nerve fibers in the skin are the outermost sentinels which protect the body by sending warning messages. They are the sensory nerve fibers that transmit to the brain the reactions of rest and relaxation to the patron. They also transmit sensations that may be disagreeable to the patron, causing his nerves to become tense.

It is easily understood why the patron immediately feels the scraping and scratching of a rough razor or the pulling of a dull razor, and that he might quickly complain of the irritating gouging of a sharp-toothed comb or the stiff bristles of a hair brush, especially if he has a sensitive or tender scalp. Such oversights aggravate a patron. Instead of receiving comfort and relaxation, he becomes irritated with the barber. He may be affected to the extent that he will decide to patronize another barber and perhaps a different shop.

Note the nerve endings that register the sensation of touch (Fig. 125). They are also near the surface of the skin, and are coiled around the roots of the hair. These nerve fibers are so sensitive that the softest feather cannot be placed on the skin without the sensation registering at the spot where it is placed. This fact being true, consider the sensation that is registered by these nerve fibers if the barber's hands feel hard, clubby or rough to the patron, especially while he is receiving a shave or massage.

The barber is most successful who acquires a light, rhythmic manner in his manipulations, and when he touches or handles a patron. The patron who is treated in this manner will enjoy a feeling of satisfaction, and will automatically relax.

Slightly deeper lie the nerve endings that register sensations of cold, and others close by record the sensations of heat. During a shave, if the bottom portion of the towel covering the lower part of the patron's neck is cool and the portion covering the eyes is hot, each of the nerve fibers registers the cold and hot temperatures of the towel at the same time. Under such careless treatment it is understandable that the patron refuses when the barber suggests a facial.

A towel that is not evenly heated is very disagreeable to the patron. It gives him the impression that the barber is indifferent or careless about his work, and with those thoughts registered in his mind he cannot relax. His only desire is to get out of the chair as quickly as possible.

The nerve endings of pressure are deep-seated sensory nerves of the skin. The sensation of pressure is most noticeable during scalp rubs or facials. The pressure of the unskilled barber's manipulations may bring tears to the patron's eyes. Such treatment is inexcusable, and it should absolutely be eliminated in all barber shops.

Follicle and Papilla

The follicle is a depression or pocket in the skin in which the hair grows. It extends from the outer surface of the skin into the dermis. (Fig. 125.)

Hair takes its shape, size and direction from the shape, size and direction of the follicles. The follicles are set into the skin of the face and scalp at various angles which regulate the "grain" of the beard and the characteristics of hair growth.

The lengths of hair follicles vary from 1/12 to ¼ inch. The follicles are permanent structures and remain in the skin even after the hairs which they contain are pulled out or shed. After permanent falling, however, they undergo an atrophic change and shrivel up.

Owing to the open mouths of the hair follicles, and their size, the scalp is a favorite site for the reception of invading micro-organisms, which produce disease conditions of varying types and characteristics.

At the bottom of the follicle is a small cone-shaped elevation called the papilla. It contains nerves and blood vessels. It is from the papilla and its blood vessels that the hair gets its nourishment. (Fig. 125.)

Disorders of the papilla and particularly of its blood supply are reflected in loss of the hair.

The Hair

The hair is divided into the hair root, the hair shaft and the point. (Fig. 125.)

The bulb is the club-shaped lower extremity of the hair at the bottom of the follicle. Its end is hollowed out into a cup-shaped cavity which fits around the upper portion of the papilla.

The root is that part of the hair contained within the follicle, including the bulb—in other words, the root is all portions of the hair beneath the surface of the skin.

The hair shaft is that portion of the hair which projects beyond the surface of the skin and terminates as a point.

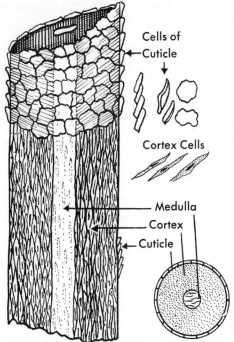

Fig. 129. Anatomy of the hair shaft.

In the cross-section of a hair we distinguish three layers, namely, medulla, cortex and cuticle. (Fig. 129.)

The medulla, the central core of the hair, is composed of round, coin-shaped cells. Air spaces sometimes form between these cells, having a tendency to affect the color of the hair.

The cortex is the second layer, constituting the greatest bulk of the shaft. It is made up of long, spindle-shaped cells, in which is contained the coloring matter in the form of minute pigment granules.

The source of pigment has not been definitely settled. It is probably derived from the color-forming substances in the blood, as are all pigments of the human body.

The color of the hair, ranging from dark to light, depends on the color of the grains of pigment. If the granules are dense, the color will be deep. If the granules are scarce, the color will be that of the granules, but lighter in tone. The presence of air in the hair brings out a lighter shade. When most of the pigment is gone and air spaces are still more numerous, the hair is white.

Canities. The turning of the hair from dark colors to white or gray color is termed canities. Gray hair in young or middle-aged persons is known as premature grayness. Albinos have complete whiteness of the hair. Here the pigment is lacking. The skin also is white or pinkish in this condition. In the vast majority of cases grayness of the hair is hereditary, and often the tendency is so strong that a person's hair turns gray at exactly the same age as did that of his parent, and in the same pattern.

Emotional shocks, worry, excitement, neuralgia, rheumatism, gout and wasting illness may lead to gray hair. The sudden, overnight change of dark hair to white has its proponents, but science has never recorded any such phenomenon up to date.

The care of gray hair will be taken up under shampooing and scalp treatments.

Cuticle or Outer Layer of Hair

The cuticle layer cells of the hair are flat, translucent, horny scales, free from pigment. These scales are piled up on each other, similar to shingles on a roof. Because of this arrangement and the density of the cells the outer layer forms a very effective shield for the inner hair structure.

The free edges of the epithelial cells point outward and upward and interlock with the cells that form the inner wall of the follicle, which point downward and inward.

The multiplication of cells, which is the true growth of the hair, occurs at the matrix cells of the bulb. Thus the point of the hair shaft represents the oldest cells, and the cells just above the papilla are the youngest.

The cells of the medulla of the hair grow from the top of the papilla, while those of the cortex originate from its sloping sides. The cuticle cells are formed where the outer rim of the bulb fits around the base of the papilla.

Arrector Muscles (arrectores pilorum). Connected with each follicle are small bundles of involuntary muscle fibers. These muscles pass from the surface of the true skin, to be attached to the neck of the follicle. When the muscles contract, as under the influence of cold or fright, the hairs are pulled up straight, and stand "on end"; the follicle is pulled upward, causing a condition of the skin known as "gooseflesh." (Fig. 125.)

There are three varieties of hair: Long hairs found on the scalp and face; short hair, such as the eyebrows and eyelashes; and lanugo, the fine, soft, downy hairs found on the forehead and other smooth parts of skin where the other varieties are lacking. Hair is absent on the soles of the feet and the palms of the hands.

The shape of the hair varies, straight hair being round; oval hair, wavy; and flat hair, curly or kinky.

The chemical composition of hair is: Carbon, about 50 per cent; nitrogen, about 18 per cent; sulphur, about 4 per cent; oxygen, about 21 per cent; hydrogen, about 7 per cent.

Life Phenomena. The life of the hair varies with age, sex, character of hair and individual peculiarities. Each hair has its determined length of life, and this is not the same for every hair of the same type. What may be the circumstances that determine the period of its existence is not known.

The lifetime of the eyelashes has been determined by Mahly as one hundred and thirty-five days. Pincus says that the life of an individual hair on the human head is from two to six years.

Some authorities think that hair grows faster by day than by night, and faster in warm weather than in cold.

The average length of an Anglo-Saxon woman's hair is from 18 to 24 inches when left uncut. Exceptionally, it may grow to 36 or even 50 inches, or more, in length. The hair of men of the same race has an average length of 12 to 16 inches, but, custom demanding that it be cut from time to time, it is rarely seen at this length.

The hair of each individual has its own determinate length, and the hair of men, even if left uncut, will not grow as long as that of women. The rate of growth varies from $\frac{3}{8}$ to $\frac{3}{4}$ inch per month. The average rate of growth may be gauged at $\frac{1}{2}$ inch per month for men and women. It must be understood that the rate of growth is slightly less for men than for women.

Number. The average number of hairs to the square inch on the scalp is given by Wilson as 1000. Withof found on a man, in one-quarter of a square inch of the crown of the head, 293 hairs; occiput, 225; anterior part of the head, 211; chin, 39; forearm, 23; back of the hand, 19.

Wilson calculates that there are 120,000 hairs upon the head of an adult. As a rule, the finer the hairs are, the more there will be per square inch of surface area. Stelwagon gives 140,000 for light blond hair, 90,000 for red hair, 109,000 for brown hair, and 108,000 for black hair.

Uses of Hair. The uses of hair are three-fold: 1. As a preservative of heat. 2. As a protective agency. 3. As a promoter of beauty.

(1) As the hair is an inefficient conductor, it serves to preserve the heat of the body.

(2) The hair of the head forms a thick, elastic cushion. Thus it is an admirable defense for the skull against blows and falls. The eyebrows are a defense to the eyes against blows, and they turn the perspiration to the outside of the eye-sockets. The eyelashes catch flying particles of dust. The hairs of the nostrils and ears prevent insects from entering the cavities which they protect, as well as guard against the entrance of other foreign substances.

(3) Little need be said of the hair as a promoter of beauty, as it is conceded that the hair is an adornment.

Shedding and Regrowth of Hair

At certain times of the year animals molt or shed their coats. A rapid fall of hair takes place and the animal's coat is thinned. At the same time, with the fall of the old hair there is a growth of new hair, and soon the coat is as thick as ever.

In the human species there is a constant daily shedding and regrowth of hair, although at certain seasons it may proceed more rapidly than at other seasons. It is stated by some observers that in many children the hair of the head falls out almost entirely in from two to six months after birth and is replaced by new growth of hair.

Each hair grows for a period of time, which is known as the life span of that hair. The bulb then atrophies and detaches itself from the papilla. The shed hair may fall out, be pulled out, or remain loose in the follicle. After a period of rest the papilla becomes active again and a new, young hair starts to grow.

The final fall of the old hair is hastened by both the pressure from the new hair below and by traction exerted upon it from above by brushing, combing or shampooing.

This new hair lives its appointed time and then undergoes the same fate as its predecessor, and thus the regular normal fall and regeneration of the hair is constantly repeated. A new hair begins to form in from 21 to 42 days after shedding.

After a severe illness, especially a fever, the shedding is more pronounced, and sometimes all the hair on the scalp will shed. This condition necessitates regular treatment by the barber, in addition to intake of nourishing, body-building foods, to be recommended by a physician.

We now understand that the follicile and papilla have everything to do with the growth of the hair, and that they will not function as they should if they do not get the proper care. The life of the hair will consequently be shortened through lack of scalp exercise and by unhygienic treatment, in which case the hair gradually grows thinner and shorter, with baldness the usual result.

The modern effort in barbering is to try to prevent baldness, rather than try to grow hair on a scalp that is already doomed to baldness.

The shedding of hair goes on for years without any sense of pain to the individual, which is the chief reason there is so little attention paid to it.

The weakening of any other portion of the body usually gives a warning; disorder of the heart causes a fluttering and faintness; disturbance of the stomach causes pain and nausea; weakening of the eyes causes headache; decay of the teeth causes toothache, etc. But growth of hair can become weaker without an individual becoming conscious of it, hence the condition often is not noticed until a thin spot appears.

The barber who is aware of the hair-growth cycle is of utmost benefit to his patrons if he impresses on them the importance of beginning the proper care of the hair at an early age. By giving it needed attention before it is too late the patron will retain his hair longer, rather than to attempt—fruitlessly— to regain it after the scalp and hair have reached the stage of deterioration where nothing can be done.

Pigment of the Skin

The pigment of the skin lies in and about the line of division between the dermis and the epidermis. The basal cell layer of the epidermis is considered the site of the pigment formation, but there is some pigment in the papillary portion of the dermis. The presence and shade of pigment is the factor which decides the color of the skin.

The pigment varies in amount according to the race of the individual and such other factors as exposure to wind and weather. The Negro has more pigment, and he is better fitted for life in tropical climates. Caucasians, whose skins have less pigmentation, cannot withstand the sun's rays unless they have developed suntan through regular exposure of the skin to ultraviolet rays. These rays fix a brown pigment in the skin.

The Nails

The barber should acquaint himself with the anatomy of the nails and their cosmetic care. Even though manicuring is not practiced by the barber, it is a standard service in barber shops, and it is necessary that he have this knowledge in order to manage this phase of his business.

The nails, like hair, are appendages of the skin. They are modifications of the epidermis, designed by nature to protect the extremities.

Nails are composed of horny cells of the epidermis compactly joined together to form horny plates. They have a convex outer surface and a concave inner surface intimately adhering to the underlying derma, called the matrix.

Divisions of the Nails: The *Nail Body* is the exposed part of the nail which lies in the nail bed.

The *Matrix* is the base beneath the nail.

The *Free Edge* is that part that extends beyond the finger tip.

The *Lunula* is the crescent-shaped marking at the base of the nail. It is a whitish area where the nail is softer and the underlying blood supply is less.

The average growth of nails is 1/32 of an inch per week.

The nail itself is translucent and devoid of color. The reddish nail bed shows through it, imparting the characteristic pastel shade of pink. This is often commonly referred to as the "healthy color" of the nails, because many disturbances of circulation or general health are reflected by changes in the color as well as thickness of the nails.

The matrix, also called the nail base, is well supplied with nerves, blood and lymph capillaries. Its function is to manufacture nail-making cells. The nails grow by a continued addition of new cells on their under surface and at the root.

The root of the nail is thin and softer than the nail proper. The nail is pale at the root, where it is outlined by the crescent-shaped lunula.

The Barber Should Have Knowledge

The barber knows from the study of the skin that the top layer (epidermis) is constantly shedding its cells, which have formed into scales.

He also has learned that the sebaceous glands supply oils to the hair and scalp, and that the sweat glands throw off perspiration.

All of these are natural functions which are constantly taking place.

But he must remember that through the chemical reaction that takes place in the formation of the epidermic scale a horny substance (keratin) is formed. Scales from all parts of the body are brushed off by the clothes and are sponged off in the bath and are seldom noticed, but scales from the scalp accumulate because they are held by the hairs of the head.

The oils from the sebaceous glands, when allowed to remain on the scalp, coagulate into a waxy substance. This substance mixes with the epidermic scales. The sweat glands throw off waste matter from the body through the sweat pores (perspiration), and this, too, goes into the mixture of excretions.

Often these elements, mingled with dust and other foreign matter, are allowed to accumulate and cake on the surface of the scalp, and the hair follicles become clogged.

The hair, deprived of air and nourishment, and under stifled conditions, often atrophies and falls out. True, each hair may be replaced, especially in the early periods of life, by a new hair, after the condition that caused it to fall has been corrected. But in many cases a recurrence of the same condition takes place through the lack of proper care, and each new growth suffers similarly. Finally the abused hair papilla gives up the struggle and ceases to produce new hair cells, thereby causing permanent baldness.

Barber shop patrons should be taught these facts, especially younger people, so that they will understand the need of hair care before it is too late. One can readily understand why the barber must first educate himself in reference to the anatomical structure of the body and the physiological functions of the skin and hair. He must equip himself to competently pass this knowledge on to his patrons and be able to serve them in keeping with their needs.

Summary of the Anatomy of the Skin

SKIN
- Epidermis
  - Cuticle or corneum layer
  - Lucidum layer
  - Granular layer
  - Mucous layer
  - Germinating layer
- Corium (dermis)
  - Blood vessels—Sebaceous glands— Lymphatics—Sudoriferous glands— Nerves—Hair follicles
- Subcutaneous Tissue (subdermis)
  - A continuation of the corium but containing a greater amount of adipose tissue

Summary of the Anatomy of the Hair

HAIR FOLLICLE
- Papilla, a cone at bottom of follicle containing arteries, nerves and veins
- Sebaceous gland, connected with upper third of follicle
- Arrector Pili muscle, from neck of follicle to epidermis

HAIR
- **Cross-Section**
- Cuticle (outer flat covering)
- Cortex (pigment layer, body of hair)
- Medulla (central pith layer)
- **Lengthwise**
- Shaft (portion of hair extending from the skin surface to the point)
- Root (portion within follicle)
- Bulb (portion capping the papilla)

Chapter 16

Electricity

ELECTRICITY is an invisible agency or force exhibiting heat, magnetic and chemical effects when in motion.

In order to understand many of the practical phenomena of electricity, which is generously used by the barber, it is persuasive that he should become familiar with some of the fundamental terms in this field.

Thus: *Magnetism* is an electric inducing force ever present in nature. Electricity in motion or moving within a conductor is termed an *electric current,* the amount of which is measured by a unit called an ampere, and its force by a unit termed a *volt.*

A *conductor* is any substance which will allow a current to flow through it easily, as a copper wire. A *non-conductor* is a substance that resists the passage of electricity.

An *ohm* is the unit of measurement used to denote the amount of resistance in an electrical system or device.

A *circuit* is the complete path of an electric current.

A *rectifier* is a device which transforms alternating current into direct current.

A *converter* is a device for changing electrical energy from one form to another.

A *rheostat* is a contrivance for regulating an electrical current by means of variable resistances.

A *cycle* is a complete positive and negative wave of an alternating current. The number of cycles per second is a measure of the frequency of an alternating current.

These electrical terms may be easily understood by drawing an analogy between a simple electric system and a water system, as in Fig. 130.

In a water system the supply comes from a reservoir or pump, while the two main sources of electricity are *batteries* or *generators.*

A battery is a device which utilizes two oppositely-charged *terminals* immersed in an *electrolite* or solution, the atoms of

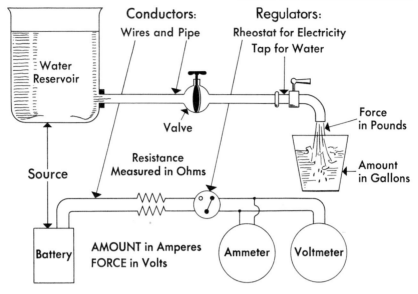

Fig. 130. Diagrammatic analogy between simple electric system and water system.

which are free-floating ions. The positive charged ions are *cations*. The negative electrically charged ions are *anions*. (Fig. 131.)

The anions are attracted to the positive terminal, and the cations to the negative terminal, as illustrated. The result is a building up of an electric charge, or an electromotive force.

When the terminals are connected by conducting wires, a current flows through them from the positive pole to the negative pole. Thus the direction of the flow of current determines the *polarity* of the wires; that is, it provides evidence as to which wire is positive and which is negative.

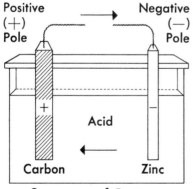

Structure of Battery

Fig. 131.

A battery current is uninterrupted or even-flowing, and therefore is designated as a direct current (D. C.), in contrast to an alternating current (A. C.), which is rapidly reversed in its direction of flow at the usual rate of 60 cycles per second.

The types of currents applicable to the practice of cosmetic therapy are: (1) Galvanic, (2) Faradic and (3) High-frequency.

Galvanism

Galvanic current is a D. C. or direct current. Its use on living tissue produces marked *chemical* effects in tissues immediately in contact with the *electrode,* as the current-conducting applicator is termed. From a physiological point of view, therefore, D. C. is a chemical current, differing in this respect from A. C., which produces changes in the tissues by *mechanical* means.

Each of the two poles in galvanic current produces a different physiological effect in living tissues. It is, therefore, necessary to determine which of the terminals is the positive and which is the negative.

An appliance, known as a wall plate, is equipped with indicators by which one may tell at a glance which is the positive and which is the negative pole. (Fig. 133.) Also, there are two simple, practical tests by which this polarity may be determined by an operator:

I. Litmus Method: Touch a piece of blue litmus paper, moistened with water, to one of the electrodes. If it turns red (acid reaction) the terminal is positive; if it remains blue (alkaline reaction), it is negative.

II. Water Method: Immerse the two terminals of the conducting wires in a glass of clear water. In a few seconds bubbles will accumulate at each terminal. Those clinging to the *negative* pole will be much larger and more numerous. It is known as the "bubble test."

Physiological and Chemical Effects of Galvanism

Positive Electrode (Anode)

1. Acid Reaction.
2. Tends to drive positive-charged (acid) solutions into skin (cataphoresis).
3. Charges adjacent tissues positive—acid.
4. Astringent—contracts tissues.
5. Sedative—decreases pain.
6. Vaso-constrictor — constricts blood vessels, tends to inhibit bleeding.
7. Hardening—hardens tissues by dehydration (drying tissues).
8. Antiseptic—tends to inhibit bacterial growth by acid reaction.
9. Decomposes metals.
10. Collects *small* oxygen bubbles.

Negative Electrode (Cathode)

1. Alkaline Reaction.
2. Tends to drive negative-charged alkaline solutions into the skin.
3. Charges adjacent tissues negative—alkaline.
4. Relaxes tissues.
5. Irritant—increases pain and inflammation.
6. Vaso-dilator—dilates blood vessels, tends to increase bleeding.
7. Electrolysis—softens and liquefies tissues by dissolution (extinction).
8. Septic—favors the growth of bacteria by alkaline reaction.
9. Does not decompose metals.
10. Collects *large* hydrogen bubbles.

Uses of Galvanism

Electrolysis

Electrolysis is the destruction of tissues by passing a negative galvanic current through them. This procedure is used in the eradication of superfluous hairs and warts, using an electrolysis needle for the electrode. (Fig. 132.)

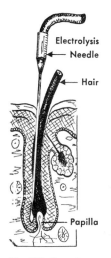

This work requires a thorough understanding of the histology involved, and a thorough knowledge of the instrument used, plus extraordinary skill and good eyesight. It should not be taken up as a casual or occasional practice, but should be studied and practiced as a specialty. The consequences of inadequate knowledge and skill may be permanent scarring and disfiguration of the skin.

To eradicate superfluous hair the procedure is to insert an electric needle alongside of the hair root in the hair follicle and papilla.

The technique requires use of the correct amperage in order to destroy the papilla without undue destruction of skin tissues, which will leave scars. Even with multiple needle instruments the work is very slow. Electrolysis is painful when administered by the unskilled. Special schooling in this art is recommended, and special licenses may be required by state law.

Fig. 132. Electrolysis.

Cataphoresis

Cataphoresis is used to introduce solutions or drugs into the unbroken skin. It facilitates greater and deeper absorption of solutions by the tissues. The current must be of very low force (voltage), its polarity depending on the type of solution to be used. The rule is to use a positive electrode with positive-acting chemical solutions such as acids; and use negative electrodes with alkaline (negative-acting) solutions.

Saturate a piece of gauze with positive-acting solution. Wrap it around the positive electrode and slide it over the face, while the patron holds the opposite electrode in his hand. (Fig. 133.) The solution is *repelled by the facial electrode* and *attracted to the hand electrode,* thus facilitating absorption of the solution by the skin. Negative-acting solutions may be introduced into the skin by the same technique, except that the negative electrode is used on the face and the positive electrode is held by the patron.

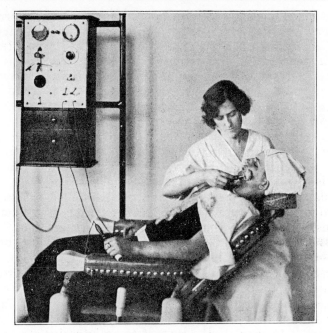

Fig. 133.

Astringent

Galvanism may be used at the finish of any facial to contract the tissues and pores in the skin. The positive facial electrode is applied to the face, with the current so adjusted that the patron is aware of a metallic taste in his mouth.

Scalp Work

Dry scalps may be greatly benefited by the use of galvanism. A metal rake, conducting a negative current of low intensity, is used to open the pores, relax the blood vessels and increase the natural flow of sebum in the scalp, thereby tending to overcome the dry condition. This treatment has been used with good success in conditioning the scalp and hair for permanent waves.

For oily scalps, the rake is attached to the positive conducting cord, resulting in an astringent effect on the tissues and glands, tending to reduce the excessively oily condition.

Faradism

The faradic current is an induced, interrupted current produced by passing either a DC current or a modified AC current through an induction coil.

An induction coil is composed of two coils and an interrupter. A current passed through the interrupter into the primary coil sets up an induced current in the secondary coil. The effect on a battery current is first to break it up into vibrations. This vibrating current becomes an induced, interrupted current of increased voltage and decreased amperage in the secondary coil.

The physiological action of faradism is the production of a fine passive exercise of all muscles through motor point stimulation; *i.e.*, the motor nerves which naturally excite action in the muscles enter them at a central point, and this current acts directly on this point and causes alternate contraction and relaxation equal to the rate of the current cycle.

This alternate contraction and relaxation of the muscles tends to milk the accumulated products of fatigue from them and quickens elimination through the lymphatic system. Thus a few minutes of faradic stimulation are equal to several hours of rest, and result in toning of muscular tissues.

Precaution must be taken in the use of this current to stimulate the tissues without fatiguing them by an overdose.

Use of an instrument with a moderate output is preferable, cutting down the probability of over-stimulation. A second precaution is to regulate the current to an intensity comfortably tolerable to the individual.

High-Frequency

A high-frequency current is one similar to the faradic, but stepped up in cycles to 10,000 or more per second, with a higher voltage and lower amperage. The current is developed by utilizing an induction coil and a d'Arson val coil.

Thus a high-frequency current is one of very high voltage, rapid alternation and very low amperage, hence the term high frequency. It is also called violet-ray, because of a violet color produced by the current in the glass electrodes, but this is a misnomer, because, technically, it is not a ray.

Because of its high frequency this current passes through the tissues without exciting the nerves, contracting the muscles or causing any sensation except heat.

The physiological effect is a direct beneficial stimulation to all tissues of the body, but especially those tissues close to the electrode.

High-frenquency electrodes are usually and preferably made in the form of vacuum glass bulbs, shaped to conform with the various surfaces of the body.

The current is conducted to the tissues from these electrodes without forming a circuit from body to instrument, as is the case with galvanic or faradic currents.

High-frequency current is applied by direct and indirect methods.

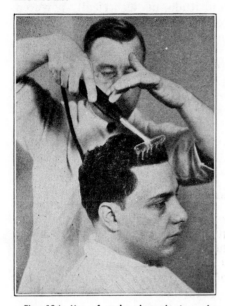

Fig. 134. Use of scalp electrode in scalp treatment.

In using the direct method, the operator should place his free hand on the electrode in making or breaking contact with the patron's skin, to insure against sparking and startling the patron. The free hand is removed when contact is made between the electrode and the patron's skin. Once a contact is made the electrode should be kept moving continuously over the tissues until it is to be removed. (Fig. 134.)

Sparking is to be avoided except when one wishes to destroy tissues, as in the case of rather large pustules, etc.

The indirect method is applied by having the patron hold a metal electrode in his hand, the current being attracted through the patron's body by the tips of the operator's fingers. This method is *not* recommended, due to the fact that contact with the fingers is not as perfect and continuous as with glass applicators, and destructive sparking is the result.

Fulguration, which means burning, is a term used to describe the practice of cauterizing small warts and other such growths with high-frequency. A fulguration needle electrode is used.

The removal of skin blemishes, warts, moles, etc., is the province of the medical profession, and the barber should not attempt this work unless it is of the simplest nature. He must be thoroughly familiar with the steps necessary and be certain of the successful outcome of his treatment. He also must be sure that state laws permit him to perform such services.

In general, high-frequency may be used to help correct a variety of conditions, both in facial and scalp work, where cellular stimulation is desired, and it is particularly effective in stimulating the sebaceous glands.

Electrical Appliances

Wall Plate

The barber relies on a multitude of electrically-powered devices in his profession. Therefore, he should have knowledge of electrical appliances usable in the modern shop, and he should know how to use them.

A wall plate is a device to transform the regular AC current (the standard 110-volt current) to the various types of currents required in a barber's work.

Most wall plates supply galvanic (chemical), faradic (mechanical) and high-frequency (thermal) currents.

Used with the wall plate are the various forms of electrodes, such as combs, brushes, massage rollers, etc., designed to apply the desired current to the scalp or face. (Fig. 133.)

High-Frequency Applicators

A high-frequency applicator is a high-frequency generating coil which generates high-frequency current. It is fitted into a cylindrical handle about two inches in diameter and about nine inches long. At one end of this handle is an opening into which can be fitted the various types of high-frequency, glass electrodes used for scalp and facial work. (Fig. 134.)

Dermal Lamps

Dermal lamps are electric appliances used to produce lights for corrective cosmetic treatments. (Fig. 135.)

I. The light elements commonly used are carbon filament bulbs of about 15 to 30 candlepower. The colors generally used are red and blue.

Red light is used principally for its heat rays and stimulating effect.

Blue light is used for its nerve-soothing effect.

Fig. 135.

II. Infra-red lamps or generators. The infra-red lamp is a reflector-type bulb of clear or ruby glass, which produces more heat than the colored lights. This lamp is used especially for introducing long heat rays into the tissues.

Infra-red generators are metal units of various shapes, which heat up as do the heating elements of an electric stove. Most of these have standard screw bases and are replaceable. There are other types that make use of permanent, nickel-chrome wires or tubes instead of light bulbs. These generators produce radiant heat useful in scalp and facial work.

The Vibrators

A vibrator, either hand or mechanical, is an electrical appliance which produces mechanical vibration.

I. The hand vibrator is a device with an electric motor or magnetic motor, and is clamped on the back of the hand. When in operation it causes the hand to vibrate, and these vibrations are transmitted to the patron's face or head. (Fig. 136.)

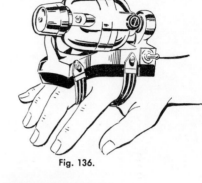

Fig. 136.

II. The mechanical vibrator is a device that transforms an electric motor's energy into vibrations. (Fig. 137.) Use of this type vibrator is now considered obsolete, but some barbers still use it.

Steamers

I. The scalp steamer is an electric apparatus

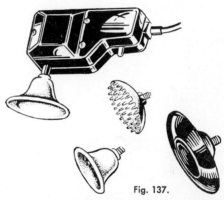

Fig. 137.

that generates and furnishes steam (water vapor) to the parts under treatment.

II. The facial steamer is similar to the scalp steamer, except that it has a hood adaptable to the face.

A hair dryer is a combination electric heater and blower which is used for rapid hair drying.

Chapter 17

Light Therapy

LIGHT THERAPY is the application of light rays in the treatment of diseases. In recent years the invisible rays, better known as ultra-violet and infra-red, have become so well established as therapeutic agents that every well-equipped hospital and sanitarium uses them. Many physicians, as well as physio-therapists, treat a wide range of diseases with them.

It is not the aim of this Textbook to show the uses of these rays as *therapeutic* agents, but rather to point out their *cosmetic* uses in the proper practice of barbering, together with the commendable results obtainable and the remuneration afforded.

It has been shown by medical authorities, such as Dr. Nagelschmidt and others, that trends toward alopecia have been checked and in some instances hair growth has been stimulated by the use of ultra-violet rays.

In order to have a practical understanding of the use of these various forms of ray generators or lamps, it is necessary to become familiar with the fundamentals of the theory involved.

One is familiar with the concentric radiations of waves set up when an object is dropped into a pool of still water. These ripples or water waves, spreading from the point of origination, have been the fascination and wonderment of every child at play.

One is also familiar with the ringing sound heard when a bell tolls, but probably he is not aware that the air surrounding that bell, if a photograph could be taken, would produce a picture of similar radiating waves. This time they are termed air vibrations, and they are recorded as sound in the ears.

If one stands near a hot stove he becomes positively aware of heat reaching his skin. He sees nothing and hears nothing, but he feels the heat. This heat is also a form of rays or radiating waves, which are known as heat waves or infra-red rays.

Continuing the analogy, look at an ordinary electric light. This time nothing is heard or felt, but a whitish light is seen. This light is a radiation of ether waves like those of heat, and of such character that the retina of the eye records them.

Ultra-violet rays are a form of ether waves, but they are so short and travel with such tremendous rapidity that they are entirely imperceptible to all human senses.

Their presence, however, can be recorded on photographic plates, due to their chemical activity. They are technically termed "actinic rays."

It is due to throwing off actinic rays that the sun and certain types of artificial generators or lamps are able to produce beneficial results in diseases. The ultra-violet rays of the sun are the life-activating and stimulating agents in all animal and plant life. It is due to chemical reaction from application of active rays on living tissues that many of life's processes (metabolism) are maintained. The fact that the shorter of these rays are bactericidal (kill bacteria), has established their use in therapeutics. Also, special ultra-violet ray equipment is now available for use in sterilizing cabinets.

Ultra-Violet Lamps

There are three types of ultra-violet lamps, two of which are suitable for use by the barber.

The carbon arc lamp produces ultra-violet radiation by means of an open arc. Carbon arc lamps, however, are obsolete. There are two great objections to this equipment. The arc sputters and sparks fly, tending to hit the patron. The open arc also is a fire hazard.

The mercury vapor arc lamp is preferable in the hands of an expert. The lamp is mounted on a pedestal and is topped by a shading device or hood in which there is a replaceable mercury-vapor unit enclosed in quartz. Its action is extremely fast, and too much exposure to its rays will develop serious "sunburn."

The "sun lamp" is a recent development. It is a reflector-type screw base globe made of special glass with a small mercury-vapor unit mounted within it. This lamp is recommended for barber services, because its action is slower, with very slight danger of over-exposure to its ultra-violet rays.

Ultra-violet rays also may be produced by an electric current passed through a vacuum tube containing mercury.

In order to understand something about measurement of these rays, presume an imaginary analysis of water waves. Assume that these ripples travel one inch per second and measure one inch across from crest to crest, or wave to wave. Technically, these waves would have a frequency of one vibration, or frequency, per second.

Light travels at the tremendous speed of 186,000 miles per second, and the frequencies of light waves are in millions of vibrations per second. Light wave lengths measure in millionths of an inch.

In order to bring these measurements down to easily understood figures, physicists have adopted a unit of measurement called the Angstrom Unit (A. U.).

The following is a comparative table showing the relation of metric measurements compared with the inch:

1 Centimeter (cm)—about 2/5th inch.
1 Millimeter (mm) (1/10 centimeter)—1/25 inch.
1 Micron (u) (1/1000 millimeter)—1/25,000 inch.
1 Millicron (uu) (1/1000 micron)—1/1,000,000 millimeter or 1/25,000,000 inch.
1 Angstrom Unit (A.U.) (1/10,000 micron)—1/10,000,000 millimeter or 1/250,000,000 inch.

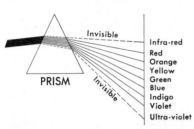

Fig. 138. Dispersion of light rays by a prism.

When a small slit of light from any source is passed through a glass prism the light disperses into rays of various lengths. The image of the dispersed rays, photographed on a screen, is a band of colors known as a spectrum. (Fig. 138.)

The spectrum of the sun is found to contain rays ranging in length from 2900 to 100,000 A. U. Those from 3900 to 7800 A. U. are the color rays (Fig. 139), the combination of which is recorded by our eyes as white light, and the separate lengths of which are divided into seven natural colors in the order of their decreasing lengths: Red, orange, yellow, green, blue indigo and violet. All other color shades and tints are combinations of these.

It may seem impossible to the layman that one can measure anything by such a small unit of measurement as the Angstrom Unit, but it suffices here to say that physicists, the scientists directly concerned with this field, are able to measure small fractions of an Angstrom Unit with exact precision.

Theory of Color Vision

All colors of objects are recognized by the reflection of certain rays from them. A red object is red because its surface reflects red rays and absorbs all others; a black object *absorbs* all color rays, and a white surface *reflects* all color rays. This fact is important in understanding changes in the color of hair, which is sometimes due not only to a lesser amount of pigment, but also

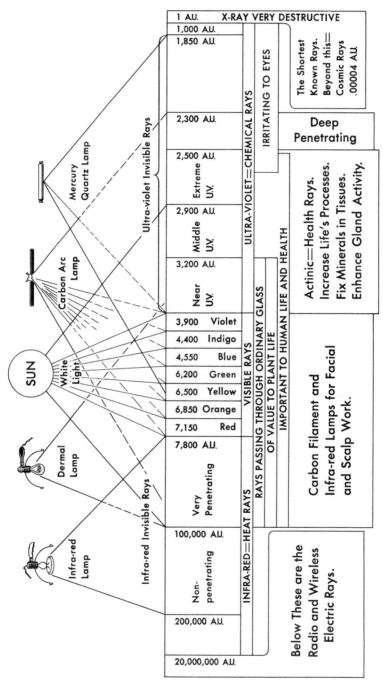

Fig. 139. Graphic diagram of approximate spectrum emitted by various forms of light generators. There are variations in spectral limits between various observers, due to differences in visual keenness. The various light bands are not sharply divided, but merge into each other, as do the colors of the rainbow.

to air spaces within the hair which reflect all color rays and become silvery in spite of the pigments in it. Conversely, a red bulb is red because it only allows the passage of red rays and retards all others. Thus the rays emitted from a red carbon filament bulb consist of red plus some penetrating infra-red rays. This fact makes the use of such a light applicable to many phases of the barber's work.

Psychological Effect of Colored Lights

Everyone is familiar with the fact that when an ordinary light of any colored or clear bulb, as from a flashlight, is pressed against the palm of the hand in a dark room, the transillumination of that light may be seen at the back of the hand. This is visual proof that these rays penetrate the tissues.

Visible rays, however, possess restricted therapeutic qualities, and it is conceded that the attributes they do have are due to the invisible rays accompanying them, plus marked psychological effects through the medium of vision. In general, their psychological effects are as follows: Yellow, orange and red are warm and stimulating. Yellow-green, green and green-blue are more neutral in effect. Blue and blue-violet hues are cool and soothing.

Red Light

1. Contains some penetrating infra-red rays, with effects as above, except less in quantity and intensity of heat. It is ideal for drying clay packs, or for use where mild, dry heat is needed.

2. Relaxes skin tissues and blood vessels, accelerates superficial circulation, and can be used to prepare the skin for the reception of cosmetics. Its action on cells makes it very efficient for increasing the absorption of fatty substances, such as creams, oils and ointments.

3. Increases the activity of the cells and glands, and excites motor response to muscles, making the tissues more resistant to infection, and validating the claim that it promotes antisepsis.

4. Increases metabolism of the cells by enhancing the blood supply to the tissue and cells.

The effects listed above are reversed with prolonged application of red light, so it must be applied with proper limitations.

Blue Light

Blue light is considered to be soothing, antiseptic and penetrating.

Infra-Red Rays

The infra-red rays, ranging from 7800 to 100,000 A. U., are just outside the red (visible) rays in the spectrum. These are the *heat* rays. Of the invisible rays, the infra-red rays penetrate most deeply into the tissues, their ability to penetrate being greater toward the short end of their light band.

Infra-red lamps and bulbs are obtainable either from supply dealers or where light bulbs are sold in department and drug stores. The bulbs are often used in hand reflectors. (Fig. 135.)

Physiological Effect of Infra-Red Rays

1. Their action is due to the effect of heat which these rays produce as they enter the tissues and are absorbed and transferred as energy in the deeper structures. The result is a general stimulation of metabolism.

2. Relieve pain.

3. Increase carbon-dioxide elimination in the body by increasing oxidation in tissues, thus promoting a beneficial series of reactions in the body.

4. Increase perspiration and secretion of sebum in the skin.

5. Meissner claims they are somewhat germicidal.

6. Dilate blood vessels, and increase blood flow to a part. Tend to *relieve inflammatory congestions* and *increase cellular regeneration.*

7. Heat tissues in area of irradiation to relatively high temperatures without increasing the temperature of the entire body.

8. Relax dermal tissues, and are thus advantageous in preparing the skin for reception of ointments, oils, creams and other cosmetics.

Ultra-Violet Rays

At the other end of the spectrum are the ultra-violet rays, designated so because they lie outside the visible violet rays. These are technically known as "actinic" or chemically active rays, because they excite chemical reactions in all photoactive substances.

Ultra-violet rays activate life in all plants and animals, and they fix mineral compounds in human tissues, stimulate glandular activity, and in general enhance the metabolic (life) processes. Their penetrativeness also varies in inverse ratio to their length, but their penetrative powers are shallow as compared with infra-red rays.

As ultra-violet rays become shorter, they become destructive to bacterial life, which adds to their therapeutic value to man.

But as the extreme end of the actinic spectrum is reached they gradually become destructive to living tissues. Most destructive of the various rays are the X-rays of one A. U. in length, which are generated by special X-ray tubes.

Due to industrial development, the atmosphere in the average city is loaded with smoke, dust, etc., which retards irradiation of beneficial rays from the sun. In winter the irradiation naturally is less than in the summer. Thus city atmospheres have become deficient in the full, health-giving rays necessary to the well-being of humanity. These rays can be given artificially to supply deficiencies.

Lamps

The mercury quartz lamp produces rays ranging from 1,850 to 6,500 A. U. with very little light, practically no heat and a greater ultra-violet range than the sun. This instrument is powerful and should be used cautiously, for the dosage of ultra-violet rays is so concentrated that the margin of safety is narrow. Overdoses may lead to untoward effects, such as third-degree sunburn. Therefore, a thorough understanding of its potentialities and extensive training in its use are advised.

A method to test the potentiality of an ultra-violet lamp is to cut a hole the size of a dime in a sheet of paper, place the paper over the arm, and allow the skin thus exposed to be irradiated by the lamp for a few seconds. Then repeat the tests on other parts of the arm and give a longer exposure, doing this in several places. Results are apparent within twenty-four hours. Each lamp manufacturer furnishes exact directions for this test.

Several forms of ultra-violet lamps which are recommended for home use are available. They are low voltage lamps, suitable for use in barber shops in connection with facial and scalp services.

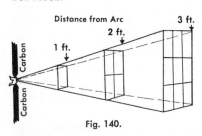

Fig. 140.

Another factor in regulating dosage is the distance between the lamp and the part being irradiated. For instance, if an object is one foot away from the lamp a certain amount of rays will be concentrated on it. If the distance is doubled, the rays are dispersed so that the same area receives only one-fourth of the rays. The intensity is diminished in inverse ratio to the distance, as shown in Fig. 140.

The color of the skin must be taken into consideration.

Persons with blond or red hair and pale skins are very susceptible to ultra-violet irradiation. People with auburn or brown hair and medium light skins tolerate slightly more of the rays. Those with brunette or dark complexions and dark skins offer considerable resistance to the rays. A Negro can tolerate a heavy dosage of ultra-violet irradiation without suffering sunburn.

Physiological Effect of Ultra-Violet Rays

1. The most pronounced physiological effect of actinic rays on the skin is the production of erythema (sunburn).

There may be varying degrees of erythema produced, depending on the dosage. Thus they are practical means of measuring doses of ultra-violet. Dosage is dependent on many factors, such as individual sensitivity of skin, intensity and composition of radiation (type of lamp), distance from which radiation is administered, duration and temperature.

Erythemas are designated in four degrees:

First degree: Slight reddening of skin, appearing several hours after irradiation without any signs of itching, burning or peeling.

Second degree: Marked reddening of skin, with or without moderate itching and smarting, with a slight shedding of thin flakes of epidermis in a few days.

Third degree: Very pronounced reddening of skin, accompanied by slight swelling and thickening of the skin without blistering, followed by a pronounced exfoliation (shedding) in a few days.

Fourth degree: Very intensive reaction with vesication (blistering), intense burning and itching, and sometimes fever.

For all cosmetic purposes no more than a first degree erythema should be given.

2. Pigmentation (tanning), as well as erythema, is produced by the ultra-violet waves, ranging in length from 2800 to 3200 A. U. Tanning is due directly to the stimulating action of these rays on the germinating layer of the epidermis. This is nature's method of protecting the body from prolonged irradiation by the sun.

3. Penetrate skin one-tenth mm. to one mm., or 1/250 to 1/25 inch.

4. Produce vitamins in sterols of skin, and fix calcium, iron, phosphorus and iodine in the tissues.

5. Increase hemoglobin (iron in the blood) and red and white cells in the blood, thereby increasing resistance to and immunity from diseases.

6. Produce a pronounced dilation of superficial and deep cutaneous blood vessels, accelerate both blood and lymph flow, and thus increase the elimination of waste products and the restoration of nutrition to the part irradiated.

7. Increase the number of active tissue cells and thereby have a direct beneficial effect on the growth of hair and regenerative process of healing. Kill bacteria.

8. Irritating to the retina of the eyes, especially in their shorter lengths. Eyes must be protected by wearing glasses fitted with lenses that filter ultra-violet rays.

DON'T BE A GOLDFISH!

The story is told of the lady who kept goldfish in a bowl.

One day, to clean the bowl, she poured the fish into the bathtub, and told them to have a good swim for themselves.

But the goldfish just swam around in little circles the size of the goldfish bowl.

Don't let yourself fall into the same practice as regards the barber business, confining your thinking to one small circle.

A successful shop is not the result only of hand-work—it takes head-work, too. Analyze your shop with the cold-blooded impersonality of an outsider. Each day strive to devise ways to improve it in every way you can think of, beginning with the shop itself, and going all the way through to the manner in which you give service to your patrons.

You'll be surprised at the improvements that can be made. But if you don't give serious, persistent thought to the matter, you will continue to operate a mediocre establishment.

You're not a goldfish, so don't confine your thinking to a tight little circle.

Chapter 18

Cosmetics
Their Properties and Uses

THE purpose of this chapter is to discuss some of the ingredients found in standard cosmetic preparations. It is not the business of the barber to suggest the use of his own formulas. Use only standard preparations and cosmetics.

Parmacology is that branch of science that has to do with the recognition, chemistry and action of drugs. Chemistry is the science that deals primarily with the composition of matter. Matter is anything that occupies space and has weight. There are three forms of matter, namely, solids, liquids and gases. Matter is made up of minute particles called molecules.

A molecule is the smallest particle into which a substance can be divided and retain its characteristic properties.

An atom is the smallest particle of an element which enters into the composition of molecules.

An element is a pure substance that cannot be separated into simpler substances.

A compound is a distinct substance formed by the union of two or more elements in a definite proportion. Acids, bases and salts are the three principal types of chemical compounds.

Acid is present in any substance having a sour taste.

A base, *also known as an alkali,* is a compound which, combined with acids, will form salts, or combined with fats will form soaps.

A salt is any compound of a base and an acid.

All matter can undergo two kinds of changes. For instance, water under various conditions exists as ice, water or steam. These are *physical* changes, because the atomic structure is not altered. When a substance is changed from one kind of matter to another, as when water is changed to hydrogen and oxygen, a *chemical* change takes place.

219

Water

Water and soap form the most universal base for the manufacture of cosmetics. It is important that some scientific facts about water be understood.

Hard water contains calcium and magnesium salts. *Temporary* hardness due to carbonates is removed by boiling, which causes the lime to precipitate (lime deposits in hot water pipes and kettles). *Permanent* hardness is due to sulphate and phosphate salts which cannot be precipitated by boiling, but may be removed by *water-softener* equipment now available.

Soft water is water relatively free from mineral salts. Minerals in water tend to retard the lathering of soap and cause a soap curd deposit to form on the hair in shampooing. Acid rinses are utilized to dissolve and remove soap film which otherwise remains on and dulls the hair.

Alcohol

Alcohol is probably the next most common ingredient used in the manufacture of cosmetics. Diluted with water to various strengths, hydro alcohol (water and alcohol) solutions are the bases of many cosmetics and antiseptic lotions and solutions.

Alcohol has physiological actions on the skin or scalp. In small concentration it is cooling and mildly astringent. In stronger concentration it coagulates tissue proteins, exerting a strong astringent action as well as some erythema (redness). At 70% strength, alcohol has germicidal action.

Alcohol is used in cosmetics such as hand lotions, face lotions, scalp preparations, hair pomades and tonics, waving and setting lotions, shampoos, etc.

Antiseptics, germicides and disinfectants are explained in the chapter on sanitation, but it may be noted here that any preparation designed for use on the skin or scalp must be considered from the possible standpoint of being toxic or irritating. Some skins may tolerate an alcoholic antiseptic, while others become reddened and irritated.

In sterilizing instruments, one should choose a sterilizing solution that is rapid in action, relatively non-toxic and non-corrosive to metals.

Detergents

A detergent is a cleaning agent. Plain water was the first detergent. Subsequently, water and clay, sand, grain meals and various skin scrapers were used. Oils and salves were also used much like cold creams are used today.

When manufacture of soap was perfected it became the detergent universally used throughout the world. For many years soap was available only in cakes or bars. Later a soap cleanser in the form of liquid soap or "shampoo" was developed.

In recent years two new types of chemical compounds (oils, organic detergents) have been developed for use as skin and hair cleansers.

The three basic types of detergents are:

1. Soap—salts of fatty acids.
2. Oils—sulphonated oils.
3. Organic detergents—these are numerous and variously designated as soapless detergents, foaming agents and surface-acting agents.

Soap and Soap Shampoos

Soap is still the most widely used cosmetic preparation in the world today.

Sodium hydroxide (soda lye) is used to manufacture solid soap. Potassium hydroxide (potash) is used to manufacture soft or liquid soaps. The best quality soaps are those in which the alkalies are neutralized as much as possible, while poor quality soaps are less refined and tend to irritate sensitive skins.

The detergent action of soaps is due to both chemical and mechanical action. Oils and other soluble substances are dissolved and emulsified by chemical action. Dust and other insoluble materials are mechanically loosened by rubbing, carried in suspension, and may then be rinsed away with water.

Shampoos are liquid cleaning agents for the hair and scalp. For many years liquid soaps were the only shampoos available. Soap shampoos are still widely used. Dandruff-removing shampoos are usually tinctures of green soap. Tar shampoos are usually the soap type, with oil of cade or tar added.

Oil shampoos, usually mixtures of sulphonated oils, may be either the plain (non-lathering), or the lathering oil shampoos containing foaming agents. They are especially recommended for use in dry hair and scalps.

"Creme" shampoos have been recently developed. They are essentially foaming agents emulsified with cream or emolient bases.

Cream oil shampoos are liquids similar to the "cremes" in composition.

Shampoo jellies are essentially soft soaps in jelly form.

Soapless shampoos may consist of one or more of a number of foaming agent solutions.

Creams

A cream is essentially an emulsion of oils, waxes and water. Some creams are simple mixtures of oils and waxes; technically these are salves.

An emulsion is a watery liquid containing insoluble substances in suspension, such as oils and waxes.

When oil and water are placed in a jar they remain separated. When the mixture is shaken, the oil breaks up into tiny droplets which are temporarily suspended in the water.

If an emulsifying agent is added and the ingredients are agitated (under proper temperature) the oil droplets remain suspended. Such a stable suspension is known as an emulsion of oil-in-water, or O/W type. By varying the conditions and ingredients another type of emulsion is formed in which the water is dispersed and suspended in the oil. Such a product is known as a water-in-oil emulsion, or W/O type.

There is a great number of cosmetic creams available, many of which are made to meet specific needs and conditions. Creams are technically classified, but for the barber's practical purposes they are termed cold creams, emollient creams, and vanishing creams. Practically all creams are available in paste or liquid form.

Cleansing cream (cold cream) is prepared with a mineral oil base of the O/W type, and is used primarily for cleansing, lubrication in massage, etc.

Emollient or skin-tissue creams are both O/W and W/O types, containing lubricating substances such as oils. They are used principally for their emollient qualities.

Vanishing or finishing creams are usually glycerin-stearic acid O/W types. They have the property of spreading on the skin and forming an imperceptible film, thus the term "vanishing." Vanishing creams are applied preliminary to giving numerous specialized services where certain ingredients such as deodorant creams, astringent creams, powder bases, sun-tan creams, etc., are applied and kept on the skin.

Astringents

An astringent, such as powdered alum or 70% alcohol, is an agent which causes contraction of the tissues. Astringent chemicals frequently contain acetic, boric, citric and lactic acids.

Hair Tonics

Hair tonic is a term now accepted to mean a liquid used on the hair and scalp for cosmetic purposes.

The purpose of hair tonic is to groom the hair and stimulate the scalp. Some tonics contain counter-irritating drugs which stimulate the scalp tissues, but with most tonic applications it is the scalp massage that achieves stimulation.

There are several types of tonics:

1. **Hydro-alcohol types,** usually containing an antiseptic, the alcohol acting as a mild irritant.

2. **Non-alcoholic,** usually an antiseptic lotion, with hair-grooming properties.

3. **Cream oil** or "creme oil" tonics, emulsions of the O/W type containing various proportions of lanolin and mineral oils.

4. **Oil mixtures,** having a large proportion of aqueous or hydro-alcohol solution, with a small portion of oil floating on top. The bottle is shaken to mix the liquids before an application is given.

Brilliantine

Brilliantines are oil compounds which are used to groom the hair and add brilliance and sheen to it.

There are three types:

1. Plain brilliantines or hair oils composed of mixtures of oils.

2. Combinations of oils dissolved in alcohol or hydro-alcohol solution.

3. Paste brilliantines, composed of mixtures of petrolatum jellies and other oils or waxes.

Hair Rinses

1. **Acid rinses** are solutions of *lemon* (citric acid) or *vinegar* (acetic acid). These acid rinses are used in diluted form to rinse the hair after a shampoo, for the purpose of softening hair by removing alkali and soap film from the hair. Dilution is juice of one or two lemons to one quart of water; one-half cup vinegar to one quart of water.

2. **Coloring rinses** are liquid or powdered coloring agents diluted in water and used as a rinse after a shampoo to brighten or color the hair. The coloring thus achieved is temporary, and lasts from one shampoo to another. Directions for use are printed on the commercial package.

3. **Peroxide rinse.** This is used as a mild discoloring agent on those persons who wish to lighten the color of their hair slightly. Use one tablespoon of peroxide to one quart of water.

4. **Henna rinse.** This is used to impart a slight auburn tinge to the hair. Pour enough hot water to cover a cupful of dry henna leaves, and place over a slow fire. Boil a short while, strain the mixture and add cold water to temper it.

5. **Blueing rinse** is used to destroy the unbecoming yellowish

tinge in gray or white hair. French blueing is recommended. Care should be taken to use a minimum amount of blueing in the rinsing water for silvery white hair, while steel-gray hair will require more. The amount of blueing used should be measured in drops.

Facial Masks

Facial masks are usually creamy mixtures of fullers earth and kaolin containing an astringent, an antiseptic and ingredients for bleaching. Such a mixture is also known as beauty clay. Other facial masks are essentially pastes compounded of various ingredients, such as almond meal, eggs, buttermilk, etc.

Depilatories

There are two types of depilatories.

1. **Wax depilatories,** a mixture of resins and waxes which are spread on the skin and allowed to harden. The hardened wax is carefully stripped from the skin, the superfluous hairs being removed with it.

2. **Depilatory creams,** containing chemicals that dissolve the hairs. Use of this depilatory requires careful timing to avoid excessive irritation of the skin.

Oils and Fats

Lanolin (wool fat). The purified fat from the wool of sheep may be procured as anhydrous lanolin, free from water, or as hydrous lanolin, containing about 30% water. It is quite similar in composition to sebum, and is easily absorbed by the skin. It is an efficient base for ointments, and its use is indicated to replace a deficiency of the natural oils of the skin, scalp or hair. Lanolin enhances the beneficial action of almost any cream or ointment. It is used in the manufacture of more than 60% of all cosmetic preparations.

Cocoa butter (oil of theobroma) is expressed from the roasted cocoa bean. It melts at body temperature. It is easily absorbed by the skin and is valuable in creams for its emollient (softening and soothing) properties. Preparations designed to soften the tissues of the scalp frequently contain both cocoa butter and lanolin.

Olive oil and **sweet almond oil** are efficient oils to be used for all conditions requiring a bland emollient. They penetrate the skin somewhat, and do not easily become rancid. Either of these two oils is highly recommended for scalps requiring hot oil treatments or hot oil shampoo.

Mineral oil (liquid petrolatum) is obtained from the distillation of petroleum. It is odorless and does not rancidify. The skin does not absorb it. It is a constituent of most hair-grooming mixtures, and is used for protecting and softening epidermal surfaces. **Petrolatum** (vaseline) is a semi-solid, purified petroleum product whose action is similar to that of liquid petrolatum.

Castor oil is obtained from the castor bean. It readily turns rancid on exposure to air, and is less efficiently absorbed by the skin than is olive oil. It should only be used when fresh, but when used it should not be left on the scalp, because the products of its rancidity become irritating to the scalp.

Crude oil is a powerful parasiticide and bactericide, but it is quite irritating to the skin. It is not recommended over other more efficient and less irritating substances.

Lard melts at body heat, and in some formulas is used as a base for ointments.

Oil of tar *(pix pini)* is produced from the distillation of pine wood. It has an offensive odor. It is stimulating to the tissues, and is parasiticidal, being especially destructive to the higher forms of bacteria. It is recommended highly to combat many skin infections, but *oil of cade* or *oil of rusci* are usually preferred, because they are similar in action and somewhat less offensive in odor. These oils are quite effective in treating various forms of seborrhoeic conditions.

Glycerine or glycerol is a thick, colorless, syrupy liquid obtained as a by-product by the saponification of natural fats and oils in connection with soap-making. It is irritating to the skin in its *concentrated* form, and therefore should only be used on the skin in 50% solutions or less, at which concentrations it is absorbed by the skin and is very beneficial in its action. Glycerine is added as a constituent of many lotions to increase their absorption by the tissues. It is an effective skin emollient and an ideal constituent of any type of lotion or cream.

Cholesterin is a white, fatty alcohol in crystalline form, found in animal and vegetable oils and fat, and is extracted from them by means of organic solvents. It is also common throughout the secretions of the body. Cholesterin is also secreted by the piliferous glands and is an indispensable item of nourishment for making the hair grow, as well as being a food for the skin. Used together with easily absorbed greasy matter it is an excellent skin regenerator. Being soluble in heated fatty substances, cholesterin is highly suitable for use in the preparation of creams.

Other Cosmetic Constituents

Substances which are constituents of many proprietary and popular cosmetic lotions, creams and antiseptics are:

Sulphur—Parasiticidal, antiseptic and stimulating to the tissues, fostering regeneration. It is mildly irritating and in large quantities is drying. It is indicated as a remedy for many infections of the skin. The form to be used is *precipitate of sulphur*. Sulphur is employed for pediculosis and the various forms of tinea, as well as chronic acne rosacea, eczema, psoriasis and seborrhoeic and other scaly conditions. Its use is valuable in allaying itching.

Iodine is an antiseptic and counter-irritant. A counter-irritant is any substance that exerts an irritating effect on an area of the skin, the result of which is to set up an inflammatory reaction. By counteracting any irritation affecting the area, it increases the regenerative powers of the cells at that point. Mild tincture of iodine is indicated in almost any form of skin lesion. It is very efficient, but its use is objectionable because of staining.

The so-called "colorless iodine," also known as "white iodine," sometimes recommended in alopecia areata, is an *iodide,* with totally different properties from iodine solutions. Its virtue is doubted.

Cantharides is a powerful counter-irritant which may cause blisters when generous portions of it are applied to the skin. In minute quantities it produces a slight beneficial erythema. It is a common remedy employed in the treatment of alopecia, being usually applied in the form of a tincture diluted with alcohol.

Capsicum is similar in properties to cantharides, but not so powerful. It is an ingredient in many hair lotions which are used as scalp stimulants for all forms of alopecia.

Alum acts as an astringent to the superficial layers of the skin. It does not have the power to penetrate deeply.

Tannic acid is a good astringent when applied in proper proportions, otherwise it acts as an irritant. It is an ingredient for ointments, and compounds containing it are of service in such skin affections as herpes and moist eczema, its action checking the discharge and allaying itching and irritation.

Zinc sulphate is often employed as an astringent, both in lotions and creams. Its penetration is deeper than alum.

Zinc oxide, employed in many types of skin creams, has a beneficial, mildly antiseptic and protective action on inflamed surfaces.

Benzoin is often used in astringent lotions for its astringent properties. It also has bleaching qualities. Mixed with glycerine it is recommended for chapped lips and hands.

Pilocarpine, in minute amounts, is an ingredient in some hair lotions. lt has a direct, stimulating action on the tissues.

It increases the secretion of the glands. (Warning: Pilocarpine is a poison, the average dosage of which is 1/120 of a grain, and its handling by others than chemists is dangerous.)

Resorcin is a strong antiseptic which dissolves epidermic debris. It is used universally in dandruff remedies. It is recommended when used in proper dosage, but may be harmful in overdosage. It tends to discolor gray and blond hair.

Salicylic acid, a powerful antiseptic, softens epidermic debris, and tends to diminish perspiration. When used in a too strong solution, or when applications are given too often, it tends to destroy the epidermis. It is injurious to inflamed or bruised skin surfaces.

Camphor, a mild cutaneous stimulant, produces redness and warmth, due to a local dilation of blood vessels. It is slightly anaesthetic and cooling in its after-effect, due to its depressing action on the nerves.

Menthol is somewhat similar in action to camphor and is often employed for its marked cooling effect. It is useful for allaying itching.

Quinine, in small quantities, is an ingredient of many hair lotions. Its effect is slightly antiseptic. In strong solutions it is irritating to mucous membranes and raw surfaces.

Arsenical compounds have a considerable, though slow, caustic action on the skin. Preparations containing it should be used carefully and not too frequently, as they may cause redness or eruptions of the skin. On abraded surfaces they will tend to increase the inflammatory conditions.

Chrysarolin, as an ingredient in ointments, is a strong local irritant and a powerful parasiticide. Its use is indicated in various forms of tinea. It stains clothing and *should be used with extreme care.*

Thymol is an antiparasitic drug, the use of which is indicated in alopecias due to ringworm and pityriasis. It has proven to be of service in ointments prepared for the treatment of psoriasis, eczema and acne.

Sodium thiosulphate is used as an ingredient in solutions designed to treat impetiginous conditions and parasitic alopecias of the beard.

The use of **sodium bicarbonate** (baking soda) is indicated in the relief of burns, itching, urticarial lesions and insect bites. It is often used as an aid to cleansing oily skins.

Sodium hydroxide and **potassium hydroxide** are two powerful alkalies. The former is used in the manufacture of solid soaps, the latter in liquid soaps.

Witch-hazel (Hamamelis solution) is mildly antiseptic and astringent. It is a soothing lotion, the use of which is highly recommended as a finishing lotion or in facial steams.

Honey is demulcent (softening). It has a tendency to relieve dryness of the skin.

Ferric subsulphate (subsulphate of iron) is a powerful styptic. It may be procured in either powdered form or in solution. It is commonly known as "Monsel's styptic."

Chapter 19

Hair, Scalp and Skin Ailments

B Y understanding common skin diseases the barber will be able to distinguish between conditions that may be *corrected cosmetically* and those which should be referred to physicians.

Dermatology is the science of the skin, its nature, structure, functions, diseases and treatment.

A *symptom* is a change in a patient occurring during disease which aids in its diagnosis. An *objective symptom,* such as a pimple or a boil, is one observable by others. A *subjective symptom,* such as pain or itching, is one only observable by the patient.

Lesions

A *lesion* is an injury or structural change usually classified into two types: (1) *primary lesions,* those occurring in the beginning stage of the disease; (2) *secondary lesions,* those changes occurring in connection with primary lesions, due to irritation or other causes.

It is necessary for the barber to understand types of skin lesions in order to be able to detect abnormal conditions, and to intelligently carry on his services in conformity with hygienic principles.

Primary Lesions

Macule: Circumscribed, non-elevated, discolored patch of any size or shape.

Papule: Circumscribed solid elevation of the skin, pinhead to pea size; does not contain pus.

Pustule: Circumscribed elevation of the skin containing pus.

Vesicle: Circumscribed, small elevation of the skin containing serum.

Bulla: A bleb or blister; larger elevation of the skin filled with fluids.

Tubercle (small knob): A circumscribed solid deep elevation of the skin, pea size or larger.

Wheal (hives): A whitish or pinkish elevation of the skin usually developing suddenly and of short duration, produced by urticaria, nettle poisoning or insect bites.

Tumors are growths or abnormal swellings, either soft or hard, such as cysts, fibromas, etc., ordinarily seated in the coreum of subcutaneous tissue.

Secondary Lesions

Scales (squamae): Dried exfoliations of the epidermis.

Crust: Dry mass of exudations on the skin. (Dried fluid from a lesion.)

Excoriations are abrasions, or removal of cutaneous tissue by mechanical means, such as an injury.

Fissures are cracks in the epidermis, caused by injury or disease.

Ulcers are circumscribed lesions characterized by loss of corium (an open sore).

Scars (cicatrices): Forms of connective tissue replacing original tissue after injury or disease.

Pigmentation (stains): Discoloration of skin (as in a bruise that has healed).

Along with characteristic lesions there often occur subjective symptoms, such as pain, itching, burning, etc., which help in ascertaining a true diagnosis.

Diagnosis is the recognition of a disease. *Barbers must not treat* diseases, but a practical knowledge of lesions will make them better barbers. If a patron has an inflamed skin full of pustules or papules, barbers should know that they should not stimulate the affected area by administering mechanical or cosmetic services and thereby aggravate the inflammation.

Dermatitis is inflammation of the skin.

Pityriasis is a term applied to various skin affections, characterized by fine, branny scales.

Pityriasis capitis, it must be noted, is a term used by Sabourand and other writers to denote the condition commonly known as dandruff.

Dandruff is a combination of dried sebum oil, dirt and epithelial scales which form a coating on the scalp, and flaky formations which cling to the hair shafts. (Fig. 141.) Dandruff is commonly considered to be the normal scaling of a normal scalp. However, there are, as has been outlined above, several

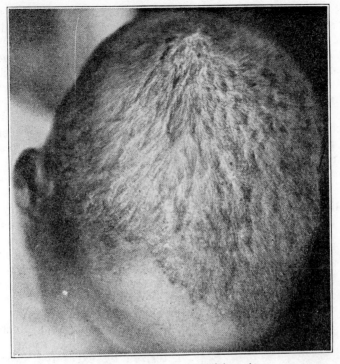

Fig. 141. A dandruff condition of the scalp.

diseases which are characterized by scales. The terminology is still somewhat confusing, because the classification of scaling diseases is still in the process of development and standardization in dermatological literature.

At this writing the term "dandruff" is still not standardized. Each dictionary and author gives a slightly different conception of it.

Dandruff scales vary in size from a very fine, almost powdery type to large and sometimes coalescing masses or crusts. The scales may be dry or oily, and they may vary in color. They may be loose or clinging, and they may or may not be accompanied by inflammation.

It is within the province of the barber to cleanse and remove dandruff scales with the use of oils, lotions, detergents, tonics and mechanical means, but when there is an inflammation, or when various lesions are present, it is his obligation to refer such aggravated cases to a physician or dermatologist.

The subject of dandruff is discussed more thoroughly in the chapter on scalp treatments.

A **furuncle** is a boil or an inflammatory infection of a single hair follicle or gland, characterized by a small tumor and pus.

A **carbuncle** has the same characteristics as a boil, except that a carbuncle involves two or more hair follicles and sebaceous glands. The area affected by it is greater, the tumor is larger, and it is more dangerous to treat.

An epithelioma is an epithelial or skin cancer. It is superficially observed as a dark, scaly blotch on the skin, or a thickened skin discoloration. Barbers have the opportunity to recognize these malignant, third-degree lesions in their early stages and recommend that the patron seek medical attention.

Diseases of the Sudoriferous Glands

Miliaria (prickly heat). An aggravating, inflammatory condition of the sweat glands characterized by papules and vesicles,

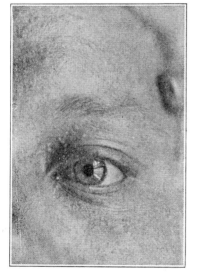

accompanied by itching and followed by desquamation (peeling). It is caused from too much acidity in the secretions from the sweat glands, and usually appears on the body in hot weather.

Hyperidrosis. A functional disorder of the sweat glands characterized by excessive sweating.

Amidrosis. A diminished production of sweat from abnormal sweat glands.

Bromidrosis. A condition in which the body throws off perspiration with an offensive odor.

Chromidrosis. A rare condition in which the body throws off perspiration that discolors clothing.

Fig. 142. Milia.

Hidrocystoma. An area of reddened skin characterized by pin-point to pea-sized vesicles on the face.

Some of these conditions, when the affection is slight, may respond to cosmetic services which include the proper use of antiseptics, astringents, antiperspirants, etc., but if good response is not gained immediately they must be referred to a physician.

Diseases of the Sebaceous Glands

Acne is an inflammatory disease of the sebaceous glands, characterized by papules, pustules and comedones. It is a common skin disease, occurring especially in adolescents, being most prevalent among persons between the ages of 14 to 24. Acne occurs mostly on the face, back and chest.

There are more than fifty types classified and named, according to their peculiarities of lesions and disposition. The most common forms are:

Acne Albida: A type of acne characterized by milia (whiteheads). Milia are whitish or yellowish non-inflammatory papules, their appearance being due to the accumulation of sebum in a sealed-over follicle. (Fig. 142.)

Acne Vulgaris: The simple or uncomplicated type, commonly recognized as pimples. Papules, pustules and some

Fig. 143. Acne vulgaris.

comedones are present in the condition. (Fig. 143.)

Acne Artificialis: A type of acne caused by some form of external irritation. This may be caused by almost any irritant or allergy, and in the barber's work may be caused by irritating cosmetic creams, lotions and soaps.

Acne Indurata: A form of acne characterized by hard, deep-seated, chronic tubercular (nodular) lesions, often of a livid appearance.

Acne Decalvans: An inflammatory disease of the hair follicle, causing atrophy of hair and scarring of the skin.

Fig. 144. Acne rosacea.

Acne Medicamentosa: A form of acne due to the internal administration of drugs.

Acne Pustulosa: A form of acne characterized by abscesses.

Acne Rosacea: A chronic hyperemic or inflammatory affection of the skin occurring around the nose, cheeks, and sometimes the forehead and chin, characterized by engorged superficial blood vessels. (Fig. 144.)

Acne Comedo (comedones) : Commonly called blackheads. A chronic disorder of the sebaceous glands, characterized by whitish or yellowish elevations, the size of pin points or pin heads, containing in their centers tiny exposed black areas.

A few simple forms of acne respond favorably to local cosmetic treatments. Many good cosmetic preparations designed to correct acne conditions are available. Manufacturers, their representatives or technicians will give the barber instructions for the proper use of their particular preparations.

If an acne condition does not respond favorably to a barber's services within two weeks it is his duty to discontinue such services and advise that the patron see his physician. Don't try to treat any but the simplest types of acne.

Asteatosis: A deficiency or absence of sebaceous secretions (dry skin).

Steatoma: A sebaceous cyst, pea to orange size, occurring on neck, scalp or back.

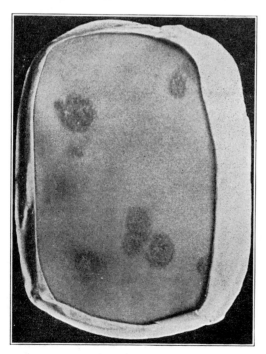

Fig. 145. Favus.

Seborrhea: A functional disease of the sebaceous glands, characterized by an excessive secretion of sebum which collects on the skin in the form of a coating of oily or non-oily crusts or scales.

The most common types are:

Seborrhea Capitis: Seborrhea of the scalp.

Seborrhea Faciei: Seborrhea of the face.

Seborrhea Ichthyosis: A variety characterized by plate-like crusts.

Seborrhea Nigra: A type characterized by dark-colored crusts, the coloration being usually from dirt.

Seborrhea Sicca: A common form of seborrhea characterized by greasy, brownish-gray scales.

Seborrhea Oleosa: A form of seborrhea characterized by excessive oiliness of the skin.

Favus *(tinea favora,* honeycombing worm) : A parasitic skin disease due to a vegetable parasite *(achorion schonleini),* characterized by a musty odor. The disease most frequently affects the scalp, and bald spots may result from scar tissue after the lesions are healed. (Fig. 145.)

Eczema is an acute or chronic, non-contagious disease of the skin characterized by papules, vesicles or pustules, plus itching and burning.

It is further characterized by a multiformity of lesions and a peculiar redness of the lesions, the redness blending gradually into the normal colored skin of the surrounding areas. The cause of this disorder is unknown. It is believed to be due to faulty metabolism.

There are many types of eczema, named according to their symptoms, such as *eczema seborrheicum, eczema madidans* (moist, weeping, raw type), *eczema squamosum* (dry, scaly type), etc. Eczema barbae is an eczema of the bearded area of the face.

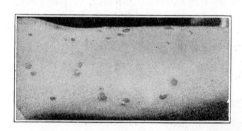

Fig. 146. Psoriasis.

Psoriasis is a chronic, non-infectious disease of the skin characterized by circumscribed, round red patches covered with silvery-white adherent scales. (Fig. 146.)

The cause of this condition is unknown. No specific treatment for it has been discovered. It is usually more active in winter than in summer.

There are several types of the disease, which are named: *Psoriasis guttata* (drop size), *psoriasis numularis* (coin size), *psoriasis capilliti* (psoriasis of the scalp).

Infectious Diseases

Impetigo. An acute, infectious skin disease characterized by vesicles, pustules and superficial crusts, usually with no itch. A raw surface is left if the crust is broken. The condition occurs most frequently on the face, and is most common among children. (Fig. 147.)

Erysipelas is an acute, streptococcus, infectious disease of the subcutaneous tissue, characterized by redness, swelling and burning, and sometimes accompanied by vesicular or bulbous lesions.

Tinea is a generic term applied to a class of skin diseases caused by parasitic fungi. The more common types are:

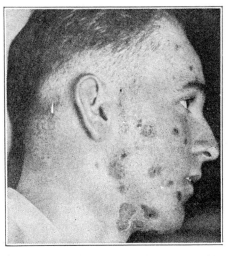

Fig. 147. Impetigo.

Tinea Capitis (tinea trichophytina capitis, tinea tonsurans, ringworm of the scalp): A parasitic disease affecting the hair and hair roots of the scalp, characterized by a rounded, grayish slightly elevated scaly patch, with brittleness and loss of hair. (Fig. 148.)

*Tinea Barbae (tinea trichophytina barbae, tinea sycosis, sycosis barbae—*ringworm of the beard, "barbers' itch"): A parasitic disease affecting the hair roots of the bearded portion of the face, characterized by rounded scaly patches that become nodular and tend to break down. (Fig. 149.)

Tinea Corporis (tinea trichophytina, tinea circinata): Ringworm of the body occurring on the non-hairy regions, characterized by spreading scaly patches tending to be smooth, with normal skin color in the center of the affected, ringed area.

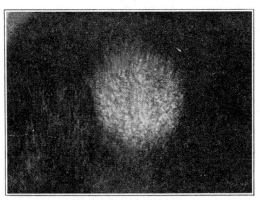

Fig. 148. Ringworm of the scalp.

Tinea Nodosa: A ringworm condition of the hair of the mustache, with thickening, roughness and fragility.

Tinea Furfurans: Seborrhea sicca.

Tinea Axillaris: Ringworm of the axilla.

Herpes, an acute inflammatory affection of the skin or mucous membrane, characterized by groups of vesicles.

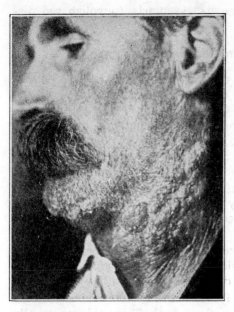

Fig. 149. Ringworm of the beard.

Herpes Facialis *(herpes labiolis,* cold sores, fever blisters), occurring commonly around the lips.

Lentigo (freckles), a small circumscribed patch of pigment, occurring mainly on the face and hands from exposure to the sun. Freckles are abnormal accumulations of pigment in the epidermis, due to abnormal pigment metabolism.

Pediculosis (lousiness), a skin affection characterized by the presence of lice. Pediculus is a small, parasitic *insect.* There are three types of pediculi: *Pediculosis capitis* (head lice); *pediculosis pubis* (crab lice) and *pediculosis corporis* (body lice).

Head lice crop up in an epidemic now and then, especially among young school children. Barbers may often check such an epidemic by recognizing the lice and the nits, and from observing the papular lesions and excoriations resulting from their bites and subsequent scratching by persons who have been afflicted by the insects.

Benign Growths—Warts and Moles

Verruca (wart). A hyperplosia (increase in number of cells) of the papillary layer of the skin. They vary in size and may be hard or soft, raised, rounded, flat, aggregated or piloform.

Verruca Vulgaris. The common wart, occurring on the hands and fingers and sometimes on the face and scalp. They are rounded, elevated, usually dry and roughened, brownish-gray, horny elevations.

Nevus (mole). A circumscribed area of pigmentation. Benign growths are common. There are many types of nevi. Some are flat, others raised and covered with soft, downy hair, and others are pierced by a profusion of stiff bristles. They vary in color, size and shape. Some types are: Nevus pilosus (pigmented growth containing hair), nevus verricosus (wart-like, usually covered with hair), nevus vascularis (purplish red discoloration, birthmark).

Alopecia (Baldness)

Alopecia is a deficiency of hair. The word is synonymous with baldness. Any abnormal deficiency of hair on any part and for any cause is termed alopecia.

Alopecia may be partial or universal, congenital or acquired. It may result from certain systemic affections, and on occasion is directly traceable to such diseases as ringworm, favus, folliculitis, syphilis, etc.

Alopecia Adnata (congenital baldness). This type, occurring with birth or soon after, may be general or localized, partial or complete. It is sometimes accompanied by malformation of the nails and teeth.

The barber may be a great benefactor by recommending proper hygienic measures, mild stimulating tonics, correct types of shampoos, check-ups by a doctor and co-operative treatments under the supervision of the patron's physician.

Alopecia Senilis (baldness of old age). The baldness usually begins at the vertex or at both the vertex and frontal regions of the scalp. It progresses symmetrically, and usually advances slowly. It is usually accompanied by graying, loss of lustre, brittleness and thinness of the hair. The scalp appears thinned, stretched and shiny.

The hair loss is permanent, due to complete atrophy of the follicle and loss of regenerative powers of the papilla. Preventive measures in the early years will delay the onset of this form of alopecia.

Alopecia Prematura, also called "alopecia simplex," is the idiopathic, premature baldness of young adults.

This form of baldness begins at an early adult age, and usually progresses by a gradual thinning of the hair. The first hairs that fall out are replaced by the successive regrowth of weaker ones. This process continues until baldness may be complete.

The causes of premature baldness are unknown, but, as research has developed in this field, many contributing factors have been recognized. Inheritance is considered by some researchers as the greatest single factor. Various mental and nervous disturbances receive the blame from other "experts."

The subjects of improper hygiene, lack of proper hair care, and improper use of cosmetic and medicinal preparations fill many pages of literature and are the bases for books on the subject.

Tight hats, too much sun, brain work and a host of other things are pointed to as causes of premature baldness. But the facts are that for the most part the *definite* causes are still unknown. Late research points to a big role being played by scalp diseases, systemic diseases and poor hygiene.

Fig. 150. Alopecia areata.

Alopecia Areata (baldness in spots). A condition in which, slowly or suddenly, one or several patches of baldness may appear on the scalp or other hairy regions of the body. Both sexes, and both young and old persons, may be affected by this condition. (Fig. 150.)

Among the many causes of alopecia areata, a few are known and more are unknown. Various diseases of the scalp and some types of nerve injuries are direct causes, and systemic diseases like syphilis, erysipelas, fevers and nerve diseases are indirect causes of it.

There are instances in which alopecia areata occurs without any known or recognizable signs of disturbances. In such instances the alopecia is usually of short duration, growth of hair reappearing within a short time. However, the new hair growth may be different in color and may be devoid of pigment.

Alopecia Syphilitica, due to syphilis.

Alopecia Cachectic, due to general malnutrition.

Alopecia Localis or Alopecia Neurotica. A form of baldness occurring in one or more patches at the site of an injury or along the course of a nerve.

Alopecia Universalis. Disappearance of the hair all over the body.

Alopecia Pityroides Capilliti or Alopecia Furforacea. A form of baldness associated with a disorder of the scalp, marked by hyperemia, itching and exfoliation of dry or fatty scales. It may be acute or chronic, and it may produce a dryness, brittleness and lack of luster of the hair.

Other Hair Disorders

Canities. Gray hair caused by loss of the natural pigment in the hair. Any change of color from natural to any degree of grayness or whiteness of hair is called canities. For the most part it is a sign of ageing.

Premature canities is premature graying of the hair of a young person. This condition is not uncommon among young people. Worry and constitutional disorders, as well as psycho-neurotic diseases, are accompanied by canities.

In some instances general systemic diseases, as well as psycho-neurotic diseases, are accompanied by canities. The alleviation of the disease is often followed by a return of natural pigment to the hair.

In general, canities demands no treatment, and as Dr. Gottlieb says, "The best thing to do is admire gray hair."

So-called "restoratives" are merely some kind of chemical coloring agent. There are numerous non-injurious dyes now on the market that can be used to successfully restore gray hair to the desired shade.

Trichoptilosis is a longitudinal splitting of the distal ends of the hairs, probably due to excessive dryness.

Hypertrichosis. This term is applied to hair growth in excess of the normal growth usually present in persons of the same race, sex and age. The condition is considered to be hereditary.

Monilethrix. An unusual congenital and hereditary disease of the hair characterized by dryness, fragility and sparseness of scalp hairs, with alternate swellings and contractions of the hair shaft. The hair tends to break at the delicate internodes. This disease is often accompanied by *keratosis pilaris* at the temples and back of neck.

Trichonodosis. A knotting of the hairs, probably due to an inability of the new hairs to grow freely from their follicles.

Trichorrhexis Nodosa *(fragilatas crinium).* The hairs in this condition are characterized by what seem to be white spots along the hair shafts at more or less regular intervals. The cortex at these points has fractured or split into longitudinal fragments. Under the microscope they appear like two brooms, stuck together end to end. The hairs break easily at the nodes.

Trichostasis Spinulosa. This is a condition in which a dozen or more fine stubby hairs, sometimes enclosed in a sheath, are found in the skin as dots resembling comedones.

Trix Annulata. This is a rare disease in which the hair has the appearance of being "ringed" or banded by alternate segments of light and dark colors when seen by reflected light. The light areas are known to contain gas, probably air, but the cause of the condition is unknown.

Pili Torti. A rare malformation of the hairs, characterized by a twisting of the hair shaft.

Chapter 20

Syphilis

Public Health Aspects for the Barber Profession

(This section on Syphilis was prepared for the Textbook by the United States Public Health Service. The Educational Council of the A.M.B.B.A. gratefully acknowledges the co-operation of the Health Service in giving this authoritative presentation of a subject of great importance to barbers.)

SYPHILIS is a contagious disease and a major public health problem. It is caused by a treponeme known as *Treponema pallidum (spirochete pallida)*, a human parasite which ordinarily enters vulnerable surfaces of the ano-genital, oral, or other mucous or cutaneous surfaces, most often due to sexual contact. It is systemic from its onset, may be either acute or chronic, and is capable of revealing itself through florid manifestations, or of lying quiescent and unsuspected for months or even years.

Syphilis can imitate most of the known diseases of man, and may involve any organ of the body at any time during its presence in the host.

If left untreated, it can cause paralysis, insanity, blindness, heart disease, and death.

Syphilis still kills thousands of persons annually. Annual maintenance of the syphilitic blind in this country costs about 12 million dollars. It also costs almost 50 million dollars each year for hospitalization of the syphilitic insane.

More than a million persons need treatment for syphilis in the United States. If they are not treated, 1 in 200 will become blind; 1 in 50 will become insane; 1 in 25 will become crippled or incapacitated to some extent; and 1 in 15 will become a syphilitic heart victim.

This problem is not confined to any race, sex, social group, or section of the country. It affects persons in all walks of life; therefore members of any profession who come into close contact with the public are involved to some degree.

241

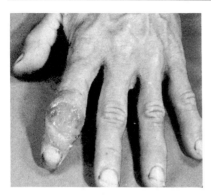

Fig. 151. Chancre of the finger.

Barbering is one of those professions closely associated with public health. Sanitary regulations and professional requirements testify to that. In this profession, opportunities occur for transmission of disease by comb, razor, towel, etc., from one patron to another or from patron to operator. Moreover, patrons frequently consult barbers for advice on venereal disease related problems.

It is apparent, then, that a general knowledge of syphilis on the part of the barber will be not only useful but necessary.

How People Are Infected

Syphilis does not just "happen." It is not spread by water, food, or air. It is NOT caught from toilet seats, door handles, drinking fountains, or eating utensils. It is NOT caught by lifting heavy things or straining. It IS caught from persons who have it—through sex relations or occasionally by other close body contact. It is possible to contract syphilis directly through handling if there is a break in the skin.

The germs of syphilis can live and grow only in an atmosphere of moisture, warmth, and protection from air, consequently they thrive in the genital organs, mouth, and similar areas, but do not live long outside the body.

The passage of the germs of syphilis from a pregnant woman to her unborn child is an important exception to the usual sexual transmission of this disease.

In very rare instances it is possible for a person to become infected with syphilis by using toilet articles and damp towels which have just previously been used by an infected person. It is important, therefore, for the barber to maintain strict sanitary conditions.

The Course of Syphilis

Although syphilis is a continuum, it may be expected to pass through several rather closely definable stages—primary, secondary, latent, and late (or tertiary).

Primary Syphilis. Approximately three weeks after infection (10 to 90 days) the first visible symptom of syphilis infection appears in the form of a chancre (pronounced "shanker"). It is found usually in the ano-genital region, but may occur wherever the treponeme first entered the body (e.g., finger, lip, tongue, tonsil, etc.). It is usually single, but may be multiple. It is usually an eroded hard papule, but may be quite soft. Uncomplicated, it is almost always painless. Any ano-genital lesion, however, must be suspected as possible evidence of syphilis.

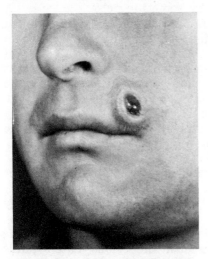

Fig. 152. Typical chancre of anterior cheek.

A very common site for a chancre in women is the cervix of the uterus, and such a chancre often is missed in examination of patients simply because of failure to examine the cervix. This is one reason why a physician, regardless of the sex of his patient, always insists upon a thorough physical examination which includes an examination of the genital organs and a blood test for syphilis.

The chancre disappears whether or not the patient receives treatment, but without treatment the germs of syphilis remain and multiply in the body. This tendency of the chancre to heal spontaneously in the natural course of the infection is often seized upon by the quack as evidence that he has cured the disease, but during this period the infection gradually spreads through the entire body.

Secondary Syphilis. This is the most contagious stage of the disease. It begins several weeks after the disappearance of the chancre. Individual patients exhibit widely varied clinical manifestations of this stage. Although constitutional symptoms such as fever, sore throat, and headache are often present, the diagnosis of secondary syphilis is made primarily on the basis of lesions of the skin and mucous membranes, which may be few or many, large or small. As a rule, the lesions do not itch or contain pus. There may also be a temporary patchy loss of hair, giving the scalp a moth-eaten appearance which becomes more evident after a close haircut. Symptoms of the secondary stage will disappear without treatment, just as do symptoms of the primary stage.

Latent Syphilis. This stage of the disease by definition is hidden syphilis. There are no clinical manifestations. A diagnosis usually is established on the basis of positive blood tests, after the possibilities of other stages of syphilis have been ruled out.

A history of exposure, or of genital lesions, or of cutaneous eruptions may be helpful to establish a diagnosis, but it is entirely possible that none of these will be remembered.

In the absence of other signs and symptoms, a positive blood test must be considered diagnostic of latent syphilis until the reaction is proved to be caused by something else.

No true line may be drawn between early latent syphilis and late latent syphilis. The disease is a continuum, and its progress depends very largely on the physiology of the infected individual. In the past, most authorities have defined "early latent syphilis" as syphilis of less than four years' duration, and "late latent syphilis" as syphilis of more than four years' duration.

Late Syphilis. As a result of untreated or inadequately treated syphilis, complications involving almost any part of the body may develop in later years. The most serious complications are paralysis, insanity, blindness, and heart disease. The bones, skin, and any of the internal organs may be involved. Syphilis of the heart and blood vessels may result in premature death.

The following are some of the differences between early syphilis and late syphilis:

Infectiousness—Early syphilis is infectious because *T. pallida,* the causative organisms, are present in the lesions. Late syphilis is not infectious, except to the unborn child of an infected mother, and *T. pallida* cannot be demonstrated from a lesion.

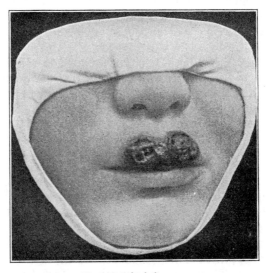

Fig. 153. Labial chancre.

Destructiveness—Early syphilis lesions are acute, nondestructive, and self-healing. Late syphilis lesions are chronic and destructive.

Reinfection—Following cure of early syphilis, reinfection is common. Following adequate treatment of late syphilis, reinfection is rare.

Congenital Syphilis

Probably the most tragic aspect of syphilis is its transmission to the unborn child. A syphilitic woman can, in any stage of the disease, pass the infection to the fetus during pregnancy. Death to the child from syphilis may occur before or soon after birth.

Manifestations of syphilis may not be evident in a living child at birth, but may develop within months or years. When symptoms of the disease are visible at birth, eruptions of the skin are the most common. As the baby grows, the permanent teeth may develop serious defects in formation, and the surface of the eyes may become cloudy, so that sight is partially or totally lost. After the child is two years of age, any of the complications of late syphilis already described may occur. It is possible, however, by keeping an infected child under the treatment and observation of an experienced physician, to maintain the child in a state of normal health.

If a pregnant woman is found to have syphilis, she should be treated at once. If she is treated before her fifth month of pregnancy, her child almost certainly will be born without syphilis. But a mother with syphilis who is not treated has only one chance in six of having a healthy baby.

How Syphilis Is Found

The diagnosis of syphilis is based upon laboratory examinations, the patient's history, and physical examination.

Infection occurs immediately on exposure, but evidence of syphilis through clinical examination or blood testing is lacking for a time. After infection (10 to 90 days), the primary chancre may appear at the site of the first contact with the disease organism. Blood tests for syphilis still are nonreactive (negative), and remain so for a week or more longer before becoming reactive (positive). Diagnosis at this time can be definitely established only by examination of fluid from the chancre under a darkfield microscope which makes it possible actually to see the *T. pallidum,* the causative organism.

Later (six weeks to six months), secondary syphilis may appear, and ordinarily at this time all blood tests are reactive (positive). The darkfield examination is also helpful in the secondary stage, since the germs of syphilis may often be demonstrated in the mucous membrane lesions and skin eruptions.

In this stage the physician will base his diagnosis upon a positive blood test, the darkfield examination whenever possible, the patient's history, and symptoms which may be present, such as a prolonged sore throat, patchy baldness, inflamed eyes and skin rash.

In the later stages of syphilis the blood tests are reactive. After many years some may become nonreactive, despite possible damage to cardiovascular or central nervous systems, but most continue to be reactive for the life of the patient.

During the latent stage there are no outward symptoms of syphilis, and the patient may be unaware that he has the disease. At this time diagnosis depends upon blood testing, spinal fluid examination and the patient's history. An untreated case of syphilis becomes noninfectious, usually after four years, although the disease may be progressing within the body toward its late, serious complications.

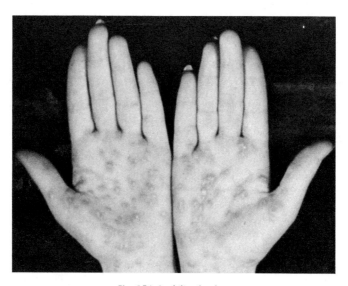

Fig. 154. Syphilis of palms.

Late syphilis may imitate many other diseases and may attack any part of the body. In this stage, the physician will rely upon a series of blood tests, a spinal fluid examination and the patient's history and symptoms in establishing his diagnosis.

The Treatment of Syphilis

Great strides have been made in technical treatment procedures for syphilis in the past few years. A satisfactory cure can now be accomplished by a number of schedules using several penicillin preparations. Thus, the treatment can be adjusted to the schedule best suited for patient, clinic or physician.

The old standard treatment for syphilis consisted of injections of arsenic and bismuth over a period of 18 months to two years. Many patients lapsed from treatment before such long-time schedules were completed. Penicillin treatment schedules now in use cover a period of only 8 to 10 days in most cases, and ordinarily it is not necessary that the patient be hospitalized.

Treatment should be started promptly after the diagnosis of syphilis is established. Even in the later stages of syphilis, one can be treated and cured of the disease. But the damage to the body can never be repaired.

Because syphilis is most frequently spread through intimate personal relations, it has long been taboo as a subject of conversation, and many persons have been victimized by quacks or misled by advertisements of fake remedies which are claimed to cure "men's diseases" and "women's disorders." As the basis of their so-called "cure," which is no cure at all, the quacks all rely on the disappearance of all outward symptoms, which is the natural course of the disease. It is important to remember that only a regularly licensed physician is qualified to diagnose and treat syphilis, and that each patient represents a special case for the physician's consideration.

Epidemiology of Syphilis

Treatment of a syphilitic patient, particularly in an early stage, without examining his or her contacts contributes very little to the control of syphilis.

Because persons who have syphilis usually are sexually promiscuous, and move among similar persons, and because of the characteristics of the disease itself, it is easy for syphilis to travel faster than individual cases can be sought out and treated. If treatment were confined only to obviously infected persons who volunteered for diagnosis and treatment, no measure of control ever would be effected.

Every sex contact to infectious syphilis should be located, examined and treated. Treatment may be administered on either of two bases: (1) treatment of diagnosed infected individuals, or (2) preventive or prophylactic treatment of all persons who have been exposed sexually to infectious syphilis who, although negative to present examination (physical examination and serology), may be in the incubation period or may have small undetected primary lesions.

Syphilis and the Individual

Syphilis is a serious disease for any individual. Because the germs of syphilis recognize no race, color or social boundaries, every person should have some knowledge of the disease. These points should be kept in mind:

1. Syphilis is a contagious disease, usually acquired through sexual intercourse, but occasionally spread by kissing or handling.

2. The diagnosis of early syphilis is based upon laboratory examinations (darkfield examination and blood testing), the patient's history and a physical examination.

3. Treatment is most effective when started during the early stages of syphilis, before the germs have done internal damage.

4. Untreated or inadequately treated syphilis may result in crippling or killing complications, such as heart disease, nervous system disorders, etc.

5. Blood tests before marriage and blood tests of all pregnant women would reduce infections in marriage and in unborn children.

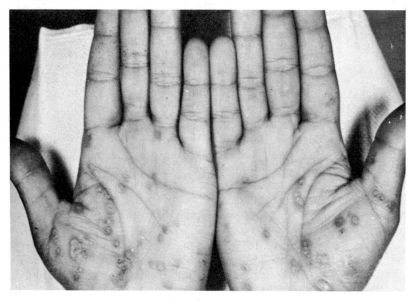

Fig. 155. Syphilis of palms.

6. A competent licensed physician should be consulted as soon as syphilis is suspected.

Syphilis and the Community

Syphilis is a contagious disease, to be dealt with as any other dangerous contagious disease. There are no isolated cases of early syphilis. Every case of primary or secondary syphilis is related immediately to at least one additional case, and must be considered with a sense of immediacy, whether it be treated in the office of the private practitioner or in the public clinic.

The control of syphilis is more than an individual problem; it is a public health problem to which the community and its citizens must direct serious attention. The United States Public Health Service has outlined the minimum essentials of a community syphilis control program. A community with an adequate program could answer "yes" to each of these questions:

1. Has your state and city or county a trained public health staff which knows how to deal with syphilis?

2. Does your state require reporting and follow-up on all cases of syphilis?

3. Are patients in your town assured of good treatment for syphilis even if they cannot afford to pay?

4. Do physicians and clinics in your town have access to free laboratory service for blood tests?

5. Is every expectant mother required to have a blood test in your state?

6. Are medical certificates, including a blood test for syphilis, required before marriage in your state?

7. Does every complete physical examination given in your town include the blood test?

8. Has your town a specific educational program aimed at age groups most frequently acquiring syphilis?

Syphilis and the Barber

Many persons have a morbid dread of syphilis, and regard diseases which have no relation whatever to syphilis as being manifestations of it. Particularly must this tendency be guarded against by those in the profession of barbering. Every skin disease is not syphilis—indeed, the vast majority of skin diseases are not. Falling hair, as every barber knows, is not caused solely by syphilis. Most insane and paralyzed persons and persons with disease of the heart and other organs do not have syphilis. Syphilis is only one cause of such disorders.

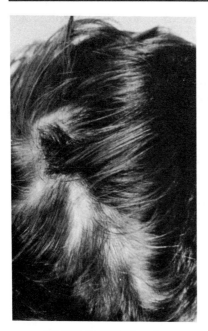

Fig. 156. Syphilitic alopecia.

Nevertheless, the barber is a very important person in preventing the spread of syphilis, because his work occasionally necessitates his coming in contact with syphilitic patrons. It is obviously impossible for him to recognize the condition by merely observing a sore, and he cannot take the chance of offending the patron by asking if he has syphilis.

Consequently, the barber should keep in mind that any sore or rash on the lips, fingers, or any other visible part of the body, or a patchy loss of hair, may be a sign of syphilis. For his own protection and the protection of his other patrons, the barber should thoroughly wash and disinfect all instruments used on all patrons, and all linens should be laundered before again being used in any manner.

The Lesions of Syphilis

Some of the more common lesions of syphilis are presented with this chapter. Where lesions are seen which resemble these pictures, they may be highly suggestive of syphilis. However, no suspicious lesions of any kind may be ruled out until syphilis itself is ruled out by serology and darkfield examination.

The following lesions are shown:

Primary Syphilis

1. Chancre of the finger. (Fig. 151.)
2. Typical chancre of anterior cheek. (Fig. 152.)
3. Chancre of the upper lip with slight induration, redness, and crusting. (Fig. 153.) Note enlarged nodes are firm in consistency and usually painless.

Secondary Syphilis

4. Maculopapular syphilis of palms. (Fig. 154.)
5. Old pigmented maculopapular syphilis of palms. (Fig. 155.)
6. Syphilitic alopecia. (Fig. 156.) Note the "moth-eaten" appearance, with numerous small areas not completely devoid of hair.

Chapter 21

The Theory of Massage

MASSAGE is any system of manipulations on the body, by hands or instruments, for therapeutic or cosmetic purposes.

The physiological effects produced by massage vary according to the type, force and duration of manipulations.

This conclusion, concurred in by the most modern scientific works on the subject of massage, was expressed in 400 B.C. by Hypocrates in these words: "Hard rubbing binds, soft rubbing loosens, much rubbing causes parts to waste, and moderate rubbing makes them grow."

There is no service more important in the whole field of barber technology than the art of giving a massage scientifically.

All the useful procedures in massage are classified as follows:

		Technical Terms
I.	Touch	
II.	Stroking	*Effleurage*
III.	Kneading	*Petrissage*
IV.	Percussion	*Tapotement*
V.	Vibration	

Massage Techniques

I. **TOUCH.** The touch of massage is not simply an ordinary touch, or contact of the hands with the body, but a *skilled professional touch applied with intelligence, control and purpose, and capable of producing decided physiological effects.*

Physiological effects:

1. Warms tissues by body heat.
2. Soothes and relaxes by influencing the cutaneous nerves and central nervous system.
3. Psychological (not occult), a subtle influence due to quality, manner and softness of hands.
4. With moderate pressure, relieves congestion and some types of pain by emptying blood and lymph vessels and benumbing nerves.

251

5. With strong pressure, stimulates by slight irritation, especially the nerves.

II. **STROKING** (effleurage):

A. LIGHT STROKING. A light touch combined with a rather slow motion. Usually two or three fingers are used. (Fig. 157.) Sometimes four fingers or the entire palm is used.

The physiological effect is principally sedative, restful and analgesic (relieving some headaches and neuralgias).

Fig. 157.

B. DEEP STROKING. This is a stroking with pressure and at a faster rate—a deep rubbing in which the underlying structures are moved, with 50 to 100 strokes per minute.

The physiological effects of deep stroking are:

1. Reflex stimulation of the vasomotor centers, increasing peripheral flow.
2. Mechanical stimulant to venous and lymph flow.

C. MODERATE STROKING. Here the strokes are executed with moderate pressure and speed. The effect is mild stimulation.

Classifying pressures as 1, light; 2, mild; 3, moderate; 4, firm; and 5, heavy, it is recommended that barbers work in the middle range of pressures, and avoid the extreme light and extreme heavy pressures.

III. **KNEADING** (petrissage). An alternate and intermittent compression of the tissues against the underlying bone surface or between the fingers, as in grasping or pinching. It differs from friction in that the skin of the parts is held in firm contact with the surface of the finger tips or hands, and the hands do not slip or move along the surface of the skin.

There are various forms of kneading:

Fig. 158.

1. PINCHING. This is sometimes executed as an alternate mild pinching and releasing of the dermal tissues. Another form of pinching is executed by grasping the tissues (Fig. 158) firmly and rolling them either between the thumb and fingers or against the underlying bony surface.

2. DIGITAL KNEADING (often called rolling). The tissues are compressed with the cushions of the fingers and thumbs and rolled against the bony under-surface.

3. PALMAR KNEADING. Same as above, applied with palm or entire hand.

The physiological effect of kneading is the production of heat. It stimulates all vital body activities, breaks adhesions and loosens scales. It increases muscle size, and tones and stimulates tissues. It increases lymph and blood flow.

IV. **PERCUSSION** (tapotement). A tapping, consisting of blows administered by hand in various ways and in varying degrees of force and speed. The speed varies from 200 to 400 or 500 per minute.

The physiological effect of tapotement is the stimulation of functional activity.

1. HACKING. A form of beating with the bony sides of the little finger, the sides of the last two fingers, and less frequently the palmar edge of the hand and little finger. It is not a slapping action, but is performed correctly by a "springy blow." The force must never be such as to bruise the tissues.

2. TAPPING. A form of alternate, springy beating with the cushion tips of two or three fingers.

The true value of massage for cosmetic enhancement of the skin and underlying tissues and for general well-being is not yet understood by the average barber. In this day of speed and social complexity, when almost everyone is influenced or affected by some form of nerve or mental tension, massage takes on a dual significance in the barber's work. Not only can he effect corrective physical changes in the skin and underlying tissues, but also he can accomplish a great deal in alleviating nerve tensions and fatigue.

V. **VIBRATION** consists of fine vibratory or shaking movements transmitted to the tissues by means of the hands, hand vibrators or mechanical (cup) vibrators. Vibrations are always used for stimulation; their physiological effect is the stimulating of functional activity.

General Physiological Effects of Massage

1. Increases blood and lymph flow.
2. Increases general metabolism of all tissues.
3. Increases glandular activity.
4. Increases nutrition to parts.
5. Increases elimination of waste from parts.
6. Increases reflex nerve activity to part.

7. Increases muscular tonicity.

8. Allays fatigue.

9. Relieves muscular and nerve tension and induces general bodily relaxation and rest via reflex nerve response.

10. Produces heat and waste of tissues when large, stimulating doses are applied.

It must be understood that proper massage means the use of proper types of manipulations to induce the desired effects. It means the use of proper technique in giving manipulations, and dosage or time of administration.

A normal skin may be soothed, mildly stimulated or strongly stimulated, depending on the type, quality and time of manipulations. On the other hand, if the skin is inflamed or sub-normal any stimulation will tend to cause aggravation instead of correction. In the latter case only soothing manipulations and applicatidns are indicated until the skin has been prepared to receive mild stimulation, which can be administered to effect further benefits.

Remember: Over-stimulation aggravates and breaks down tissues. Use massage technique with moderation.

Chapter 22

Facials

The Scientific Rest Facial

THE purposes of the **Scientific Rest Facial** are:
1. To thoroughly cleanse and nourish the skin.
2. To tone fatigued and sagging muscles, and to relax chronically tensed muscles.
3. To delay the onset of ageing lines or wrinkles, and to delay the development of undesirable contours.
4. To preserve youthful skin textures, complexions and features.
5. To relieve tired eyes and transient headaches.
6. To induce *rest* and *relaxation,* for when the Scientific Rest Facial is properly administered, it is restful, and imparts a feeling of buoyancy and well-being.

These facts are important for the barber to understand, so that he can advance them to patrons in recommending this service. Just as important are the adequate knowledge and skill the operator must possess of all the underlying principles involved in the proper administration of this facial. If he does not know the locations and actions of the muscles of the face and neck, he will not be able to manipulate them properly.

If the barber has no idea of the anatomy of the nerves and the physiological reactions from the sensory nerves and the nerve centers as discussed in the chapters on The Nervous System and The Theory of Massage, he cannot direct his manipulations in the manner required to secure desired results.

He must further be familiar with the relative virtues of different cosmetic preparations, in order to use the right formulas on the various types of skins.

The importance of the histology involved becomes apparent when we consider some of the causes of skin wrinkles:

1. Gradual natural loosening of the delicate, elastic-fiber cells which constitute a part of the derma, causing a slow loss of dermal elasticity.

2. Gradual atrophy of subdermal adipose tissue, coincident with advancing age.

3. Abnormal relaxation of muscles, due to lack or loss of muscle tone, which may be caused by prolonged nervous or physical strain.

4. Abnormal tension of muscles, due directly to mental or physical strains, or prolonged unpleasant facial distortions.

5. Excessive dryness, due to insufficient sebaceous secretions, resulting in undue creasing and furrowing of the epidermal structure.

6. Excessive oiliness, causing roughness and sometimes abnormal folding of skin tissues.

7. Creasing and folding of the skin from normal facial expressions.

8. Improper hygienic skin care, ill-advised cosmetic applications and incorrect manipulations.

In order to gain the fullest benefits, there are several precautions to be considered before giving the *Scientific Rest Facial.*

The mental attitude of the operator has much to do with the benefits of the facial to the patron. An indifferent facial, or one applied when the operator is overtired, will probably prove to be unsatisfactory to the patron. Every effort should be directed toward making the facial as restful, refreshing and soothing as possible. Every thought should be centered on the comfort of the patron, for there can be no relaxation without comfort.

Be thoroughly sanitary in your work. Use nothing but clean, sterile linen on each patron. Sterilize all instruments before using them.

The hands must be washed before a patron is touched, and special attention should be given the fingernails, which should be trimmed short and always kept clean.

Never lean over a patron's face while giving a facial—the exhaled breath is obnoxious to the patron.

Never use tobacco in any form while working on a patron, and make sure that the breath is not otherwise offensive. All barbers should use a germicidal mouth wash frequently.

All used linens should be disposed of immediately.

Use nothing but standard creams and lotions, and have all the necessary materials at hand, ready for use. Do not leave the patron during the course of the service, unless absolutely necessary, and never converse with the other barbers or with waiting patrons while giving the facial.

Procedure

As soon as the patron is comfortably seated in the chair, and the chair cloth has been neatly arranged, the operator must wash his hands.

Next tuck a small towel across the back of the neck to protect the garments from the creams; place another towel folded diagonally over the headrest, and recline the patron at an angle that will be comfortable to him.

To bring about a condition of relaxation in the patron, gently stroke his forehead and hair a few times. Fasten the towel on the headrest around the patron's head to protect the hair from the creams. Tuck another towel neatly in front of the neck.

Deposit the proper amount of cleansing cream in the palm of the left hand, using a spatula or cream spoon. (Never take creams out of jars with the fingers.) By rubbing the hands together, spread the cream over the palms and fingers of both hands.

Apply the cream gently and deftly over the entire face with spreading, stroking and rotary movements, thereby working the cream into the tissues and cleansing the skin. Remove the cream with a smooth face towel, sanitary cleasing tissue or a warm steam towel.

Steam the face mildly with three or four warm towels. The towels must not be hot, because it is necessary to relax the tissues, and too much heat will contract them. Be sure the towels are *evenly* heated; a towel partly hot and partly cold is very disagreeable to the patron.

Try to acquire a graceful as well as an efficient technique in handling towels.

Soak the steam towel evenly, wring it out thoroughly, and bring it folded to directly in back of the patron. Raise both arms extending above the patron's face, unfold the towel just above the chin level and place it carefully and neatly on the face, with the body of the towel extending from the Adam's apple up over the face, and the ends over the forehead, the right end overlapping. Be sure that every part of the face is covered evenly, with the exception of the nose, which must be uncovered to permit easy breathing by the patron.

In placing the second steam towel, which should be a little warmer than the first, carry it neatly folded in the right hand in such a manner that the left end can be readily grasped with the left hand. Gently lift the first towel from the face with the left hand. Holding the first towel in the left hand, grasp the left corner of the second towel with the left hand and spread it over the face. (Fig. 159.)

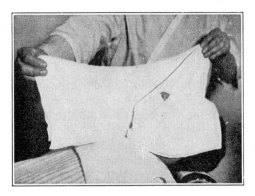

Fig. 159.

After steaming the face with several hot towels, cream the patron's face again in the same manner as previously explained, in preparation for the movements of the facial.

Since the primary purpose of this facial is to give rest and relaxation, all the movements must be rhythmically firm, but gentle. Although the movements are explained in serial fashion, *the aim of the operator must be to make all the movements continuous, without taking the fingers off the face during or between movments,* and to rhythmically shift from one movement to another with a light sliding stroke.

In all these movements only the cushion tips of the fingers come in contact with the patron.

Movements for Rest Facials

Movement No. 1 (Fig. 160). This movement is executed by placing the first two fingers of both hands at the left temple, and proceeding with an up-and-down stroke, the fingers of the right

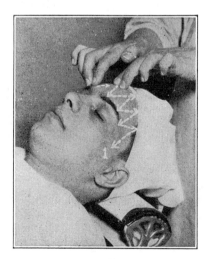

Fig. 160.

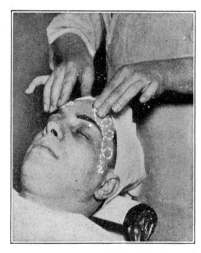

Fig. 161.

hand going upward as the fingers of the left hand go downward, alternating in this manner as the fingers move across the forehead to the right temple, and pausing while applying a slight vibration over the semi-lunar ganglion. Then proceed in the same manner back to the left temple, and vibrate over the semi-lunar ganglion on the left side of the face. Execute this movement a second time, returning to the starting point at the left temple. Now slide the fingers of the right hand lightly across the forehead to the right temple. The operator now has a hand at each temple.

Proceed with Movement No. 2 (Fig. 161), which is a circular movement, with the fingers of both hands working simultaneously toward the center of the forehead, pressure being applied as the strokes move upward and outward. Now slide the fingers of both hands lightly back to each temple and execute the movement a second time. After completing this movement the fingers of both hands will be at the center of the forehead. (The entire skin surface between the hair line and eyebrows must be manipulated in Movements 1 and 2.) The muscle involved is the frontalis.

To execute Movement No. 3 (Fig. 162), slide the second finger of the right hand across the bridge of the nose at the inner margin of the left orbit, and, with a stroking movement, move upward over the procerus muscle. The second finger of the left hand performs an identical stroking movement at the right of the nose. Alternate three movements in this manner. In executing this movement the finger of one hand must not be lifted from the patron's face until the other one has been placed.

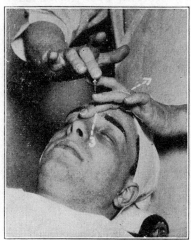

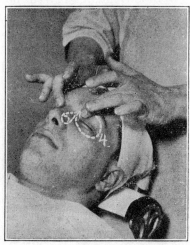

Fig. 162.   Fig. 163.

In Movement No. 3, the operator is working over the procerus muscle and a portion of the frontalis muscle.

Movement No. 4 (Fig. 163). Slide the second finger of each hand lightly to each side of the nose, and execute a rotary movement three times over the wings of the nose. Then slide the fingers with a stroking movement over the bridge of the nose to the inner margins of the eyes, proceeding around the eyes and along the eyebrows back to the inner margins of the eyes again. Now slide the fingers lightly back to the starting points on the wings of the nose. Execute this complete movement a second time.

In Movement No. 4 the operator is working over the following muscles: Nasalis, dilator naris (posterior and anterior), procerus, corrugator and orbicularis oculi.

Movement No. 5 (Fig. 164). After completing Movement No. 4 the second time, slide the fingers of both hands across the forehead to the temples, and execute five wide rotary movements over the surface between the corners of the eyes and the ears, finally working into Movement No. 6.

In Movement No. 5 you are working over a portion of the orbicularis oculi muscle and the temporal muscle.

Movement No. 6 is executed with a rotary motion downward in front of the ears, upward behind the ears, over the mastoid process and back to the temple. The pressure of this movement must be on the upward strokes. Repeat the movement three times. These first six movements are very effective in relieving some types of headaches, and are restful to tired eyes.

In Movement No. 6 the operator is working over the auricular

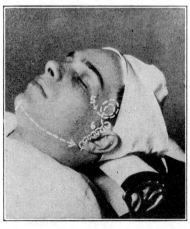

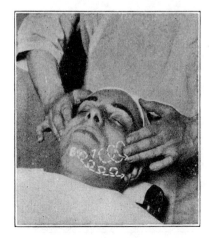

Fig. 164.   Fig. 165.

muscles (superior, posterior and anterior), masseter muscle and a portion of the sternocleidomastoid. (Fig. 164.)

Movement No. 7 (Fig. 165). Slide the fingers of both hands lightly to the corners of the mouth. With the first three fingers of each hand execute Movement No. 7 by rotating upward over the cheeks to the temples. Vibrate with slight pressure over the semi-lunar ganglion. Slide the fingers lightly back to the starting point and execute this movement a second time.

In Movement No. 7 the operator is working over the angular, infra-orbital and zygomatic portions of the quadratus muscles; the caninus muscle, zygomaticus muscle, buccinator muscle, and the risorius muscle. These muscles are all inserted into the orbicularis oris.

Movement No. 8 (Fig. 165). Gently slide the first three fingers of each hand downward to the tip of the chin in position for the eighth movement. Use a rotary movement along the lower jawbone from the tip of the chin to the ear, vibrating near the otic ganglion. Slide the fingers back to the tip of the chin. Execute this movement a second time, and at the finish shift to Movement No. 9 (Fig. 166), by alternately cupping the hands over the chin, first with the right hand, which the operator slides back with a stroking movement to the ear, then performing the same movement with the left hand. Keep in mind that one hand or the other must be in constant contact with the face in executing this movement. Repeat the movement four times.

In Movements No. 8 and No. 9 the operator is working over the mentalis muscle, depressor labii inferioris muscle, triangularis muscle, platysma muscle, and a portion of the masseter muscle,

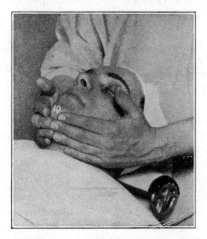

Fig. 166

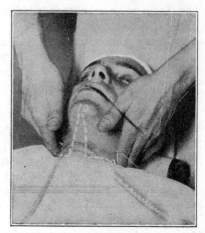

Fig. 167

also, the oval-shaped otic ganglion, which lies slightly in front of the lower lobe of the ear, alongside the mandibular nerve.

Now slide the fingers of both hands back to the tip of the chin and execute Movement No. 10 by placing the tips of the fingers of each hand together just beneath the chin (Fig. 166). Slide the hands in this position downward over each side of the neck to the point where the fingertips have passed over the Adam's apple. Lift the wrist upward, thus turning the hand so that the fingers will be pointing downward. Slide the hands in this position across the lower portion of the neck (Fig. 167), and continue the movement until the fingers meet at the back of the neck. Then rotate with all the fingers over the back of the neck, slide them upward back of the ear and around the ear to the temple, and pause with application of slight pressure. Now slide the fingers lightly over the face back to the starting point. Movement No. 10 is highly soothing to the patron, and it is exceedingly effective in inducing relaxation.

Repeat this movement a second time. Upon again reaching the temple, slide the fingers of the right hand lightly across the forehead, placing them in position for Movement No. 1, and repeat with all ten movements. These movements should be given three times. After the operator has completed all the movements for the third time, he may then proceed to cleanse the cream from the face, and be ready to complete the facial.

In movement No. 10 the operator is working over the following muscles: platysma, omohyoid, sternocleidomastoid, trapezius and occipital.

For a standard finish the following procedure is advised:

Remove the excess cream with a soft towel or tissue. Sponge the face with a cotton pledget saturated with witch-hazel to eliminate traces of cream.

Cover the face with a steam pad, which may be made by saturating a face towel with witch-hazel and placing it on the face so that the entire face is covered. In case of an oily skin use a drying lotion with high alcohol content, and in case of a dry skin use mild witch-hazel.

After the steam pad has been soaked with the witch-hazel or other skin-solution, apply a series of three hot steam towels. After steaming with the third towel, a *cool* towel may be applied if the patron desires it. Never use a *cold* towel.

Remove the last towel and apply a mild toilet water. In the case of an oily skin, apply a small quantity of vanishing cream. In the case of a dry skin apply a small quantity of tissue cream. Dry the face thoroughly, and evenly apply a suitable shade of face powder, taking care to keep it off the patron's clothing.

With the corner of a towel wipe the powder from the lips, eyes and eyebrows. When the patron is again upright in the chair, give him a brisk scalp rub and carefully comb his hair. A perfectly finished appearance will augment his feeling of well-being. He will not only feel well, but also will look well, and he will be fully satisfied with the benefits derived from the *Scientific Rest Facial*.

The Amplified Facial

The *Amplified Facial* is administered with twin hand vibrators. Preliminary preparations are the same as for the *Scientific Rest Facial*, with a towel in front of the neck, another in back of the neck, and a third over the head to protect the hair.

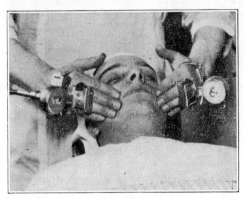

Fig. 168

The procedure in this facial is the same as in the *Scientific Rest Facial*, the twin vibrators being used when giving the movements.

Place the vibrators on the backs of the hands by inserting the hands, with the exception of the thumbs, through the long wire grips, the second and third fingers being inserted through the short wire grips (Fig. 168). Vibrations are transmitted through the fingers of the operator to the patron's face. All the movements should be executed with the cushion tips of the fingers.

The movements are much slower than in the *Scientific Rest Facial*, and the full ten movements need be given but twice.

This is an ideal stimulatory facial, and is very beneficial in cases in which the complexion is pale from lack of circulation. It also tones up the muscles of the face.

The following precautions should be observed: Adjust the rheostat so that the vibrations are not too rapid. Do not use heavy pressure. When manipulating around the eyes use but one finger, relaxed, so that the pressure will be very slight. Do not make many, if any, movements directly over the patron's closed eyelids.

Note: Some operators, in giving a *Scientific Rest Facial* or an *Amplified Facial*, reverse the order of the movements, starting with No. 10 and ending with No. 1. This is especially true in cases where the patron is exceptionally tense or tired, and is in proportionately greater need of immediate and complete relaxation. Further, they lean to the theory that by beginning with Movement No. 10 they bring a greater flow of arterial blood to the face, thus increasing the supply of nourishment to the muscles and integument of the face.

The Face Refresher

Can the number of facial services given in a shop be increased? The answer is that any business can be stimulated, and any phase of a business feels the effect of special emphasis on it. The suggestion, "Try a Face Refresher," a new name for a hot weather facial, emphasizes to a patron the benefits to be had from this refreshing facial service.

Here is a modern method of giving a quick facial that is cleansing, refreshing, relaxing and pleasing to patrons. The gentle movements of this cold cream facial soothe the patron, and the few minutes consumed while the service is being given are relaxing to him.

During the summer season the idea of a treatment that gives a patron a refreshed feeling is appealing to him. Hot weather causes discomfort because of sweating about the face and neck. There is mopping of faces, and grime appears on handkerchiefs. "Face Refresher," in the true meaning of the words, is the remedy.

Face Refresher treatments are given with a slightly mentholated cleansing cream, because of the cool, refreshed sensation that lingers after the service. The operator distributes a small amount of the cream over the surfaces of the face and neck so that ample lubrication of the area is assured. The treatment then merely requires slow, rhythmic strokes UPWARD in a face-lifting movement, all movements being gentle—not harsh. The thin cream cleanses the skin; the slow, rhythmic action is relaxing to the patron, and relaxation induces a rested feeling.

Briefly, the treatment is as follows: Two or three comfortably warm towels; application of a slightly mentholated cleansing cream, using upward, gentle, stroking movements; removal of the cream with Kleenex or other soft tissue; and final application of several warm towels, a mild astringent, and a thin dusting of good talcum. High quality creams, astringent lotions and talcum powders are being produced by leading barber and beauty supply manufacturers, and these standard cosmetics can be secured from your local dealers. Use only the best materials—it pays!

Acne Facial

Acne vulgaris or "pimples" is the most common skin disease encountered in barber shops. It is often called the disease of the healthy because it frequently occurs in otherwise healthy individuals, and most frequently among people between the ages of twelve and twenty.

The chief underlying cause of the disorder is the physiological changes occurring in an individual during the adolescent period. Among the changes are the sudden development of long hairs on the faces of boys, and development of sebaceous glands in both boys and girls. There may be temporary over-activity of the sebaceous glands, with an excessive production of oil.

For some unknown reason these oil glands are more subject to infection at this stage, causing pustules, papules and comedones, which are the characteristic lesions of acne. The predisposing and aggravating causes of chronic acne tax the ingenuity of the best dermatologists.

Though it has become traditional for barbers to treat acne cases cosmetically, it must be pointed out that medical treatment may be necessary. All cases not positively responding to cosmetic treatment within two weeks should be referred to a physician or a dermatologist.

However, there are many mild cases that will respond to treatment, and barbers can do much towards alleviating the condition.

The following is a practical treatment for acne disorders:

Outline of Acne Facial

1. Cleanse the skin with a good cleansing cream. Remove the cream with a dry face towel.

2. Steam the skin with three moderately hot towels.

3. Sterilize the skin, using a good, non-irritating antiseptic.

4. Extract comedones. Open and evacuate pustules. Express any milia that are present. (See principles of procedure, page 266.)

5. Apply a good, *non-irritating* germicide or antiseptic acne lotion.

6. Apply a good acne cream and work it gently into the skin with light, stroking movements.

7. With pledgets of cotton moistened with witch-hazel, cover the eyes to protect them from lights.

8. Irradiate with red dermal light from three to five minutes.

9. Stimulate glands and tissues with a two- to three-minute application of high-frequency current. (Do not spark.)

10. Remove excess cream and apply three warm towels.

11. Apply a good, non-irritating astringent lotion.

12. Apply two cool towels. Finish by applying an acne lotion or an antiseptic finishing lotion, such as witch-hazel.

13. Fan or pat dry, and finish with a very thin film of face powder.

Principles of Procedure

The first prerequisite of this, as well as all other facials, is absolute cleanliness of hands, nails and instruments. Assemble and have ready for use all materials needed for the treatment. Follow the instructions under Outline of Acne Facial.

To evacuate comedones the best method is to lift the skin tissues between the two index fingers, which are covered with sterile gauze. Gradually rotate the fingers inwardly, with pressure applied *below* the comedone. To avoid inflaming the tissues, care must be taken never to press hard or express too many comedones at one sitting.

To evacuate milia, pierce the overlying cuticle with a sterile needle or instrument designed for that purpose and express the "whitehead," either by pressure exerted between the two index fingers, or by use of an instrument known as a blackhead remover. Take care to sterilize the instrument before using it.

The barber must constantly bear in mind that sterile hands, instruments and linens are imperative. There is no halfway point. A thing is either sterile or it is not sterile. Therefore, before removing whiteheads or blackheads, he should completely sterilize not only the instrument (needle or comedone extractor) which he employs, but also his hands and the skin of the patron.

His purpose is defeated if he works with a sterilized instrument but takes no precautions to sterilize the skin, for bacteria on the skin may enter when it is pierced (for removal of a blackhead or whitehead), and infection may set in.

Asepsis of the skin may be accomplished by painting the portion to be worked on with any one of the colorless alcohol-acetone mercurial antiseptics now obtainable from supply dealers. As soon as the antiseptic dries, removal of the whitehead or blackhead may be safely accomplished, because both the skin and instrument are in a sterile condition. Evidence of this care on the part of the barber will cause the patron to appreciate the soundness of the barber's procedure.

In treating pustules, pierce the sac when "ripe," and gently press or clean the lesion, being careful not to further injure the inflamed surrounding tissues. Each treatment should be of short duration, and may be augmented by heat from a stand-type dermal lamp.

Applying a germicide to the skin is best done with a piece of saturated cotton. A non-irritating antiseptic is preferred. Special care should be given to each pustule that has been ruptured.

In applying acne cream rub it well into the skin with light, gentle, rotary movements.

Irradiation is most efficiently done with a new-type infra-red lamp or a red carbon filament bulb. Irradiate three to five minutes in the more inflamed cases. This lamp is recommended because of its penetrating red and infra-red rays, which serve three purposes: (1) Increase absorption of creams and lotions by the skin; (2) increase superficial blood flow and metabolism, producing a beneficial action in the tissues; (3) soothe and relieve inflammation.

High-frequency stimulation may be given for three to five minutes. Avoid sparking. High-frequency acts to tone the tissues and enhance their regenerative powers by stimulatory action on cells, glands and nerves.

To complete the treatment, remove the acne cream with two warm towels, apply an astringent lotion, follow with two cool towels, and finish. Use medicated powder sparingly.

Acne Rosacea Facial

This condition should be treated by a physician. Its etiology indicates that it is in great part due to systemic factors. However, barbers can do a great deal in improving the local condition cosmetically, in its mild forms.

Cosmetic treatment for acne rosacea:

1. Cleanse with cleansing cream.
2. Remove cream gently with soft towel.
3. Sponge face with soda solution (half teaspoon soda to cup of water), using cotton pledget.
4. Apply astringent cream.
5. Use blue light for three to five minutes.
6. Use *mild* high-frequency up to ten minutes.
7. Sponge face with witch-hazel. Dry and powder.

No hot towels are used in this facial.

The positive electrode of the galvanic current may be used.

Facials and Packs

There are several types of facial packs, in addition to the clay pack (see page 270), which may be applied for the purpose of stimulating blood circulation and assisting the skin in performing its function of excreting waste matter.

Physiologically they induce the same results as are obtained by the clay pack, but may contain an astringent, bleach or other ingredient, when it is desired that the action of the facial pack be predominantly astringent or bleaching.

Most facial packs are of a semi-solid consistency and are applied directly to the skin surface, but some are applied over a piece of sterile gauze, which is first placed snugly and smoothly over the face.

Packs are allowed to remain on the face from ten to fifteen minutes, and most of them exert their physiological action on the skin because the preparations contract as they dry. Packs usually dry in from eight to ten minutes. Drying of clay packs is usually speeded up by the application of infra-red heat rays.

Types of Facials and Packs

Commercial packs are products designed to achieve various results, and the rule for their use is to follow the manufacturers' instructions.

1. **Milk and Honey Facial.** This pack, bearing many trade names, is principally a mixture of two parts honey, one part powdered milk, and two parts almond meal, compounded into a thick paste.

2. **Bleach Packs.**
   A. A mixture of peroxide and almond meal, which may be freshly prepared by the operator. Some operators prefer to add two or three drops of ammonia to hasten the action.
   B. A paste compounded of peroxide and magnesium oxide. In using bleach packs it must be remembered that the hairs of the head and eyebrows must be protected from the pack mixture. This is done by applying a heavy cream on the eyebrows and along the hair outline to form a protective film against the bleach, and by exercising extreme care in keeping the bleach from touching the hair.

3. **Egg White Packs.** There are various formulas in which fresh egg white is the principal ingredient. Some operators use pure egg whites, beaten to a thick, frothy consistency. Others mix almond meal with egg albumen to make a paste. Usually an egg white mixture is a "runny" liquid which is applied over sterile gauze placed over the face and allowed to dry. The drying may be augmented by using an infra-red lamp. The pack is removed with towels wrung out of tepid or cool water.

4. **Witch-Hazel Pack.** Various preparations containing almond meal or other powdered substances mixed with witch-hazel.

General Outline for Giving Facials and Packs

1. Comfortably recline the patron.
2. Place neck towel as for facial. (Fig. 96.)
3. Place head towel as for facial to protect hair. (Fig. 96.)
4. Clean the skin with cleansing cream. Remove the cream with a dry face towel.
5. Steam the face by applying three hot towels.
6. Prepare cotton pledgets by soaking two small squares of cotton with witch-hazel or boric acid (saturated) solution. Squeeze out any excess solution and place the pledgets on a clean surface, ready for use.
7. Mix facial pack ingredients in a small, deep, sterile dish, and have it ready for use.
8. Remove hot towels from the patron's face and carefully place previously prepared cotton pledgets over the patron's eyelids.
9. If a bleach pack is to be used, protect the hair outline and eyebrows from the bleach by carefully coating them with a heavy cold cream or a protective cream designed for that purpose.
10. If the pack mixture is to be applied directly to the skin, smooth it out carefully to uniform thickness.
11. In instances where a thin, liquid mixture or preparation is to be used, arrange moistened sterilized gauze snugly and smoothly over the entire face, leaving an opening at the nostrils for breathing. Apply the preparation over the gauze.
12. In all cases permit the pack to "set" for two minutes, and make sure that the liquid packs are under control and do not "run."
13. After the two-minute "setting" period, apply infra-red or dermal light to hasten the drying. Masks must remain on the face from ten to fifteen minutes to be of true value.
14. To remove most types of packs, apply a hot, wet (not dripping) towel to soften the pack. When the pack is softened, gently and carefully sponge it off the face with two or three towels. To remove an egg mixture use a cool, wet towel to soften the preparation. Carefully remove the gauze and gently sponge the face with two warm towels.

Plain facial packs are finished with the application of proper creams, lotions, etc., in the manner in which facials are finished, with a final application of a thin film of powder.

Most facial packs, however, are followed by facial manipulations before being finished, as described on page 258.

The Clay Pack

The use of clay packs dates back to the ancient Egyptians and Persians. From Egypt this custom spread to Greece and Rome, where large edifices called *termes* were built and dedicated to beauty culture.

The early Greek physicians, Hippocrates and Galen, both wrote about the virtues of the clay massage, not only as applied to the face, but also as applied to the entire body. It was perhaps one of the first remedies used by primitive man to heal skin lesions, and it proved beneficial as an antiseptic and protective coating, just as gauze bandages serve those purposes today.

The substances used in the manufacture of beauty clays usually come from volcanic deposits in certain areas of the United States, Hungary, Germany and Italy.

A clay pack acts as a mild tonic to the muscles, nerves and tissues generally, and when properly applied is beneficial in promoting suppleness and preventing undue wrinkling of the skin. This is accomplished by constricting the superficial tissues. It is mildly hyperemic.

The service is generally recommended (except for dry skins) because it is drying in effect and the clay tends to absorb oils from enlarged pores. Clay also has a mild bleaching effect, and it is a good facial for toning up the complexion.

Method of Giving Clay Packs

In the application of clays, they are more effective and pleasant in action when used warm.

It is recommended, therefore, that the tube of clay be immersed in a vessel of hot water while the patron is being prepared for the facial.

It is necessary in the arrangement of the linen to fasten a towel around the head to protect the hair (Fig. 96). Cleanse the skin with a good cold cream, then proceed to prepare the skin for the reception of the clay by the application of three moderately hot towels.

Before removing the last steam towel, place a sufficient amount of the warm clay in the palm of the left hand. Remove the towel with the right hand, and with the finger tips of the right hand distribute equal portions of the warm clay to the forehead, chin and cheeks.

As soon as the clay is distributed on the face, proceed immediately to spread it evenly over the entire face, using gentle, continuous, stroking or rotary movements. Be careful to not obstruct the nostrils. (Fig. 169.)

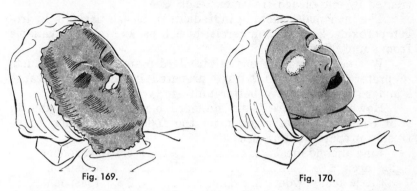

Fig. 169.   Fig. 170.

Place over each eyelid a small pledget of cotton, moistened with a little witch-hazel (Fig. 170), and dry the pack with a red dermal lamp. The red dermal lamp is recommended because it is necessary to dry the substance slowly in order to get the most pleasant and effective results.

There is no objection if a hand fan is used with a slow rhythm, but the use of electric hair dryers is condemned, because of discomfort to the patron and the deleterious effect on the skin from fast drying.

Remove the pack. This is neatly and comfortably done by carefully moistening the pack and removing it with a warm, damp steam towel. The clay adhering to the towel may be easily rinsed out in warm water. Three towelings should suffice in removing the clay, and care must be taken that this is done gently.

Apply a good cold cream or nutrient cream, as the case requires, using light, soothing, rest facial manipulations.

For a more elaborate treatment the use of a blue light is recommended at this point for its soothing, beneficial effect.

Remove the cream with a soft face towel and steam the face with three comfortably warm towels. Finish by applying two cool towels, a mild astringent or antiseptic lotion, dry well and apply a thin coating of face powder.

The Bleach Pack

The purpose of the bleach pack is to whiten the *outer* layer of skin when it has lost its natural tint from exposure, neglect or other causes.

It must be noted that the effect of any bleach on the skin is at best only temporary and limited, and that naturally dark skins or those containing excessive pigment *cannot* be cosmetically bleached. Some mild cases of freckles may be successfully treated by one bleach treatment each week.

The principal bleaching ingredient in bleach packs is hydrogen peroxide. Several commercial bleach packs are now available from supply dealers.

We recommend the use of standard manufactured products in preference to any mixtures prepared in the shop, because standard products have better uniformity and textures.

However, if there is no standard bleach pack available in your community, we recommend the following formula, to be freshly prepared before use:

Fine almond meal	4 or 5	teaspoons
Starch	1	teaspoon
Citric acid powder	1/3	teaspoon
Tincture benzoin	10	drops
Peroxide	2 or 3	teaspoons, or sufficient to make a good spreading mixture.

Procedure

Follow the General Outline, page 269.

Prepare the bleach mixture previously referred to if a standard product is not available.

After removing the pack (point 14, page 269), apply a lemon or bleach cream with *light,* rest facial movements.

Remove excess cream and finish.

Dry Skin Facial

The dry skin facial is to be recommended in those conditions in which the skin is either abnormally dry, somewhat thin, or perhaps tender and scaly.

These conditions are due primarily to a lack of sebaceous secretion, which may be caused by a deficiency in dermal nutrition, some general nutritional disturbance, or perhaps some occupational or environmental condition, such as working in excessively dry rooms, lack of exercise or poor hygiene.

The facial stimulates the sebaceous glands and increases the metabolism of the skin.

Procedure

Prepare the patron for the facial. To cleanse the skin apply a good *cleansing* cream evenly over the entire surface of the skin of the face. Remove the cream by using a soft, dry towel or tissue. Sponge the face with a cotton pledget saturated with witch-hazel. Steam the skin moderately with three or four warm towels.

Apply a nutrient cream or dry skin cream containing lanolin, as this substance is very soothing to the skin and is more quickly absorbed than any other type of lubricant. Using the cushion tips of the fingers, massage the cream gently but thoroughly into the skin, with circular movements over the forehead and with rotary movements over the cheeks and nose. Use deep, stroking movements across the chin, lower jaws and neck.

At this point apply cotton pledgets, soaked in a mild solution of witch-hazel, over the eyes. Radiate the skin with a red dermal light or infra-red lamp for from two to five minutes. This will effect better penetration of the cream into the tissues, because the heat thins the cream, making it easier for the cells to absorb the essential oils. Proceed by picking up the tissues between the ends of the fingers and thumb of each hand and gently twisting the tissues first to the right and then to the left. This movement tends to build up and stimulate the tissues.

After these manipulations apply high-frequency for three or four minutes with a glass facial electrode. This will stimulate activity in the sebaceous glands. Remove excess cream with a soft face towel or tissue. Steam the face with three or four warm towels. Apply one cold towel. Dry the face with a soft, dry face towel.

Place a few drops of skin oil or tissue cream in the palm of the left hand. Rub both hands together until the oil is evenly spread on the surface of both hands, then apply it to the face with even, soothing strokes, working the oil into the tissues. This will leave a very delicate film coating on the face, soothing and velvety smooth to the touch. Apply a thin film of face powder.

This facial will leave the skin in a smooth, pliable condition, and the patron will be well pleased with a service that has benefited him. He should be advised to take regular treatments each week. When the skin is again in a normal condition, the patron should be advised to avail himself of this facial service at least once each month.

To augment professional treatments, the barber should suggest to the patron that he purchase a jar of tissue cream for home use during the intervals between visits to his shop.

Egg and Honey Facial

The virtues of this facial lie in the fact that when these

ingredients are properly combined and allowed to remain on the skin a few minutes, they exert a beneficial effect on the tissues by causing a mild superficial hyperemia, which in turn has a tonic effect on the cells. The tissues are also slightly contracted, and there is a mild bleaching effect. The cells become more turgid, thereby increasing the suppleness and smoothness of the skin, a phenomenon that is noticeable after such a facial.

In general, it is a luxuriant type of facial, especially when the skin is irritated by exposure to cold, sun, or by some sudden change in weather conditions or climate. The egg and honey pack is recommended for restoring softness and beauty to the skin. It is also a good cleanser which does not irritate delicate skins.

Formula

White of egg, well beaten.   Fine almond meal, enough
Honey, one tablespoon.   to make a smooth paste.

Procedure

Follow the General Outline, page 269.

Apply the pack mixture previously referred to. Do not get mixture into nostrils, eyes and ears. Use dermal light for five minutes.

After removing the pack (point 14, page 269) apply glycerine and rose water lotion with cotton pledget. Gently fan the face dry and apply a thin film of powder.

Milk and Egg Facial

This facial is highly beneficial to skin that is sensitive to soaps or other chemicals, and which easily becomes dry and scaly.

Formula

White of one large egg.

Powdered milk, enough to form a paste.

Whip the mixture into a smooth paste.

Powdered milk can be purchased in package form, and is rich in butterfat. The white of egg is nourishing, and gives the skin a supple and smooth feeling.

The facial causes a mild, superficial hyperemia, which brings an added blood supply to the cells of the skin.

The treatment is especially good for a delicate skin which may be in need of a facial treatment, but for which most treatments are too harsh.

Procedure

Follow General Outline, page 269.

After removing the pack, spread a few drops of tissue oil evenly over the face, and work it into the tissues until the oil disappears, before finishing.

Coarse Pore and Oily Skin Facial

This facial is recommended for excessively oily skins, or any skin showing signs of enlarged, engorged, or sluggish sebaceous glands, and enlarged pores.

Since such conditions are due in part to faulty hygienic habits, it may be advisable to urge the affected patron to attend more rigorously to simple, daily measures of eliminating such conditions, such as cutting down on excessive intake of starchy or fatty substances in the diet, drinking plenty of water and regulating elimination.

Procedure

1. Clean the skin with a good cleansing cream, or with soap and warm water.

2. Steam the skin with three hot towels.

3. While the face is still warm, evacuate the engorged sebaceous glands, by pressing the contents out as gently as possible between the fingers, as described in the Acne Facial, page 265.

4. After this has been done, pat the face with an antiseptic lotion, and follow with a good astringent cream.

5. Follow the application of cream with five minutes of moderate stimulatory hand manipulations. The purpose of this is to work the cream well into the pores and follicles, where it is most required, and to stimulate the circulation. The dermal light (red) is not used here, because the oils should not permeate the tissues.

6. Follow the manipulations with a two-minute application of *mild* high-frequency current.

7. Remove the astringent cream thoroughly with a soft, dry face towel, steam the face with two warm towels and sponge the face with a good astringent lotion.

8. Cover the face neatly with two layers of cheese cloth or a piece of linen. Saturate the cloth with a good astringent lotion and leave the astringent on the face for two minutes. Steam the face with two hot towels. Follow with one or two cool towels.

9. Apply an antiseptic lotion on the face, dry and finish with a good face powder.

The Faradic Facial

The faradic facial is a general stimulatory facial massage, to be recommended in any condition where the facial tissues show a marked sign of fatigue or chronic flabbiness; where there is a tendency toward sagging, drooping or premature aging lines; or where the expression is dull or apathetic from muscular atony (lack of tone), due either to prolonged fatigue from general run-down conditions or to fatigue from lack of proper rest or living at an excessively fast pace.

The principal purpose of this facial is to give the muscles and tissues of the face an ideal form of mild, passive exercise, combined with a remedial, soothing relaxation of the nerves, thereby enhancing and restoring the general tone of these structures; brightening the expression or appearance, and revitalizing nerve energy.

The soothing effect on the nerves makes this facial more than just a temporary remedy. It tends to improve the condition, and weekly administrations bring about a permanent improvement.

The faradic current, unlike the galvanic, has no chemical effects, and its action is due directly to the effect on the motor nerve points in the muscles.

The technique of its application, therefore, should be slow movements, with momentary pauses of slightly firmer pressure over the center of each muscle, for it is at this region that the motor nerves enter the muscles. The current acts directly on these motor nerve points.

The manipulations for this facial are usually given with the finger tips, in which case they are the same as those of the *Scientific Rest Facial.*

Usually the amount of current comfortably tolerable to the patron is the amount tolerable to the operator, but there may be times when the operator is over-sensitive to this current, or when the patron requires more than the operator can stand. In such circumstances, which are the exception, a roller electrode may be employed. However, care should always be taken that in any event the current should be adjusted to the comfortable, easy tolerance of the patron.

Procedure

Cleanse the face with cleansing cream and remove the cream with a soft, dry towel. Steam the face with three warm towels. Apply a cold cream or lubricating cream, such as cocoa butter cream, choosing one most adaptable to the individual skin.

Place the carbon cylinder electrode, covered with moist cotton, in the hands of the patron. The wrist electrode is adjusted to the left wrist of the operator, with wet cotton over the disc. Connect both electrodes to the wall plate terminals with the conducting cords.

Adjust the current slowly, accepting the patron's decision as to the degree of intensity, and apply the movements as suggested in paragraph 5 under Faradic Facial.

After the required amount of current has been given, proceed with the rest facial movements. (See page 258.) Remove the cream with a couple of warm towels and finish with two cool towels, a good antiseptic astringent or finishing lotion, and application of a thin film of powder.

THE RESPONSIBILITY OF REPUTATION

A great responsibility rests upon the man with a laudable reputation. You cannot LIVE ON the reputation of a successful barber business, but must continually strive to LIVE UP to it.

Chapter 23

Shampoos
and Scalp Treatments

Plain Shampoo

Preparations for barbers' use in giving plain shampoos are available from supply houses, and usually consist of soaps or detergents that are easily and quickly handled in giving this service.

Gently massage the scalp for a few moments. Apply small quantities of the shampoo preparation over the scalp area and massage into the scalp with the finger tips until the scalp has been thoroughly covered. Add small quantities of water and continue massage, removing the suds and soap foam as it collects.

When the shampoo preparation appears to be thinned out on the scalp, and the hair seems well free of shampoo suds, proceed to rinse at the lavatory. A further application of shampoo, brought to a quick suds by vigorous rubbing, and again rinsed, may be necessary to insure a clean scalp and hair. Dry the hair with a coarse towel and/or a hair dryer, and comb to suit. (Review shampooing techniques, pages 105 to 108.)

Tonic Shampoo

The tonic shampoo is given exactly like the plain shampoo, except that a choice of tonic selected by the patron is gently rubbed into the scalp before shampooing and rinsing. Also, an application of the tonic is applied after the shampoo is given and the hair has been slightly dried. The hair is combed damp after an application of hair tonic.

Medicated Shampoos

The plain shampoo procedure is again utilized, except that

a medication, either liquid or salve, may be first applied and heated into the scalp with an infra-red lamp. Or, the medicated shampoo may be in one combination of ingredients to be applied, worked into the scalp, treated with heat, and the hair washed and dried. Selected medications may be heated into the scalp or otherwise applied following the shampoo.

Medicated shampoos are not designed to cure diseases or treat diseases. This type of shampoo is recommended to induce healthy scalp conditions. The ingredients may include pine tar, creosote, lanolin, sulphur, ammoniated mercury, salicylic acid, vaseline, etc. There are numerous preparations made available to the barber profession by leading manufacturers.

Hot Oil Shampoo

The hot oil shampoo is recommended especially for the correction of, and to be used in conjunction with treatments of, dry scalps, where it is advisable to replace any deficiency of the natural oils.

The shampoo softens and soothes any dry and abraded scalp surfaces, and facilitates the dislodgment and removal of scales without mechanical or chemical injury to the sensitive tissues, thereby protecting the irritated surface. It tends to alleviate inflamed and irritated conditions. Its use is justifiable under any circumstances, because of its thorough penetrating and non-irritating detergent effect.

Procedure

The shampoo should be recommended to those who are exposed to more than the usual amount of dust, and to those who must wash their heads frequently, depleting their scalps of the normal amount of oil necessary to the proper growth and appearance of the hair. It is an excellent treatment for people who lack a normal amount of natural oil.

1. Prepare the patron as described for the Plain Shampoo in Part One of this Textbook, page 106.

2. Massage the scalp as explained in Scalp Manipulations, page 283.

3. Apply warm oil to scalp with a small brush or cotton swab and spread it with a few circular movements. Fresh olive or sweet almond oil should be used; olive oil is preferred.

4. Irradiate the scalp with a red dermal lamp or infra-red ray generator for five minutes. It is important that adequate time be taken to thoroughly heat the scalp.

5. Apply a good liquid soap shampoo; work up plenty of soap lather, using movements explained under Shampoo in Part One.

6. Rinse the hair thoroughly with warm water, and repeat the lathering if necessary.

7. Dry thoroughly with a clean towel.

8. Apply a small quantity of oil directly to the scalp with a cotton pledget or finger tips. The oil for the finish need not be warm. An oily hairdressing tonic may be preferable.

Egg Shampoo

The chief virtues of egg shampoos lie in the fact that egg cleanses the hair and scalp without removing much of the natural oils, and without causing irritation to skins that are sensitive to other cleaning agents.

The main difference between oil and egg shampoos is that the former tends to replace oil to oil-deficient scalps, while egg washes very little of the oil from the scalp or hair.

The egg shampoo is recommended, therefore, where there are signs of scalp irritation, or where an emollient is not necessary. It is highly beneficial for those who wash their hair frequently because of occupation, those who have light-colored hair, or those who work indoors and have weak, lusterless hair, due to a lack of fresh air, light and bodily exercise. It leaves the hair soft and glossy. It is a great boon to those who have such naturally sensitive scalps that they are allergic to almost any soap.

There are available some commercial egg or egg-like shampoos which are excellent products and do an efficient job. These are preferred, but if they are not available you may use the following:

Egg may be used alone or in combination with salt, witch-hazel or any other ingredients that may enhance its action in any way. Some prefer the use of egg white only, but there is no objection to the use of the whole egg.

Formula

One large egg.	Salt, one teaspoon.
Witch-hazel, one tablespoon or less.	Mix thoroughly.

The quantity of the above formula is sufficient for a head of short hair, but may be inadequate for long hair. If necessary, double the amount of the ingredients.

There are two general precautions to be observed in its use. First, care must be taken not to permit the substance to run or drip down on the patron's neck or face, for, unlike lather, it has a tendency to run freely. Consequently, it is advisable to apply it in small quantities, rubbing it thoroughly into the scalp before more is applied. Enough of the mixture should be applied to saturate the hair. Second, the rinse water should be lukewarm, not hot enough to cook.the egg mixture.

Procedure

1. Prepare the egg mixture freshly for each shampoo. Prepare the standard linen setup and massage the scalp, as explained in Scalp Manipulations. Apply one-half of egg mixture carefully and massage it into the scalp and hair, being careful not to let any of the mixture drip from the head.

2. Rinse with tepid water. Care must be taken that the water is not hot enough to coagulate the albumen of the egg mixture.

3. Apply the remainder of the egg mixture with massage.

4. Rinse thoroughly, dry carefully and finish.

Special Shampoos

There is a number of proprietary shampoo mixtures advertised and recommended for specific purposes, some of which are to be given according to special procedures.

The barber should use these according to the instructions of the manufacturers and for the conditions specified, and he should compile a record of the results, as a physician does in a hospital or clinic. In this way the relative merits or demerits of such products may be referred to by the expert shampooer, who should not conduct his business by chance, guesswork or hearsay.

Types of Shampoos

1. Medicated: Tar, sulphur, proprietary.
2. Oils: Plain, reconditioners.
3. Soapless: Creams, milks, foaming oil, neutralized oils, etc.
4. Soap: Dandruff-removing, green soap, coconut base, etc.
5. Albumin-base (egg, processed albumin).

The Scalp Steamer

Whenever it is necessary to steam a scalp in a Barber Science treatment, the most effective way to do so is to use a scalp steamer.

The patron's head is covered by a hood, inside of which circulates a constant supply of controlled steam. This is an improvement over the towel method, with which the operator finds it necessary to frequently replace the cooling towels on the patron's head with hot ones.

Another decided advantage of the steamer is that the hood contains an opening on each side, through which the operator may give hand manipulations while the scalp is steaming, thus rendering the treatment more effective.

The scalp steamer is necessary equipment for scalp treatments, because through its use the pores of the scalp are opened, impurities and secretions are excreted from the glands, and foreign materials and encrustations are loosened.

The steaming process conditions the scalp for deep penetration of such medications (oils, salves and lotions) as are indicated for alleviation of a condition of the scalp.

The scalp steamer, from the viewpoints of business-building and patron-satisfaction, cannot be recommended too highly.

Many shops have built up an extensive patronage in scalp treatments by giving the service in booths and by appointment.

Scalp Manipulations

Scalp manipulations are designed to stimulate the scalp covering that portion of the skull called the *cranium*—the occipital, frontal, sphenoid, ethmoid, parietal and temporal bones.

The preparation of the patron is the same as described under the subject of shampooing. The linen around the neck should be comfortably loose, to allow free circulation of blood.

The following is an outline of a standard set of scalp manipulations recommended in Barber Science. They may be modified to suit the individual needs of various types of shop services. Some shops are able to charge higher fees than others, and render a more elaborate service. One shop may feature a 35- to 40-minute service, whereas another shop may limit the service to 20 or 25 minutes.

There are six manipulations in the complete set to be discussed. The first three of these are linear stroking, and are executed mostly with the cushion tips of the fingers, pressure being applied with upward strokes. Upon completing each stroke the fingers are slid back without pressure, and pressure is re-applied as the upward movement is repeated. Each manipulation is executed four times before moving on to the next one.

The chief purpose of these linear manipulations is to stimulate the flow of blood in the scalp. As the fingers move upward, enough pressure must be applied to move the tissues of the scalp, but undue pressure must be avoided to guard against pulling the hair. It is important that all the manipulations be given *slowly*.

Manipulation No. 1

Stand directly behind the patron. Place the fingertips of each hand at the edge of the hairline on each side of the patron's head, the fingers pointing upward (Fig. 171). In that position move the fingers firmly upward. At about an inch above the ear spread the fingers *gradually* and continue the manipulation on both sides until the fingers meet and interlock in the center of the top of the scalp. Repeat this manipulation four times. This manipulation stimulates the flow of the blood in the superficial temporal artery and its two branches, frontal and parietal.

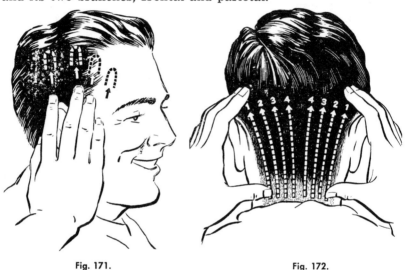

Fig. 171.   Fig. 172.

Manipulation No. 2

Place the fingers of the hands on the sides of the patron's head, and, with the thumbs at the bottom portions of the scalp below and behind the ears, manipulate upward about four inches toward the crown, as indicated by the dotted straight lines in Fig. 172. Repeat this manipulation four times, changing the position slightly each time so that the thumbs almost meet low on the neck for the fourth manipulation. Repeat the series of movements four times. These manipulations stimulate the flow of blood in the posterior auricular and occipital arteries.

Manipulation No. 3

Move to the right side of the patron. Place the thumb, first two fingers and the contiguous portion of the palm of the right hand against the forehead, just above the eyebrows. Relax the fingers and applied portion of the palm so that they conform to the contour of the forehead, making sure that they cover the whole area immediately above both eyebrows, and further making sure that the third and fourth fingers and the entire palm of the hand are not touching. Place the left hand in a similar position on the back of the head at the base of the skull. After making the proper contact, using mainly the first two fingers of each hand, proceed upward firmly and slowly with both hands to about two inches past the hairline with the right hand and to the crown of the head with the left hand (Fig. 173). Repeat the manipulation four times. (This stimulates the blood flow in the supra-orbital and frontal arteries to the frontal area, and in the posterior auricular and occipital arteries to the back portion of the scalp.)

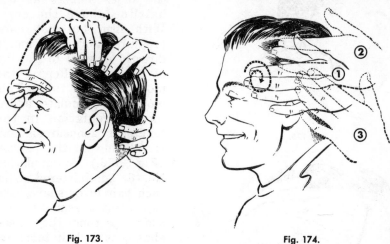

Fig. 173.   Fig. 174.

Manipulation No. 4

Move to the back of the patron. Place the hands on each side of the patron's head at the temples, just in front of the hairline, and with a rotary movement, executed with the cushion tips of the fingers, rotate four times as indicated in Fig. 174. Now move the hands back about an inch and manipulate in the same manner. Make four or five such movements, depending on the size of the head.

Then bring the hands forward without pressure, this time a little higher up on the scalp, and proceed toward the back of the scalp as before. Complete three or four series of rotations on each side of the head, executing the lowest series first. (Fig. 178.) This manipulation is most gracefully executed with the first three fingers held closely together. The frontal and parietal branches of the superficial temporal artery are stimulated.

Manipulation No. 5

Place the fingers of each hand on the patron's neck and rotate low in back of the ear, but move gradually upward as indicated in Fig. 175. Repeat four times. Posterior auricular arteries are stimulated.

Manipulation No. 6

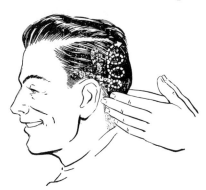

Fig. 175.

With the fingers close together, place the hands at the side of the head with the index fingers at the hairline above the ears. With firm but not hard pressure move the hands directly upward to the top of the head. Repeat the movement four times. This movement stimulates added blood circulation in the tendinous aponeurosis and is relaxing to the patron. (Fig. 176.) Manipulation No. 6, administered after each haircut or shave, acts as a silent salesman to persuade patrons they need shampoos or hair tonic applications. Barbers should include the manipulations as a routine when serving patrons.

Using Twin Vibrators

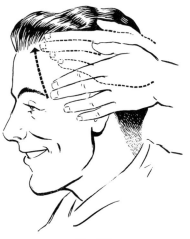

Fig. 176.

When twin vibrators are used in giving scalp manipulations, place the vibrators on the backs of the hands by inserting the hands, with the exception of the thumbs, through the large wire grips, the second and third fingers being inserted through the smaller wire grips. (Fig. 177.) When the machine is in operation, the vibrations are applied to the patron's scalp through the fingers of the operator.

Most of the manipulations should be executed with the cushion tips of the fingers. Care should be taken not to make the vibrations too harsh, as a result of using too much current. The current may be regulated by a rheostat manufactured especially for use with the vibrator and its use is highly recommended. Harsh vibrations tend to break down and destroy tissue, whereas properly regulated vibrations soothe and build up tissue. For this reason it is advisable to use a vibrator with mild vibrations. Follow the outline for scalp manipulations just explained.

Fig. 177.

Twin vibrators are very effective in giving scalp manipulations. Metabolism, glandular activity and circulation are greatly stimulated by this type of equipment, and all barber shops should have them. The best results are obtained when the barber executes these manipulations with a knowledge of the nerve points of the scalp and the arteries which supply the scalp's nourishment.

The Scalpial

In the chapter on Shedding and Regrowth of Hair it is explained how unhygienic neglect of the scalp may give rise to factors that noticeably lead to loss of hair.

The importance of healthy, vigorous hair follicles and papillae cannot be over-emphasized. Normal hair shedding takes place at the rate of 50 to 80 hairs a day, and these hairs should be normally replaced at the same rate. Any abnormal condition of the scalp will tend to weaken and thin each successive regrowth of hair.

When a thin spot makes its first appearance, it is not an indication that the hair is just beginning to fall out. It means that the condition of alopecia has reached quite an advanced stage in its development, and that the actual decline of hair growth probably has been going on for five years or more.

The most important principle in all hair work is to apply treatments primarily for the *prevention* of baldness, rather than its "cure," for if one waits until the hair follicle has become so devitalized that it ceases to produce a new, healthy hair in place of a recently shed, weak hair, it is often too late to revive the follicle and papilla to normalcy, even with efficient treatment.

However, if the operator informs the patron of the importance of hygienic daily care of his hair, and points out to him the value of regular, systematic treatments given by his barber, a great deal will have been done in offsetting many scalp conditions that lead to baldness.

In order to be able to impart such knowledge to patrons, and to give proper, systematic treatments for the various conditions that may present themselves, it is necessary for the barber to understand the principles of Barber Science. These principles explain the wonderful possibilities open to practitioners from careful study of Barber Science, for it reveals new and worthy services which will benefit a barber's patrons. These services bring not only complete satisfaction to them, but also a higher respect for the operator and justified remuneration.

In order to label a general, all-around scalp treatment concisely, the word "Scalpial" is used to designate a procedure for proper care of the scalp and hair.

Procedure

Manipulate the scalp according to directions given under "Scalp Manipulations," on page 286, using twin vibrators.

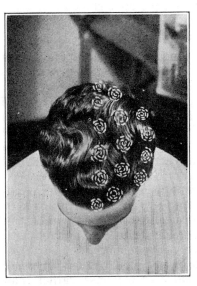

Fig. 178.

1. Shampoo the scalp according to its needs. The shampoo must be selected to fit the conditions encountered. For instance, if the scalp is deficient in oil, use an oil shampoo; if it is oily, use a tar shampoo; if the hair is dry and the scalp very tender, use an egg shampoo. Prepare the patron and proceed with the proper type of shampoo according to the instructions given in the chapter on shampoos.

2. Dry the scalp. Short hair should preferably be dried with an absorbent turkish towel. Long hair should be dried with a dryer, especially if time is to be conserved. The hair should not be dried too rapidly, either

with heated air or with a strong blast of air, for too rapid drying
may have a deleterious effect on the scalp tissues.

3. Apply a good antiseptic with a few massage manipulations, using light, rotary movements. (Fig. 178.)

Then apply a stimulating ointment directly on the scalp,
being careful not to get any perceptible amount on the hair. To
apply an ointment efficiently and expertly, remove a small amount
of it from the jar with an ointment spoon and place it on a clean
piece of white, waxed paper. From this paper, conveniently
placed, the operator may pick up single applications of ointment,
with a cotton applicator, and spread it on the scalp area exposed
by the parted hairs, as illustrated in Fig. 179.

After applying ointment to one scalp area, make another
part in the hair about one inch from the first part, and again
apply the ointment. Continue in this manner until the entire
scalp is covered.

4. Irradiate the scalp with a red dermal lamp or infra-red
lamp. This may be done from two to four minutes, depending
on the patron's needs. This procedure increases penetrability
of the ointment and improves
superficial blood circulation.

5. Stimulate the scalp from
three to five minutes with high-
frequency current. This is for
the purpose of enhancing glandular and nervous activity in the
scalp.

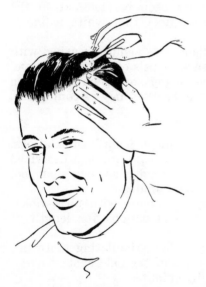

Fig. 179.

Comments About Scalp Treatments

The scalp treatments de-
scribed in this Textbook are not
presumed to hold any virtue for
the treatment of abnormal conditions of the scalp, and the barber, ever keeping this in mind,
should not treat a scalp disorder
not within the field of legitimate
barbering. He should refer aggravated conditions to a compe-
tent physician. The chief aim of the barber is to assist the patron
in keeping his scalp clean and in a condition of natural health, to
promote the growth of hair, and to prevent abnormal loss of hair.

The patron should be informed that it is essential, if he
desires to promote these desirable ends, to take regular, system-

atic treatments. No improvement can be assured unless the patron utilizes the services of the barber at least once a week, and in extreme cases two or three times a week until eradication of an undesirable condition warrants treatments less frequently, perhaps one treatment a week. These facts should be explained to the patron before he obligates himself to receive a series of treatments.

In abnormal conditions that require the advice of a physician, the barber is in a position to assist recovery by applying the particular scalp treatments the doctor may prescribe. Today many physicians work in co-operation with Barber Scientists in the treatment of scalp disorders.

Treatment for Alopecia Areata

In the case of bald spots, *where the cause is determined to be a parasite,* the treatment must first be directed toward the eradication of the inciting cause.

Tincture of iodine may be painted on the spots until a marked peeling is produced. As has been pointed out in the chapter on cosmetics, however, remember that white iodine is much less efficient.

Along with this treatment, the scalp should be washed with care and all measures taken to insure asepsis of instruments and materials, to avoid a scalp disorder being spread on the patron being treated or to others, for a scalp disorder may be contagious.

Procedure of Treatment

1. Massage the scalp as directed under Scalp Manipulations.
2. Shampoo with a good shampoo, using method described under Shampoos (page 279). If scalp is tender, use egg shampoo.
3. Apply high-frequency for five minutes.
4. Irradiate scalp, especially bald spots, with ultra-violet, following the lamp manufacturer's instructions for length of exposure.
5. Apply sulphur ointment or other stimulating ointment, working it thoroughly into the tissues of the bald spots.
6. Use red dermal light for five minutes.
7. Dress hair, using comb only.
8. Discard all linens used in treatments, sterilize all instruments and thoroughly wash the hands. Apply a disinfectant to the hands.

Note: Iodine may be used in this treatment in painting over the bald spots, but when it is used the ultra-violet lamp and sulphur ointment should be eliminated from treatment. It is acceptable procedure to alternate, using the lamp and sulphur ointment for one treatment, then changing to iodine for the next treatment, etc.

Iodine and ultra-violet should never be applied at the same time, as both treatments peel the scalp.

Dry Scalp Treatment

This treatment is suggested for those cases in which there is a chronic deficiency of natural oil on the scalp and hair, uncomplicated by any other condition. These are cases that are caused by indoor occupations, too frequent washing with strong soaps, and the use of irritating tonics or lotions.

Procedure

1. Give manipulations as directed under Scalp Manipulations, page 283.
2. Give an egg shampoo. If scalp is exceedingly dry, hot olive oil should be *thoroughly massaged into the scalp* before the shampoo is given.
3. Give a stimulating application of high-frequency for 3 to 5 minutes.
4. Dry the scalp thoroughly, because the oily substances which are a part of the treatment are best applied to a dry scalp.
5. Apply a scalp food cream, or a mildly stimulating cream, containing a considerable amount of highly absorbent materials, such as lanolin, cocoa butter, etc. The type of cream must be judged according to the condition. Sulphur ointment may also be used.
6. After the ointment has been spread and worked into the scalp with rotary, frictional movements (Fig. 178), give a four-minute application with a red dermal light.
7. Finish by dressing the hair neatly.

Eczema of the Scalp

If the condition is severe, it should be referred to a physician. In mild cases where the skin is dry, the following local treatment will bring relief:

Procedure

1. Prepare the patron as described in Shampoos on page 105.
2. Give gentle manipulations. Scalp Manipulations (page 283).
3. Apply olive oil to the scalp by parting hair. (See The Scalpial, page 287.)

4. Use red dermal light for five to eight minutes.

5. Cleanse scalp with egg shampoo or oil shampoo.

6. Apply sulphur ointment. (See The Scalpial.)

7. Dress hair cautiously and neatly with the comb.

Note: An ointment containing oil of cade is also indicated in this treatment where it is seen that sulphur does not give the proper results.

Psoriasis

Psoriasis is a skin disorder that should always be referred to a physician, for even if the condition is eradicated for the time being, it is liable to recur at any time, and it may be more severe than ever before.

The barber may serve admirably in applying local treatments as recommended and directed by a physician.

Olive oil is effective for removing scales.

Ammoniated mercury, oil of cade, sulphur ointment, ultra-violet and high-frequency are all indicated in the treatment for psoriasis, but should be applied only on the advice of a physician.

Oily Scalp Treatment

This treatment is designed to be used in almost any form of simple seborrhea—oleosa or sicca—uncomplicated by pityriasis. Give manipulations as indicated in Scalp Manipulations. Remember, however, that the manipulations should be gentle and soothing in order to relax the nerves, instead of stimulating them.

1. Apply oily scalp ointment containing oil of cade. Thoroughly manipulate the scalp.

2. Wash the scalp with a good tar shampoo. Accompanying the manipulations there should be some pressing and squeezing directed toward the evacuation of plugged or enlarged sebaceous glands in the scalp.

3. Dry excessive moisture from the hair, leaving enough moisture for the reception of a lotion.

4. Apply a non-irritating astringent lotion and steam it into the scalp. This is best applied to the scalp with a pledget of cotton, as indicated in Fig. 179. Dry excessive moisture with a turkish towel.

5. Irradiate the scalp with ultra-violet, following the manufacturer's directions.

6. Dress hair with a comb only.

Dandruff Treatment

This treatment is suggested for the ordinary, simple type of pityriasis.

1. Shampoo according to the need of the individual scalp, and dry fairly well. It is not necessary to dry the scalp thoroughly when an alcoholic or aqueous solution of any kind is to follow, for, unlike ointments, such lotions are better applied to damp scalps. Just as a damp cloth will take up water more quickly than a perfectly dry one, the tissues are more receptive to lotions when already damp.

2. Apply high-frequency for two minutes.

3. Irradiate the scalp with ultra-violet rays. *If a mercury quartz lamp is used, the manufacturer's directions should be followed implicitly.*

4. Apply a proven dandruff lotion, or a good, non-irritating antiseptic lotion. This is more expertly done by applying it to the scalp with a pledget of cotton.

Lotions should contain glycerine to prevent drying and to soothe inflamed tissues. The chief drugs used are tar (oil of cade), resorcin 2%, sulphur and ammoniated mercury in lanolin and olive oil. These drugs are compounded in commercial products usually available from supply dealers.

5. Steam the lotion in well, preferably with a scalp steamer, or with five or six hot steam towel applications, as described on page 110. Dry the hair and scalp thoroughly.

6. Manipulate the scalp as described in Scalp Manipulations.

7. Apply a good dandruff ointment, and use a red dermal light for four or five minutes. Ointment should be applied as indicated in Fig. 179.

The following sulphur ointment may be used for this purpose:

1 oz. yellow vaseline.	½ teaspoon quinine.
1 oz. lanolin.	10 drops carbolic acid.
1 teaspoon of sulphur precipitate.	Mix thoroughly.

Care must be taken that the ointment is applied only on the scalp, and not smeared into the hair. The ointment is left on the scalp until the next treatment.

8. Finish by dressing the hair neatly, using a comb only.

THINK AND ACT

The creative business man accepts the changes of the times and the tribulations that come with them as a golfer accepts bunkers, sand traps, water hazards, rocks, trees and other temper-testing things on the course over which his skill triumphs. To overcome them by superior thinking and acting is his task. To whine over them is to play the part of a cheap sport.

Chapter 24

Coloring the Hair

Dyeing-Tinting

COLORING, tinting or dyeing is the process of changing the natural color of hair to a different shade, or adding color to gray—all three terms are used to mean the same thing.

Hair tinting should never be given on abraded scalps or on patrons found to react "positively" to a patch test for hair dye, an allergy, or dermatitis reaction.

Virgin hair is hair that has *not* been bleached, dyed, or treated with color restorers.

Practically all the precautions given in previous chapters of the Textbook are applicable here. An important precaution must be added: Never give a coloring treatment without first giving a patch test, and until you are positive that the test has a complete negative reaction.

Excessive coloring and softening will tend to make hair dry, brittle, heavy, unruly and temporarily lose its natural curliness.

Dyes cannot be guaranteed as to results of desired shades or to their lasting qualities, because of variable or uncontrollable factors, such as the effects of heat, shampoos, chemicals, acid rinses, permanents, tonics, etc.

Making a Patch Test

A patch test is a skin test to determine a person's sensitivity to a chemical. To test a hair dye, a patch of skin the size of a quarter is cleaned with alcohol and painted with the dye. The dye is prepared exactly as it would be for dyeing the hair. The skin surrounding the test area is protected with collodion or a small non-absorbent bandage.

If a rash, swelling or inflammation occurs within twenty-four hours (time of testing), the reaction is "positive," and that person is sensitive to the dye and *must not* be given a hair dye. If there is no reaction, the test is "negative." Persons with negative reactions may be given hair dyes.

In the best dyeing practices a "test for color" is made. A small strand of hair is selected upon which the procedure for giving a complete dye is followed.

Such a test will reveal a more definite evaluation of both the choice of shade, and the timing required for the best results.

Classification of Dyes

I. **Organic chemical derivatives.** They are derived from aniline. These are also referred to as aniline-derivatives or acid-derivative dyes, instant dyes, synthetic or peroxide dyes.

II. **Vegetable dyes.**
1. Henna, a red harmless dye.
2. Wood extracts. Progressive or slow in action, gives hair brownish shades.
3. Camomile. Gives warm, yellowish highlights.
4. Sage. Gives greenish-brown tones.
   Hair colored with vegetable dyes can be permanent-waved.
   Hair dyed with sage may discolor if permanent-waved.

III. **Compound dyes.** These are combinations of vegetable dye (usually henna) and metallic or other dyestuffs.

IV. **Metallic or mineral dyes** are made of lead, silver, or copper salts. They are progressive, coat the hair and may be toxic. Their results are more uncertain and hair-shading is less controllable.

Instructions

Due to the natures of various dyes and tints, it is absolutely necessary that the operator follow the manufacturers' instructions carefully in order to obtain the best results. Such instructions usually accompany the products, and if further information is needed it can easily be obtained either from the manufacturers or their representatives.

Precautions

1. Keep hair-tinting service confidential.
2. Do not scratch the scalp or irritate it with strong soaps in preliminary shampooing, or loosen scales by brushing or combing before the shampoo. Wash preferably with soft water and mild soap. Leave the hair moist.
3. If hair is to be dyed a lighter shade, it must first be bleached, for any shade added to another shade produces a darker color.
4. Hold small, outspread strands of the hair away from the scalp while applying dye.

5. The hair shafts closest to the scalp are more resistant and are always dyed first.

6. Keep the hair moist and remove the excess dye with cotton to prevent streaking. A towel may be placed over the head to prevent drying and hasten the oxidizing process.

7. Distilled water will dilute a dye; additional peroxide will lighten the color.

8. Be sparing with dye in touch-ups.

9. Do not save left-over dye.

10. Keep a record card of each patron whose hair has been dyed.

Retouching

An entire head of hair should require tinting only once, but the new growth should be retouched about every six or eight weeks. The following method should be employed for tinting new growth of hair.

Exercise great care not to touch any hair dyed by previous applications. Overlapping colors cause the appearance of a streak. To prevent this, apply the tint with a swab made by wrapping a thin piece of absorbent cotton around the end of a dye-applicator stick.

Leave an untouched space of about one-eighth of an inch between the new application and the line of the previous one, starting the retouching process at the scalp. Use a comb to spread the color over this untouched space. In this way it is possible to blend the color in with the previously dyed hair.

Tipping

Tipping is the act of dyeing small strands of hair a different shade than the mass. For instance, a dark-haired man may have a streak of gray hair dyed into the mass of hair that is combed back from the forehead. Other contrasting shades may be preferred in accordance with a patron's wishes. The dyeing process, applied to the strands of hair to be treated, is the same technique used in dyeing an entire head of hair. No opinion is advanced as to the advantages or disadvantages to one who affects this type of hair coloring.

General Comment

Hair coloring is becoming a more popular service in barber shops, due principally to the desire on the part of older and gray-haired men to look younger. Barbers are becoming conscious of the opportunity to develop a profitable source of revenue through hair dyeing. Any first-class practitioner should know the techniques of hair dyeing, just as he should know the techniques of haircutting, shaving, beard-trimming, facial work and the other services—it is part of the barber profession.

The Henna Pack

Egyptian henna is a pure vegetable dye and will not injure the hair except when overlapped too often in trying to cover dark hair. The principal, active ingredient is a reddish-yellow, soluble dyestuff.

Compound henna is mixed with different chemical colors to modify the red effect and produce other shades. It is a commercially mixed powder, and is available in various shades. Compound henna and Egyptian henna are applied with the same technique.

The hair is parted as for liquid dyeing, and the tint is first applied where the strongest result is desired, on the hairs close to the scalp, so that it will have more time to become set while work proceeds on the balance of the hair.

To make an Egyptian henna pack, place about three or four ounces of henna powder in a double boiler and add enough warm water to make a creamy paste. Heat the paste to boiling point, but do not boil it. After the hair has been thoroughly shampooed and dried, apply the paste as hot as possible to all hair of head, using a long-bristled brush.

Dip a thick turkish towel in hot water, and after wringing out the surplus water, wrap it over the head to keep the paste warm. If the paste is to be left on the hair any length of time, apply a fresh hot towel on the head every five minutes.

Bleaching the Hair

Bleaching is the process of removing natural coloring matter from the hair. A bleach should not be used on a patron whose scalp shows any signs of inflammation, scratches or sores. A bleach may be applied in either of two forms:

1. Liquid form, consisting of hydrogen peroxide. (A few drops of ammonia may be added.)

2. Paste form, made freshly by mixing peroxide with white henna (magnesium oxide), soap flakes or fine almond meal powder.

Hydrogen peroxide (peroxide) is the safest and most dependable agent for bleaching human hair. Seventeen- or twenty-volume peroxide is commonly used, as a weaker solution acts too slowly. The action is hastened by ammonia or steam.

Three to five drops of ammonia will not affect the shade, but too much of it will add a reddish cast to the hair.

Bleaching makes the hair porous in texture, as well as lighter In color, and repeated bleaching will make hair over-dry and brittle.

Precautions in Bleaching

1. Hair must be clean. Do not irritate scalp or use acid rinse with the preliminary shampoo.

2. Protect patron's skin and clothing. Bleach should not touch skin, face or neck, or the hands of the operator. (Use rubber gloves.)

3. Do not use strong bleach or too much ammonia. Be careful not to leave bleach on too long or overlap the applications.

4. Be sure bleach is fresh. Measure peroxide and ammonia proportions carefully.

5. To prevent dripping and overlapping, do not have excess moisture on swab at any time. Work rapidly.

6. A towel, cellophane or paper may be placed on the head to prevent rapid drying.

7. Carefully watch development of the bleaching action. When the desired shade is obtained, remove the bleach by immediate rinsing, followed with a shampoo. An egg shampoo is recommended. The hair should then be dried with towels. *Do not use a hairdryer.*

8. Keep a complete record of all bleaching treatments. If bleached hair is to be permanent-waved, be sure to give a shorter processing time.

The Bleach Touch-Up

For a "bleach touch-up" the bleach should be applied to the new growth of the hair only. A paste bleach is preferred because it is more easily controlled. Use a swab to apply the touch-up mixture. Sometimes more than one application is necessary to blend the coloring of the hair.

Technique for Frequent Tinting

Scientific research has led to the development of products that enable practitioners to tint both men's and ladies' hair with preparations that color the hair while at the same time barely coloring the skin tissue. The tinting products are sold by suppliers and are provided in containers with shaker tops.

The preparations are applied in the same manner that tonics

are applied to the hair—a sufficient amount to thoroughly wet the hair, followed by finger massage to evenly distribute the coloring agent, which is then left on the hair and scalp for 15 to 20 minutes to allow for penetration of the ingredients into the hair shafts. The patron is then given a mild shampoo to wash away the excess tinting agent.

If the skin tissue at the edges of the hair shows "color" after the shampoo, a cotton pledget, dipped in a 40% alcohol solution of toilet water, may be used to remove the color. Care must be taken not to permit the alcohol solution to neutralize the tinting by carelessly wetting the edges of the hair with the solution— *remove the tint only from the skin.*

This tinting process should be used at least once each week on a patron's hair. This insures that new growth of hair will also be tinted, and avoids periods when the roots of the hair will contrast with the color of the tint desired by the patron.

BE YOUR OWN CRITIC

Your patron may be easy to please, but don't make the mistake of stopping there. Set your own high standards, then live up to them. When you finish the job and know that it is good according to your own best ability, you have gone farther toward pleasing the man in the chair than anything else you could have done.

Chapter 25

Technique of Finger - Waving

FINGER-WAVING is the fashioning of the hair, while wet, into "S"-curved waves with the fingers and comb. Finger-waving has an advantage over marcelling, since no hot irons are used, and it is almost equally adaptable to every type of hair, leaving beautiful, deep, natural-looking waves when dry.

The popularity of finger waves shows an ever-increasing growth, and the barber who becomes adept in this art adds to his income. It is pointed out that finger-waving is not restricted to women; men in large numbers are utilizing this service each day for the enhancement of their appearance.

Procedure

The first requisite for a finger-wave is clean hair. This does not necessarily imply a thorough shampoo, unless one is needed, but rather a hair wash, in order to remove dust and oil from the hair. This will insure a more lasting wave.

Following the shampoo, remove the excess water by blotting with a towel. Leave the hair quite wet.

Apply a good waving lotion. In general, waving fluids or lotions are aqueous solutions of mucilaginous mixtures, which in their original state are more or less gelatinous in nature. These lotions are diluted in most cases to suit the individual type of hair to which it is applied. If the hair is naturally wavy or perfectly permanent waved, the lotion may be diluted considerably. When the hair is straight and coarse, it may be used undiluted. There are instances where water alone may be used. A rule to follow is to use the lotion as thin as possible, the purpose being to reduce to a minimum any flakiness that may result from an excess of dried lotion.

Another rule that must be followed in order to secure the best results is to saturate the hair thoroughly without using an excess quantity of the lotion. The liquid should not be permitted to drip.

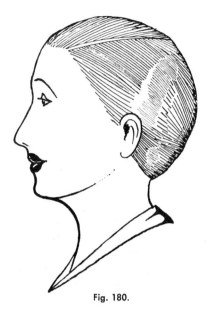

Fig. 180.

Apply the waving lotion with a shaker top container and work it through the hair with the finger tips.

After the hair has been properly saturated with the lotion, proceed to comb it free from all snarls with the coarse end of the comb, always beginning close to the hair points and working toward the scalp. This procedure avoids pulling or causing undue snarling with the comb.

After all the hair has been straightened out, fashion the part. With the fine end of the comb, smooth all the hair diagonally back on both sides from the part, as shown in Fig. 180.

Before attempting to wave an entire head of hair, it is necessary that the student master a few finger-wave movements, for no matter how simple the procedure may seem when viewing the work of an accomplished operator, a perfect wave depends on correct execution of many fine details in the movements. Therefore study the movements carefully and practice them until the technique becomes easy, speedy and perfect.

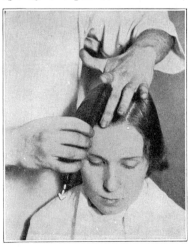

Fig. 181.

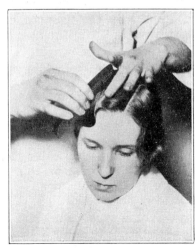

Fig. 182.

Making the First Ridge

After the hair has been combed back smoothly, place the second finger of the left hand firmly against the hair about an inch away from the part, on the long side of the part, in the manner indicated in Fig. 181, the forefinger being held up and away from the head. Holding the comb vertically, insert the edge (coarse teeth in practice) into the hair through to the scalp, and comb a strand forward, being careful not to scratch the scalp. Press this ridge up with the first and second fingers.

To Deepen the Ridge

In many cases the ridges can be made deep enough with the above movements by the knack of rolling and pressing with the fingers of the left hand, but there are situations in which it is necessary to make them deeper.

To do this, leave the second finger of the left hand in the same position alongside and above the ridge. Now, holding the second finger firmly against the head, place the edge of the comb about a quarter of an inch in front of the ridge, push the ridge up against the second finger and then pinch it up with the first and second fingers.

Completing the First Ridge

Place the second finger of the left hand in a position farther back on the head, in line with the first position, with the tip extending past the rear end of the first-formed ridge, as shown in Fig. 182, and repeat the above technique, this time combing the hair forward so that it reaches the first ridge and matches continuously without a break. Repeat this movement back to the crown.

This completes the first ridge on the long side of the part, and the results should be a smooth, unbroken ridge from forehead to crown. For later reference this ridge is designated as ridge No. 1.

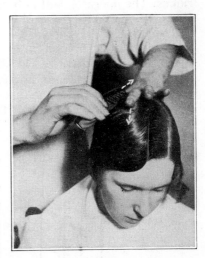

Fig. 183.

Making the First Wave and Second Ridge

The *first wave* is that wave which lies between the first and second ridges, and is made as a consequence of the formation of the second ridge.

The second ridge begins at the crown. (See Fig. 183.) This time the hair is combed backwards, and the ridge is formed by pressing strands together as the operator works toward the forehead.

The width of the waves is determined by the distance between ridges. These may vary in different styles of waves from one to two inches in depth, the average being from $1\frac{1}{4}$ to $1\frac{1}{2}$ inches.

Matching Waves

In order to complete the wave it is necessary to continue the waves around the back of the head and match them perfectly. This process of matching the waves of both sides around the end of the part at the crown is commonly spoken of as "horseshoe waving."

To make the horseshoe wave it is necessary to drop one wave close to the part on one side, and match the second wave of that side with the first wave of the opposite side.

In the diagram below are depicted two simple methods of matching waves around the end of the part. Since waves are fashioned as a consequence of the formation of a ridge, it is easier to judge the matching process by studying the direction of the ridges. The operator will note then that the first ridges on either side of the part are forward-running ridges, therefore the second ridge of the left side must be matched with the first ridge on the right side, as is the case in the left-hand diagram (Fig. 184), or the second ridge of the right side must be matched with the first ridge of the left side, as in the right-hand diagram. (Fig. 184.)

There are other combinations. In a swirl it is sometimes necessary to match the first ridge of one side with the fourth

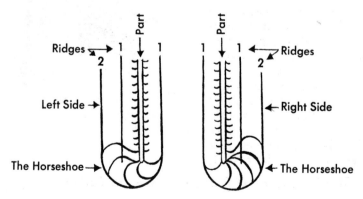

Fig. 184.

ridge of the opposite side. There is no arbitrary rule to follow.

This gives the fundamental principles for the practice of finger-waving. It would require an entire book of this size to expound the vast number of styles, modes and variations of finger-wave coiffure. The operator is referred to textbooks devoted solely to this art, if he wishes to further his knowledge in this field.

The Push-Up Wave

The push-up finger-wave is a natural-like wave set in a pompadour fashion. It follows the natural wave tendency found in most textures of hair. This natural wave tendency is not found in excessively coarse, hard textures or in extremely fine, limp textures.

To find the wave tendency, dampen the hair slightly and comb it backward, pushing up the hair mass with the left hand, thus finding where the hair "breaks" into natural wave lines.

After the natural wave lines and line directions have been found, proceed to finger-wave the hair according to instructions.

Set the waves to the natural lines.

Trifles make perfection, but perfection is no trifle.

PART III
Business Principles

Chapter 26

Shop Management

THERE is a multitude of factors concerning the management of a shop, that in the aggregate may attract or repel patronage.

One of the purposes of the Research Department of the Associated Master Barbers and Beauticians of America is to delve into the subject of shop management, to assimilate statistical data on it, and to disseminate knowledge fostering standardization and efficiency, at the same time eliminating those factors that make for general inefficiency.

The Shop

A primary physical asset to a shop is an attractive front. It should be well painted, and the windows should be kept scrupulously clean.

Window signs should be well chosen, neatly arranged, and not too large. The dignity and class of any type of establishment are lowered by large, gaudy wording, and especially by such cheap, shallow names as "Pete's Eat Shop," "Micky's Tailor Shop," or "Dinty's Barber Shop."

It is not only bad taste, but also quite unprofessional, to have prices emblazoned on windows in box-car letters, especially cut prices. In some states laws specifying that shop prices may not be displayed in a manner so that they are visible from outside the shop show the unmistakable trend toward this phase of professional conduct. Price is the poorest argument that can be used in selling, because any barber work that is sold at a cheap price usually has no other argument in its favor.

The familiar red, white and blue barber pole has stood the test of centuries as the identifying emblem of the barber shop, and every shop should display a modern, attractive pole because of its instant meaning to the public.

The interior of the windows, in turn, should not be used as a store room for supplies, or as a reading table, to be littered with papers or a dusty accumulation of unsightly objects.

The display part of the window should always be neat, clean, and attractively decorated, with a more or less permanent artistic feature, or well-chosen selling displays. This is the place for artistic placards advertising feature services, slogans, and for displaying organization cards.

Comfortable waiting chairs for patrons are as essential as other proper equipment. The patron who relaxes while waiting is pleased from the start, and is in the proper mental condition for the barber's services.

The first impression on entering the shop itself should be one of cleanliness, for cleanliness is the immediate suggestion of sanitation, which is one of the most important factors in a barber's work. Remember, a floor covered with hair may be a sign *of* business, but it is not a good advertisement *for* business.

A shop owner need not have the most expensive furniture and fixtures to create interior attraction, for a simple outlay, chosen and arranged well, and tidily kept, may be made very attractive.

A great deal of attention and good judgment should be given to interior decoration. The shop owner should strive to choose a color scheme that is harmonious, restful and attractive.

The best interior, on the other hand, may be spoiled by ill-placed and badly-chosen pictures, calendars and signs. In their stead, however, a well-placed mirror will not only add to the decoration, but also will serve as a dressing mirror for patrons.

One should also give some attention to the choice, number and placement of advertising signs and cards. Such sarcastic signs as, "Cash makes friends; let us be friends," "We do not cash checks; this is no bank"; or "Your credit is good, but" so-and-so, are not only a breach of good business etiquette, but certainly portray poor business or managerial ability.

As to fixtures, they are, of course, usually regulated by the amount of capital a barber wishes to invest, but certain minimum standards are advocated, such as individual sterilizing cabinets or equipment. Individual wash bowls should be the rule in all modern shops.

The installation of semi-private booths is among the more advanced standards in this field.

Illumination

The subject of illumination is of very great importance, not only as a means of creating attractiveness and proper atmosphere, but especially in increasing efficiency in work and in promoting better health.

Lights should not be extremely bright and glary, but should be adequate to furnish sufficient illumination for easy reading for the waiting patrons, and easy vision for the operators. They should be so placed as to cast as few shadows as possible around the working chair, as shadows are very annoying, straining and retarding to the work.

Advertising

The most important type of advertising in the barber business is that which directs attention to uniform high grade, artistic, comfortable and courteous service.

Individual shop advertising may consist of window displays, plus exterior and interior signs. There is the possibility of distributing numerous items, such as individual cards, printed match books, baseball schedules on cards, postal cards, blotters, pencils and calendars at Christmas time.

Larger shops may advertise in community periodicals, theater programs, and even on neighborhood theater screens.

Circular letters calling attention to new services, added equipment, etc., prove highly effective. These should be sent to a selected mailing list, and may be made a regular procedure, sending them out at regular intervals.

The latest form of advertising which has proved quite fruitful among organized shops, which portrays one of the manifold powers of the strength of organization, and which is becoming popular, is collective advertising in local newspapers, periodicals, and over the radio.

What kind of haircut will the patron receive in your shop? An ad may tell the story by utilizing one or more of these adjectives: Attractive, fitting, dressy, good-looking, latest, new, novel, popular, smart, striking, stylish, suitable, different, individual, chic (for the ladies), exclusive.

The student is requested to procure the book on advertising known as **Advertising Principles, Latest Edition,** by Hugh E. Agnew and George Burton Hotchkiss, in order to familiarize himself with this phase of business activity.

Service

Each shop should have, in a sense, some mark of shop individuality, for pitiable is the case of the place whose individuality lies in the personality and work of one or more operators. It is essential, of course, that each operator possess ability and personality by which constantly to build up his own clientele; but this virtue must not go to such extremes as to react unwholesomely on the good will and efficiency of the shop as a whole.

Fair play should be the aim of the manager, and this is best established by insistence on uniform adequate service to all, and favors to none. A manager should never allow any operator to give more or less service than the standard of the shop requires, because of possible tips or lack of tips. For instance, if one hot towel and a cream finish is the shop's standard for a shave, no operator should be allowed to give any patron more or less than the standard calls for.

Therefore, the first two by-words of service are adequacy and uniformity. These principles should be practiced in all shops, for if one shop in a whole town is known to give extra services for the same fee, it not only creates intolerance and ill-will among other shops, but is one of the worst forms of competition.

Uniform, adequate prices should be another aim of all shops in a community and the aim of each individual manager.

Service actually begins when a person enters the door. The person should be received with courtesy, treated in every respect with courtesy, and leave the shop satisfied. Thus, another great principle of shop service is courtesy.

It is superfluous to add that one of the principal practices in every shop should be sanitation with a capital "S."

Next to sanitation, the up-to-date barber shop should emphasize Relaxation. Relaxation implies a great many things. It means aiding the patron by judicious elimination of extraneous or loud conversation. It means a whole atmosphere of calmness and pleasantness. Last of all, it means much to the future progress of professional barbering.

There are many things that can be said about service that we cannot delve into in detail. However, we point out some of the outstanding features, such as sanitation, relaxation, courtesy, uniform and adequate service and price. The aim is to create constructive progressive thought in this field.

Selling

All of the facts referred to, such as uniform, courteous service, advertising, etc., are factors in selling. Among the *direct* principles to be considered are:

The owner or manager should make it an iron-clad policy to use and dispense only pure, high-grade standard materials and products, such as soaps, creams, lotions and shampoos.

Too often a shop owner is blind to the fact that a few cents saved on a jar of cream may mean the loss of enough income from dissatisfied patrons to have purchased several jars of the best cream obtainable.

High-pressure salesmanship, by which the patron is literally forced to buy everything but the chair itself, is slowly fading and is being rapidly replaced by a method that is far superior, a method which is based on truth and facts, and one that fosters repeat business, thanks to the educational program of the Associated Master Barbers and Beauticians of America.

For example, a patron's hair may be getting thin on the top. Instead of using this misfortune as an excuse to put a worthless mixture on the head and squeeze another quarter out of the patron, the educated and expertly-skilled operator will explain the anatomy and physiology of the hair, its shedding and the conditions that impede its regrowth. He will further portray the advantages and benefits that may be derived from proper manipulations and various appliances, and through the channel of positive, truthful suggestion he will create a desire and demand in the mind of the patron for specific added services. When he has sold the patron these added services he will execute them with knowledge and skill, and prove their value.

Most barber shop patrons shave themselves, and many shampoo their own hair at home. The patron who gets an occasional shampoo at the barber shop usually washes his hair at home between his visits to the barber shop. Many patrons use some kind of hair tonic, hair oil, face lotion, massage, vanishing and cold cream and talcum powder. There are also the razor blades, electric shavers, strops, shaving cream, soaps, combs and hair brushes that men use. Look over this list of items and figure out how many patrons buy these articles from their barbers.

The patron almost invariably goes to the drug store for these necessities. This is really the barber's fault, because the patron is seldom, if ever, asked by the barber if he needs for home use any of the articles mentioned above. The barber has as much advantage in retailing his wares as he has in using them when serving his patrons.

If a patron should ask for a specific brand, do not try to substitute and say that another is just as good, for eventually the operator will find that he has lost the confidence of the patron if he is not satisfied, and he may buy elsewhere of someone who will recommend a good quality of merchandise. It is just as essential to satisfy the patron when selling him tonsorial necessities for home use, as it is to satisfy him with good barber service, for a patron who is well pleased with his services or purchases will go out of his way to be a booster. It will please his pride to say: "He is my barber, and he is a good one."

What words should be used in selling merchandise? The following should prove effective:

choice	dependable	excellent	exceptional
extraordinary	genuine	reliable	satisfactory
standard	substantial	superior	effective

The student is requested to procure the book on salesmanship known as **The Sales Promotion Handbook,** by John Cameron Aspley, in order to familiarize himself with this phase of business activity.

How to Figure Yearly Profits

Some barber shop owners keep very little record of their annual income and outgo; in fact, if they do any bookkeeping at all, they merely add the receipts and deduct the ordinary expenses, such as the employes' salaries, rent, light, heat, laundry and barber supplies, and figure the balance as clear profit.

This, however, is a mistake, for there are other items that should be given consideration before the actual profits can be arrived at.

In order to assist shop owners in figuring their net profits after a year's business, the following method is outlined:

1. Total the actual investment by figuring the cost of the following items: Equipment, such as barber chairs, mirror cases, workstand, lavatories, plumbing, sterilizing cabinets, barber pole, cash register, display stand, waiting chairs, clothes tree, hatrack, urns, shampoo stool, therapeutic lamps; light and ventilating equipment, such as special light fixtures, wiring, electric fans and other electrical equipment; scalp steamers, and all other items that make up the total investment in equipping the shop.

This amount is business investment.

2. Total the general overhead, such as rent, electricity, barber supplies, laundry, cost of linens, cleaning equipment, water taxes, advertising, magazines and newspapers, insurance, all taxes (federal, state and local), repairs, replacement and breakage expenses.

Now add 10 per cent depreciation of the total investment, as given in paragraph 1, plus salaries and commissions to employes and the salary paid to yourself.

The total of these amounts is the total expenses for the year.

3. Total the gross receipts taken in by the barber shop.

4. Deduct the total expenses, as determined in paragraph 2, from the total receipts. The remainder is the shop's actual profits for the year.

For information on allowable deductions on shop furnishings and fixtures for income tax purposes, consult federal and state income tax authorities.

Bookkeeping

Years ago the barber, along with other small business men, may have borne the unhappy stigma of being known as a poor business man because of his carelessness in keeping books. Usually his records comprised a ten-cent note book in which he tabulated the daily gross receipts in one column and the daily gross expenses in another column. Then, at the end of each week, he subtracted his gross expenses from his gross receipts. The resulting figure he called his net income!

Today this picture has changed. The advent of federal and state taxes and payroll deductions has perforce made the barber adopt a more accurate system of bookkeeping, comparable to that of other professional and small business men.

A course in bookkeeping cannot be incorporated in the Standardized Textbook of Barbering. However, we will endeavor to outline the necessary bookkeeping that will aid the barber in keeping adequate records.

Through the generous co-operation of A. C. Clayton Printing Co., 608 N. 21st St., St. Louis 3, Mo., we are privileged to reproduce charts this company has prepared for barbers' use in keeping their business records. It is called the "Easy to Use" ledger and can be secured at any barber supply house.

THE RECEIPTS AND PAY ROLL RECORD (Fig. 185) provides for recording all receipts from all sources, as well as the pay roll records, including the deductions for Social Security, Withholding Taxes, Unemployment Tax payments, etc.

At the end of each day the proprietor should post the day's receipts on the Receipts and Pay Roll Record form. Each employe should be credited with the gross receipts collected on his services for the day. Spaces are provided in the Receipts and Pay Roll Record for each day of the week for these entries. Also, a space is provided for total receipts from all sources for each day. Further, spaces are provided for the weekly totals of receipts, deductions and wages.

EXPENSE RECORD (Fig. 186) provides for recording each expense incurred each day and for the week in operating the business, including salaries, light, heat, phone, taxes, supplies, etc. A recapitulation column is provided in order that the proprietor may arrive at the correct figure of profit or loss each week. Also, there are spaces to enable the proprietor to carry his balances forward each week so that he may have an accurate knowledge of cash received and paid out in his business for the entire year.

COMMISSIONS COMPUTATION SCALE (Percentage Table) (Fig. 187). Possession of this Commissions Computation Scale

BUSINESS RECORD FOR WEEK
RECEIPTS AND PAY ROLL RECORD

WEEK BEGINNING_____19____

DATE	FIRST CHAIR	SECOND CHAIR	THIRD CHAIR	FOURTH CHAIR	FIFTH CHAIR	SIXTH CHAIR	SEVENTH CHAIR	EIGHTH CHAIR	SHINES	SHINES	MANICURE	MANICURE	LAUNDRY	SUNDRIES	DAILY RECEIPTS
MONDAY															
TUESDAY															
WEDNESDAY															
THURSDAY															
FRIDAY															
SATURDAY															
SUNDAY															
RECEIPTS FOR WEEK															
SALARY OR ___% COMMISSION															
DEDUCT O.A.B. (SOCIAL SEC.)															
WITHHELD TAXES (FEDERAL)															
OTHER DEDUCTIONS															
TOTAL DEDUCTIONS															
NET WAGES PAID															

TOTAL SALARIES OR COM-
← MISSION FOR WEEK

TOTAL O.A.B. (SOCIAL
← SECURITY) FOR WEEK

TOTAL WITHHELD TAXES
← (FEDERAL) FOR WEEK

TOTAL OTHER DEDUCTIONS
← FOR WEEK

TOTAL DEDUCTIONS
← FOR WEEK

TOTAL NET WAGES
← PAID FOR WEEK

Fig. 185.

BUSINESS RECORD FOR WEEK

Week Ending_____ 19__

EXPENSES

DAY	SALARIES	LAUNDRY & LINEN SERVICE	SUPPLIES	LIGHT, HEAT, AND WATER	RENT	INSURANCE	FEDERAL TAXES	STATE TAXES	EMPLOYER'S SHARE TAXES	TELEPHONE AND MISC.	DAILY EXPENSES	RECAPITULATION	
MONDAY													
TUESDAY												RECEIPTS FOR WEEK	
WEDNESDAY												EXPENSES FOR WEEK	
THURSDAY												NET PROFIT FOR WEEK	
FRIDAY												NET LOSS FOR WEEK	
SATURDAY												NET PROFIT PREVIOUS BUSINESS (FROM LAST WEEK'S RECORDS)	
SUNDAY												NET LOSS PREVIOUS BUSINESS (FROM LAST WEEK'S RECORDS)	
EXPENSES FOR WEEK												NET PROFIT TO DATE	
												NET LOSS TO DATE	

REMARKS

CASH BEGINNING OF WEEK: ON HAND $_____ IN BANK $_____ TOTAL

RECEIPTS FOR WEEK

TOTAL CASH AVAILABLE

LESS { EXPENSES FOR WEEK $_____ OWNER'S DRAWINGS $_____

CASH END OF WEEK: ON HAND $_____ IN BANK $_____ TOTAL

Fig. 186.

COMMISSIONS COMPUTATION SCALE

AMOUNT	50%	55%	60%	65%	70%	75%	80%
1.00	.50	.55	.60	.65	.70	.75	.80
2.00	1.00	1.10	1.20	1.30	1.40	1.50	1.60
3.00	1.50	1.65	1.80	1.95	2.10	2.25	2.40
4.00	2.00	2.20	2.40	2.60	2.80	3.00	3.20
5.00	2.50	2.75	3.00	3.25	3.50	3.75	4.00
6.00	3.00	3.30	3.60	3.90	4.20	4.50	4.80
7.00	3.50	3.85	4.20	4.55	4.90	5.25	5.60
8.00	4.00	4.40	4.80	5.20	5.60	6.00	6.40
9.00	4.50	4.95	5.40	5.85	6.30	6.75	7.20
10.00	5.00	5.50	6.00	6.50	7.00	7.50	8.00
11.00	5.50	6.05	6.60	7.15	7.70	8.25	8.80
12.00	6.00	6.60	7.20	7.80	8.40	9.00	9.60
13.00	6.50	7.15	7.80	8.45	9.10	9.75	10.40
14.00	7.00	7.70	8.40	9.10	9.80	10.50	11.20
15.00	7.50	8.25	9.00	9.75	10.50	11.25	12.00
16.00	8.00	8.80	9.60	10.40	11.20	12.00	12.80
17.00	8.50	9.35	10.20	11.05	11.90	12.75	13.60
18.00	9.00	9.90	10.80	11.70	12.60	13.50	14.40
19.00	9.50	10.45	11.40	12.35	13.30	14.25	15.20
20.00	10.00	11.00	12.00	13.00	14.00	15.00	16.00
21.00	10.50	11.55	12.60	13.65	14.70	15.75	16.80
22.00	11.00	12.10	13.20	14.30	15.40	16.50	17.60
23.00	11.50	12.65	13.80	14.95	16.10	17.25	18.40
24.00	12.00	13.20	14.40	15.60	16.80	18.00	19.20
25.00	12.50	13.75	15.00	16.25	17.50	18.75	20.00
26.00	13.00	14.30	15.60	16.90	18.20	19.50	20.80
27.00	13.50	14.85	16.20	17.55	18.90	20.25	21.60
28.00	14.00	15.40	16.80	18.20	19.60	21.00	22.40
29.00	14.50	15.95	17.40	18.85	20.30	21.75	23.20
30.00	15.00	16.50	18.00	19.50	21.00	22.50	24.00
31.00	15.50	17.05	18.60	20.15	21.70	23.25	24.80
32.00	16.00	17.60	19.20	20.80	22.40	24.00	25.60
33.00	16.50	18.15	19.80	21.45	23.10	24.75	26.40
34.00	17.00	18.70	20.40	22.10	23.80	25.50	27.20
35.00	17.50	19.25	21.00	22.75	24.50	26.25	28.00
36.00	18.00	19.80	21.60	23.40	25.20	27.00	28.80
37.00	18.50	20.35	22.20	24.05	25.90	27.75	29.60
38.00	19.00	20.90	22.80	24.70	26.60	28.50	30.40
39.00	19.50	21.45	23.40	25.35	27.30	29.25	31.20
40.00	20.00	22.00	24.00	26.00	28.00	30.00	32.00
41.00	20.50	22.55	24.60	26.65	28.70	30.75	32.80

AMOUNT	50%	55%	60%	65%	70%	75%	80%
42.00	21.00	23.10	25.20	27.30	29.40	31.50	33.60
43.00	21.50	23.65	25.80	27.95	30.10	32.25	34.40
44.00	22.00	24.20	26.40	28.60	30.80	33.00	35.20
45.00	22.50	24.75	27.00	29.25	31.50	33.75	36.00
46.00	23.00	25.30	27.60	29.90	32.20	34.50	36.80
47.00	23.50	25.85	28.20	30.55	32.90	35.25	37.60
48.00	24.00	26.40	28.80	31.20	33.60	36.00	38.40
49.00	24.50	26.95	29.40	31.85	34.30	36.75	39.20
50.00	25.00	27.50	30.00	32.50	35.00	37.50	40.00
51.00	25.50	28.05	30.60	33.15	35.70	38.25	40.80
52.00	26.00	28.60	31.20	33.80	36.40	39.00	41.60
53.00	26.50	29.15	31.80	34.45	37.10	39.75	42.40
54.00	27.00	29.70	32.40	35.10	37.80	40.50	43.20
55.00	27.50	30.25	33.00	35.75	38.50	41.25	44.00
56.00	28.00	30.80	33.60	36.40	39.20	42.00	44.80
57.00	28.50	31.35	34.20	37.05	39.90	42.75	45.60
58.00	29.00	31.90	34.80	37.70	40.60	43.50	46.40
59.00	29.50	32.45	35.40	38.35	41.30	44.25	47.20
60.00	30.00	33.00	36.00	39.00	42.00	45.00	48.00
61.00	30.50	33.55	36.60	39.65	42.70	45.75	48.80
62.00	31.00	34.10	37.20	40.30	43.40	46.50	49.60
63.00	31.50	34.65	37.80	40.95	44.10	47.25	50.40
64.00	32.00	35.20	38.40	41.60	44.80	48.00	51.20
65.00	32.50	35.75	39.00	42.25	45.50	48.75	52.00
66.00	33.00	36.30	39.60	42.90	46.20	49.50	52.80
67.00	33.50	36.85	40.20	43.55	46.90	50.25	53.60
68.00	34.00	37.40	40.80	44.20	47.60	51.00	54.40
69.00	34.50	37.95	41.40	44.85	48.30	51.75	55.20
70.00	35.00	38.50	42.00	45.50	49.00	52.50	56.00
71.00	35.50	39.05	42.60	46.15	49.70	53.25	56.80
72.00	36.00	39.60	43.20	46.80	50.40	54.00	57.60
73.00	36.50	40.15	43.80	47.45	51.10	54.75	58.40
74.00	37.00	40.70	44.40	48.10	51.80	55.50	59.20
75.00	37.50	41.25	45.00	48.75	52.50	56.25	60.00
76.00	38.00	41.80	45.60	49.40	53.20	57.00	60.80
77.00	38.50	42.35	46.20	50.05	53.90	57.75	61.60
78.00	39.00	42.90	46.80	50.70	54.60	58.50	62.40
79.00	39.50	43.45	47.40	51.35	55.30	59.25	63.20
80.00	40.00	44.00	48.00	52.00	56.00	60.00	64.00
81.00	40.50	44.55	48.60	52.65	56.70	60.75	64.80
82.00	41.00	45.10	49.20	53.30	57.40	61.50	65.60

AMOUNT	50%	55%	60%	65%	70%	75%	80%
83.00	41.50	45.65	49.80	53.95	58.10	62.25	66.40
84.00	42.00	46.20	50.40	54.60	58.80	63.00	67.20
85.00	42.50	46.75	51.00	55.25	59.50	63.75	68.00
86.00	43.00	47.30	51.60	55.90	60.20	64.50	68.80
87.00	43.50	47.85	52.20	56.55	60.90	65.25	69.60
88.00	44.00	48.40	52.80	57.20	61.60	66.00	70.40
89.00	44.50	48.95	53.40	57.85	62.30	66.75	71.20
90.00	45.00	49.50	54.00	58.50	63.00	67.50	72.00
91.00	45.50	50.05	54.60	59.15	63.70	68.25	72.80
92.00	46.00	50.60	55.20	59.80	64.40	69.00	73.60
93.00	46.50	51.15	55.80	60.45	65.10	69.75	74.40
94.00	47.00	51.70	56.40	61.10	65.80	70.50	75.20
95.00	47.50	52.25	57.00	61.75	66.50	71.25	76.00
96.00	48.00	52.80	57.60	62.40	67.20	72.00	76.80
97.00	48.50	53.35	58.20	63.05	67.90	72.75	77.60
98.00	49.00	53.90	58.80	63.70	68.60	73.50	78.40
99.00	49.50	54.45	59.40	64.35	69.30	74.25	79.20
100.00	50.00	55.00	60.00	65.00	70.00	75.00	80.00

AMOUNT	50%	55%	60%	65%	70%	75%	80%
5 CENTS	.02½	.02¾	.03	.03¼	.03½	.03¾	.04
10 CENTS	.05	.05½	.06	.06½	.07	.07½	.08
15 CENTS	.07½	.08¼	.09	.09¾	.10½	.11¼	.12
20 CENTS	.10	.11	.12	.13	.14	.15	.16
25 CENTS	.12½	.13¾	.15	.16¼	.17½	.18¾	.20
30 CENTS	.15	.16½	.18	.19½	.21	.22½	.24
35 CENTS	.17½	.19¼	.21	.22¾	.24½	.26¼	.28
40 CENTS	.20	.22	.24	.26	.28	.30	.32
45 CENTS	.22½	.24¾	.27	.29¼	.31½	.33¾	.36
50 CENTS	.25	.27½	.30	.32½	.35	.37½	.40
55 CENTS	.27½	.30¼	.33	.35¾	.38½	.41¼	.44
60 CENTS	.30	.33	.36	.39	.42	.45	.48
65 CENTS	.32½	.35¾	.39	.42¼	.45½	.48¾	.52
70 CENTS	.35	.38½	.42	.45½	.49	.52½	.56
75 CENTS	.37½	.41¼	.45	.48¾	.52½	.56¼	.60
80 CENTS	.40	.44	.48	.52	.56	.60	.64
85 CENTS	.42½	.46¾	.51	.55¼	.59½	.63¾	.68
90 CENTS	.45	.49½	.54	.58½	.63	.67½	.72
95 CENTS	.47½	.52¼	.57	.61¾	.66½	.71¼	.76

Fig. 187.

COPYRIGHT 1948, A. C. CLAYTON PRINTING CO., ST. LOUIS, MO.

enables the proprietor to arrive at the wages due an employe in a matter of seconds. He merely utilizes the percentage figure he uses as the basis of paying wages, refers to the gross amount credited to an employe for the week, deducts Social Security and Income Tax withholding, and thus arrives at the amount the employe is to be paid. For example:

```
Employe's  gross  receipts — $150.00
Employe's commission @ 60% ..................                    $90.00
O. A. B. (Social Security) ..........................$ 2.70
Income Tax Withholding (Federal) .......... 12.00
Income Tax Withholding (State) .............   5.00
                                              _____
                                               $19.70       $19.70
```

Wages paid for the week, after taxes $70.30

(Note: Commissions as low as 50% on gross receipts are paid in some large city shops. In other areas commissions may be as high as 75%. Hence wages in relation to gross receipts are governed by commission rates.)

For information on payment of unemployment taxes consult with the State Division of Unemployment Compensation. For information on payment of Social Security and Income Tax Deductions on payrolls consult with the Director of Internal Revenue for your district.

At the end of each fiscal year the shop owner will make a recapitulation of his cash receipts. He will also make a recapitulation of his expenses for the 52-week period.

Subtracting his gross expenses from his gross income, however, will not give him his actual earnings for the year. There are other items to be taken into consideration for income tax purposes.

For instance, fixtures purchased during a fiscal year may or may not be deducted for the full value in one year. Usually only a percentage of the costs, depending on the life of each fixture, may be deducted in one year. Such deduction is termed depreciation, and the portion of the expense of each fixture that may be deducted for income tax purposes is set forth in a schedule approved by the Federal Government.

As an example, presume a shop owner purchased a barber chair on January 1 and paid $600 for it. He could not deduct the entire $600 at the end of that year as an expense on his income tax return. The Federal Government has estimated the life of a barber chair as 12 years. Consequently the cost of the barber chair must be deducted over a 12-year period—$50 each year for 12 years.

Another item to be considered for income tax purposes is

termed amortization. As an example, let us suppose that a barber leases a shop for five years. Before he can occupy the premises he must, at his own expense, lay linoleum on the floor at a cost of $300. The Federal Government would acknowledge the expense of the linoleum as a leasehold improvement, but no doubt would not allow the entire deduction of $300 in one year. Instead, it would insist that the $300 be amortized over the period of the lease of five years. Hence the shop owner, under this circumstance, would be eligible to deduct only $60 per year over the five-year period of the lease.

Income Tax Return. The barber shop owner should not "fear" filling out his annual income tax return. On the contrary, if he keeps an accurate account of his income and expenses (and all disbursements should be made by check), at the end of the year he may take the figures of his gross income and expense to the office of the Director of Internal Revenue in his district, who will cheerfully aid him in filing a correct report.

Things to be Considered When Looking for a Barber Shop Location

Outlying Districts and Small Towns

Check the number of pedestrians passing the desired location during the full period between opening and closing hours planned for the shop each working day of the week. The location checking the largest number of pedestrians is the logical point, other factors being equal.

The building should have an attractive-looking front, and a large window for display purposes.

Doors should be easily accessible to the street.

The side of the street that is shadiest the greater portion of the working day is preferable.

A location next door to a bank or some other well-patronized business establishment is of value. Next door to or close by a bank is always desirable, for the reason that a bank draws people from a large surrounding territory.

Avoid locating a shop near an old-established barber shop or a large barber shop. These two types of shops have a distinct advantage over a new competitor.

Avoid any district where too many shops are located.

Avoid any district where cut-rate barber shops are located.

Inspect the interior of the storeroom, to make sure it permits well-planned inside arrangement of fixtures. Supply dealers can advise you on this point.

The general color scheme, lighting, and the right treatment of floors and ceiling are important items to consider.

No location should be selected unless it can be given the appearance of a spotlessly clean and sanitary shop.

Basement locations should be avoided.

A shop handy to parking space for cars is advantageous. Shopping centers usually offer good opportunities.

Locations near schools, factories, and transfer points of local transportation services are also advantageous.

The surrounding agricultural conditions often play an important part in the business life of a community.

Office Building Locations

Locations for barber shops in rooms across from elevators or as nearly as possible thereto are good.

Check the working population of the building, and make sure that the percentage of tenancy in the building offices is high enough to insure a proper amount of business from the tenants in the building.

Office buildings make good locations for appointment shops.

Arrangements should be made for special booths for scalp treatments and hair piece fittings.

If the barber shop space has a window facing the street, and is located on the second floor, a barber pole may be displayed on the second floor to attract street patronage.

General Observations

In all cases, whether in an outlying district or the business section, or in a small town, be sure no more rent is paid than a business of like income would pay for the same space.

Some communities are progressive, while others tend to stand still. Some measure of this progressiveness can be obtained by determining the standards of the public schools, also by ascertaining the activity of the civic and business associations and the extent to which they aid local business and operate to secure new industries or hold old ones.

Do not contemplate opening a barber shop unless sufficient funds are available to establish a high caliber, good-looking, sanitary shop, and an additional surplus of money on which to operate for at least six months without much profit. This will enable the shop owner to get acquainted and build up a steady clientele, so that, other factors being equal, at the end of six months he will have a well-established, profitable business. To go into business on a shoestring means an inevitable temptation, in many cases, to cut prices—a step that can result in nothing but harm to all members of the profession.

By all means refrain from starting a cut-rate shop. Barbering is not like merchandising articles of food, clothing, etc. Barbering is a profession. Remember that most of the barber's revenue is derived from personal services rendered directly upon the patron. A barber shop displaying cut-rate prices openly declares and advertises the inferiority of its standards and its services. Be professional, and charge professional prices.

Patrons' Card Index

An indexed card record of regular patrons should be part of each shop's equipment. On each patron's card should be entered his name, address, condition of hair and scalp, history of general health, hereditary health factors, type of scalp treatment given to secure a desired result, and any other pertinent facts that will aid in retaining him as a satisfied patron.

The style of haircut that pleases him should also be listed, including special points to be observed as regards any difficult places on the head, where the hair should be cut shorter or longer than might ordinarily be the case, the size of clipper blade used (1, 0, 00, etc.), and all other important information that will tend to insure a pleased patron.

If he has registered satisfaction with a certain tonic or shampoo, that fact should be entered on his card.

Public Relations

The barber has done little and knows little about conducting public relations programs. Barbers are small business men, usually allied to each other through membership in either a union or in the Associated Master Barbers and Beauticians of America. It is a hard task to properly conduct a public relations program for them because it is difficult to find the financial resources required in the promotion of such a planned activity.

It is beyond the present ability of barbers to contract for a sequency of public statements in nationally-recognized mediums such as radio, television, newspapers, the better periodicals, etc. Bill boards and posters also require heavy financing if a comprehensive program is attempted.

However, effective public relations are not entirely beyond the ability of barbers to promote. The barber is an interesting person with considerable public appeal. Through his dealings with famous people he can secure widespread publicity. The public is intensely interested in children and babies, and the barber frequently makes news because of his contact with them—baby's first haircut, a barber shop full of youngsters getting haircuts, a haircut with a smile through tears, and other human interest touches which rate features in newspapers and magazines.

Good public relations are developed when groups of barbers let it be generally known that the profession accepts responsibility for keeping orphans and other unfortunates well groomed. Hundreds of photos and favorable news stories for barbers have resulted from visits to orphanages, hospitals and public institutions by groups of barbers who make realistic the slogan: "It Pays to Look Well."

Good public relations for barbers have been tied in with public relations programs promoted by allied industries such as linen suppliers, cosmetic manufacturers, and makers of instruments the barber uses. Also, barbers have had favorable presentations of their art in motion pictures, through television and in wide-spread advertising campaigns conducted by large corporations.

Public relations can be effectively promoted only when barbers are banded together in an organization, club or society which pursues the task of elevating the prestige of the profession. As organized groups the barbers can join in civic drives for new hospitals, libraries, civic centers, public playgrounds and a host of other enterprises which are coincident with community life. Good will for barbers nationally can be augmented by their participation in the Red Cross and Community Chest campaigns, heart and cancer drives, polio and tuberculosis programs.

Good public relations for barbers is the promotion of any activity, or the participation in civic and national affairs, which blesses them with public good-will. The successful barber affiliates himself in organizations and associates himself with activities which develop better public relations and greater good-will for his chosen profession.

The student is requested to procure the book on public relations known as **Public Relations Principles and Problems,** by Bertrand R. Canfield.

SALES TECHNIQUE

Today every alert industry selling either commodities or service is giving its best thought to the development of sales technique, for increased sales resistance and intensive competition make it necessary that sales efforts be backed by better education, higher training and every needed item of shop equipment.

Chapter 27

The Barber and His Business

The Necessity of Organization

I T HAS been the experience of all business and industry that representative trade associations are the beacon lights to which the members of any industry may confidently look for guidance and help under every-day difficulties, and upon which they may rely for the preservation of their business and industrial interests in times of unusual stress, such as the depression that began in 1929, and during the Second World War.

Think what would happen if there were no organized effort in the barber profession. The results are obvious. There would be a gradual and continuous decline from present standards of operating efficiency, more accelerated departure from ethical standards, fewer and less effective barber license laws, and the development of a more destructive form of competition throughout the entire barber profession. Of course the ultimate result would be chaos, and in the course of reaching that point confusion would reign.

Organization is the method for putting order into any undertaking. It is the one method by which barbers can co-operate in the creative and educational work of the profession. Organization makes possible human contact and links together the minds of all. Each barber is a human intelligence center, and organization makes possible the transmission of thought current throughout the group, stimulating all to greater activity.

For these reasons no barber can afford to disregard organization. The ideals and purposes of the national organizations in the barber profession are: To bring about a reasonable standard of barber service prices, which will prove profitable for the shop owner, and at the same time insure a fair wage to employes. To enact legislation that will raise the standards of the barber business in regard to sanitation and cleanliness. To promote efficient and courteous service for the protection of the public. To bring into the barber business a better-educated and more highly-trained class of barbers. The raising of the standards of

barber school training is one of the outstanding factors that
has brought much improvement and will further develop these
purposes.

National organization activities, founded on the right principles, never end. The more that barbers see of its activities,
and the more they become acquainted wth organization work,
the more they will be convinced that it is a big, never-ending
job that must always enlist the best in time and effort that all
members of the barber profession can possibly give to it.

The bringing about of better standards for the benefit of the
barber business cannot be accomplished through any individual.
This will have to come through the medium of organization.

There are two national organizations of and for barbers—
the Associated Master Barbers and Beauticians of America,
which is the shop owners' and managers' organization, and the
Journeymen Barbers', Hairdressers', Cosmetologists' and Proprietors' International Union of America, an organization that
solicits the membership of all barbers, employers as well as
employes.

Personality and Skill Inspire Confidence

In every line of business there are outstanding men who
are more successful than others. These men, as a rule, are doing
well and getting results, regardless of conditions. These men, in
most cases, have pleasing personalities that attract patrons to
them. They stand out because they have something in common,
in that they are intensely interested in their work. Patrons sense
that they consider themselves part of the business they represent.

Each and every member of the barber profession should
develop a pleasing personality, for it is a characteristic of an
outstanding barber in any community. Accomplishment of this
ideal hinges in no small measure on the barber resolving to himself: "I am going to make my patrons like me, and the best way
to do this is to give them superior service, and show them I
like them."

The barber's mental attitude when a patron enters the
barber shop should be: "This man is proud of his appearance,
enjoys good service, and is pleased when he is given a becoming
haircut and a smooth, clean shave; therefore I shall do everything
in my power to gratify him in those respects."

A discourteous act, an unpleasant attitude, or using a dull
razor on a patron who is known as a "squirrel," may bring satisfaction to some barber, if it results in discouraging that patron
from further patronizing that barber shop. But the barber forgets
that he may have led that patron to advise his son, father,

mother, wife, brother, sister, or other relative or friend against patronizing that barber shop, by informing them of the ill manner in which he was treated, or the poor service he received there.

There are few, if any, barbers who can boast of never having lost a patron for one reason or another. Consequently, in order to eliminate these mishaps to the greatest possible extent, the barbers of a shop should hold a consultation occasionally, and openly and frankly discuss such patron-losses and the reason or reasons therefor, and devise steps to prevent such occurrences. All barbers in a shop should use every means in their power to give their personal and courteous attention to each and every individual who comes into the shop for service, so that, in addition to being pleased himself, the patron will say to his friends that the service in the shop is excellent. The barber will find this is very good advertising which will bring more business to his shop.

It is folly for any shop owner or employe to take an "I don't care" attitude. This does not win new patrons or replace those lost; nor is such an attitude of self-satisfaction one that compensates for the loss of income.

It is an old saying that business goes only where it is made welcome, and stays only where it is well treated.

These are vital points for the barber school student to consider and to observe while attending school.

High Ideals in the Barber Business

How many barbers have ever given any thought to the importance of the work of the barber, in connection with the welfare and happiness of the whole community, and the important part he plays in keeping the public well groomed?

Nothing gives a person such an air of distinction, nothing adds such a strikingly immaculate note, as does a good head of hair, well-groomed. Hence it follows that what appeals to us also appeals to others, so it is equally important that we ourselves present an agreeable appearance.

Give a thought to this. Suppose that every barber should close his doors tomorrow and stop rendering service for about six months. Not a pleasant thought, is it? The benefits derived by a barber's patrons are in direct proportion to the frequency of their visits to his barber shop.

Every man and woman should give his or her hair every possible chance for health and growth. This is done by according it intelligent attention which, sad to relate, should be much greater than is the case with the majority of individuals today.

This fact in large measure accounts for the unwarranted prevalence of partial or total loss of hair.

Hair—its observance, study and care—is the primary work of the barber. This is only natural, for without hair there would be no barbers. Hence it follows that the barber is in a front-line position so far as knowledge of that portion of the human makeup is concerned. For this reason the services of the barber profession of today have progressed to the point where they are no longer a matter of guesswork, but are based on solid, undeniable certainty, with a background of scientific research and intensified investigation.

The successful men in any business are not "jog-trot men," "take-your-time men," "placid, peaceful road travelers," "easygoing followers of a routine." It takes an energetic man to get things done today, a man with eager energy, a man intensely awake, a man with ambition, his heart full of hunger for achievement, a man with a sincere desire to equip himself with newer and better ideas to operate his business.

Business is a battle, and those who use the best strategy, secure the finest and most efficient equipment, keep on the alert for newer things, prove their knowledge, and then put these elements into practical use are the ones who will lead in their chosen vocations.

A barber can insure his business success if he will stop loitering, break out of the rear ranks and make a dash for the front of the parade where he can get a good view of the prospects ahead and where he will be sure to be seen. He must bring his powers into play—go in for all he is worth.

The Profession of the Barber

Barbering is a profession, because it is based on science. Barbers who are qualified as skilled artists, the same being certified by a State Barber Board created by due process of law, can be included in the class giving professional service, without presuming to be doctors of medicine, or surgeons, or anything else, except what they claim to be, namely, skilled artists in barbering. Doctors of medicine are skilled in the science and art of medical practice. Barbers are skilled in the art and science of barbering. Both are skilled artists or professionals when qualified; neither are amateurs nor students. The physician is registered under the law as a Medical Doctor and uses the letters M.D. after his name. A registered barber is privileged to use the letters R.B. after his name.

The amateur student performs the act of haircutting, but for lack of actual experience and knowledge he cannot repeat his acts in a systematic, explicit way. When, by experience and knowledge, the amateur attains the skill to complete his acts in a systematic manner he has acquired the *art* of barbering. Barbering, then, is a skilled art. And, as distinguished from the amateur, the skilled artist is a professional. And, when qualified, barbers perform professional services.

Fortifying the qualifications of the barber as a professional—the qualifications set forth above—is another factor, one to which the greater portion of this Textbook is devoted: Barber Science. The subjects covered in Part II of this book make no pretensions to being an entry into the field of the physician. Rather, they are made up of basic facts concerning the human body, and the manner in which it functions to insure a condition of healthy balance.

Barber Science teaches the barber to supplement his skillful and artful knowledge with an understanding of the processes directly affecting those portions of the human body to which his efforts are directed. Without this understanding he would still be a professional; with it he is doubly so. Add to his skill a solid foundation of pertinent facts concerning the chemical, physical and mechanical behavior of man as a living entity, and the barber's professionalism assumes a solidity and reality that point up his continued advancement from the dark ages of his calling, now happily far behind.

Suggestions To Teachers

An instructor must be a model in his deportment. Through his example a student learns much about proper conduct in his business. The instructor should guard himself in all his habits, refrain from smoking in the class rooms or work areas, refrain from using any foul language, keep himself reserved in the presence of students in order to command respect, refrain from the use of liquor while on duty, and be punctual in meeting his obligations to start classes exactly on time and keeping appointments.

An instructor should keep himself super-clean, bathe daily, shave each morning, secure a haircut at least once each week, wear a clean uniform, wear neatly-pressed trousers, keep his shoes gleaming with fresh shines, guard against bad breath, keep his hands washed, and his finger nails short and clean.

An instructor should apply himself to studying the books listed as references on page 345 of this Textbook, and prepare and deliver lectures on the subject matter contained therein. He should particularly prepare himself to lecture on SALES PROMOTION, PUBLIC RELATIONS and ADVERTISING when his class is studying the chapter on BUSINESS PRINCIPLES.

An instructor should know that in so far as he presents himself to his students as a high class teacher, so will his students become high class practitioners. And so will the reputation of the teacher, the reputation of the school and the prestige of the students be enhanced.

Good judgment comes from experience and experience comes from poor judgment.

Chapter 28

Ethics of the Barber

ONE word that is woven into the fabric of the barber business, and whose meaning applies in equal measure to employer and employe alike, is Ethics. In order to give an understandable definition of Ethics, we quote from Webster's Unabridged Dictionary:

"The science of moral *duty;* more broadly, the science of the ideal human character. The problems with which ethics deals concern the origin and validity of the sense of duty, and the character and authority of moral obligation."

Every business transaction, as well as every personal act, is subject to the rules of ethics. In the barber business, therefore, every contact with the patron gives opportunity for the observance or disregard of a high standard of honesty, responsibility and service.

The ethical barber is he who carries in his mind a picture of himself as the patron, with the patron's desires, needs and attitude. With that picture in mind he should make few errors.

Ethics indicates the barber's outward attitude toward the business itself. As a result he is a champion of practices that reflect *credit* to the profession, and he should oppose any and all practices that have no place in the ethical barber shop. With intelligence and earnestness he offers, explains and sells those things that are of actual benefit to the patron, letting nothing that detracts from true professionalism enter into his conduct.

Consider the word *character.* The ethical barber speaks only good of his fellows. If he cannot speak good, he says nothing. Reduced to common parlance, no ethical barber "knocks" another barber.

He does not pick his patrons, either by rushing or holding back, in order to get a favorite "good spender." Nor does he, by word or deed, cast reflection on his employer. The barber owes to that employer unrestricted loyalty while in his employ.

The employer owes a similar duty to those who make the operation of his shop possible. Each operator is as good as the other. In the ethical shop there is no room for favoritism or dissension. The motive of one is the motive of all—to serve to the highest possible degree the obligation incurred by the patronage of those who seek service in the shop. In observance of this responsibility the employer only speaks well of his employes.

In recognition of the need and importance of a definite understanding of the relationship between the ethical barber shop and the public, the Associated Master Barbers and Beauticians of America at its 1929 National Convention, held in St. Paul, Minn., unanimously adopted a Code of Ethics. This Code sets forth in unmistakable language the responsibility of the shop to its patrons. Every member of the Association, through the action of the St. Paul Convention, is bound to observe the Code, and in similar fashion every operator accepts the Code as part of his responsibility.

This Code of Ethics, copyrighted by the Associated Master Barbers and Beauticians of America, is as follows:

CODE OF ETHICS

A Statement of the Responsibility of This Shop to Its Patrons

We recognize the fact that you are entitled to every possible protection against infection and contagion while in this establishment, and we endeavor to discharge this responsibility by scrupulous adherence to all sanitary precautions.

We believe that you are entitled to the same courteous, careful and conscientious treatment from every practitioner in this establishment, whether you wish all of the services we have to offer or only one, and we sincerely try to carry out this principle.

The preparations dispensed in this establishment and sold for home use are all standard merchandise of the highest quality, bearing the original manufacturer's label, undiluted and guaranteed by the manufacturer to be free from injurious ingredients.

We consider it our professional duty to suggest and explain to our patrons such services and applications as we think may be needed in any particular case. However, we do not mean to be offensive, overbearing or insistent, and will at all times respect the wishes of our patrons.

We regard the cosmetics for sale in our shop not as "hair-growers" or "baldness cures," but as legitimate aids to the preservation and beautification of hair and the proper care of the skin and scalp.

We feel that we owe the responsibilities enumerated above to every patron of this establishment, regardless of the frequency of his, or her, visits, and the owner would appreciate having called to his or her attention any lapse on his or her part or on the part of any of our co-workers.

Observance of the Code of Ethics by all shop employes insures a standard that will result in general public approval. Its provisions embody principles decided upon after considered thought and deliberation. With the Code of Ethics as a rule and guide, the barber takes a full step toward true professionalism. He establishes a relationship with his patrons that will bring rewards to the entire barber profession.

GLOSSARY

(Pronounce ā as in *ale;* ē as in *eve;* ī as in *ice;* ō as in *old;* ū as in *use.*)

Abducent nerve (ab-du'-sent): Sixth cranial nerve.

Abnormal (ab-nor'-mal): Not normal. Not conforming to nature or general rule.

Abnormality (ab-nor-mal'iti): A deformity or malformation.

Abrasion (ab-rā'-zhun): Broken skin. Excoriation of cutaneous surface by mechanical means.

Abscess (ab'-ses): A localized collection of pus surrounded by wall of lymph.

Absorption (ab-sorp'-shun): The act of taking in, as a blotter takes up water.

Acceleration (ak-sel-er-a'-shun): A quickening or speeding up.

Accessory nerve (ak-ses'-o-ri): Eleventh cranial nerve.

Acid (as'-id): Any substance having a sour taste.

Acne (ak'-ne): An inflammatory disease of the sebaceous glands.

Acne vulgaris (vul-gar'-is): Ordinary acne.

    Acne albida (al'-bi-da), Acne artificialis (ar'-ti-fish-i-al'-is), Acne cachecticorum, (ka-kek'-ti-co'-rum), Acne indurata (in-du-rat'-a), Acne rosacea (ro-za'-she-a).

Actinic rays (ak-tin'-ik): Those rays of the spectrum capable of producing chemical changes (violet and ultra-violet).

Acute (a-kūt'): Sharp, severe; having a rapid onset, short course and pronounced symptoms.

Adipose (ad'-i-pos): Fatty. A fatty tissue.

Adnata (ad-nat'-a): Alopecia. Baldness from time of birth.

Afferent (af'-er-ent): Carrying toward the center; nerves conveying impulses toward the central nervous system.

Ala (a'-lah): 1, Wing. 2, Any wing-like part.

Albinism (al'-bin-ism): The condition of the skin in which there is a congenital absence of pigment involving its entire surface, including hair and eyes.

Albumen (al-bu'-min): A protein substance; chief constituent of animal tissue.

Alcohol (al'-ko-hol): Any compound of an organic hydrocarbon radical with hydroxyl.

Alimentary (al'i-men'ta-ri): Nourishing. A canal or system or tube; the digestive tube from lip to anus, with its accessory glands.

Alkali (al'-ka-li): The hydroxides of alkali metals; they are chemically electro-positive and strong bases.

Alkaline (al'-ka-line): Having the qualities of an alkali.

Allergy (al'-er-je): A hypersensitivity to certain foods. An altered ability of reaction to specific substances.

Alopecia (al-o-pe'-she-ah): Deficient hair (baldness). Alopecia adnata (ad-nat'-a). Alepecea areata (a-re-a'-ta). Alopecea prematura (pre-matu'-ra). Alopecea senilis (se-nil'-is).

Alternating (awl'-ter-na-ting): Occurring successively.

Alum (al'-um): A substance having astringent action.

Alveolus (al-ve'-o-lus): An air cell of the lungs.

Amitosis (ah-mit-o'-sis): Multiplication by direct division.

Ammonia (am-o'-ne-ah): A colorless, pungent gas, very soluble in water. Strong ammonia water—a 28% solution of ammonia in water.

Ampere (am'-par): A unit of measurement of an electric current.

Anabolism (an-ab'-o-lism): Constructive or synthetic metabolism, building up process.

Anatomy (an-at'-o-me): The science of the structure of organs or of organic bodies.

Anemia (an-e'-me-ah): Deficiency of blood as a whole, or deficiency of the red blood corpuscles, or of the hemoglobin.

Angiology (an-je-ol'-o-je): The science of the blood vessels and lymphatics.

Anhidrosis (an-hid-ro'-sis), also anidrosis: Partial or complete absence of sweat secretion.

Aniline (an'-il-in): A basis substance of analine dyes.

Anion (an'-ion): Ion carrying a negative charge.

Anode (an'ōd): The positive pole of galvanic battery.

Anterior (an-te're-or): Situated in front of.

Antiseptic (an-te-sep'tik): Having the power to prevent the growth of bacteria.

Aorta (a-ort'-ah): The large blood vessel arising from the left ventricle and distributing its branches (carrying arterial blood) to all parts of the body.

Aponeurosis (ap-o-nu-ro'-sis): A fibrous expansion of a tendon.

Arrector Pili (ar-ek'-tor pī'-lī): Smooth muscles, the contraction of which erects the follicle.

Arteriole (ar-te'-re-ōl): A very small artery.

Artery (ar'-ter-e): A vessel that conveys blood from heart.

Asepsis (a-sep'-sis): Absence of pathogenic micro-organism.

Aseptic: Free from germs.

Asteatosis (as-te-at-o'-sis): Deficiency or absence of sebaceous secretion.

Astringent (as-trin'-jent): Causing contraction. An agent producing contraction of organic tissues.

Atom (at'om): The ultimate unit of an element for ordinary chemical purposes.

Atrophy (at'-ro-fe): Diminution in size of a tissue, organ, or part. The result of degeneration of the cells.

Atrium (a'-tre-um): The auricle of the heart.

Auditory (aw'-dit-o-re): Pertaining to the act or the organs of hearing.

Auricle (aw'-rik-l): The expanded portion of the wing of the ear. One of the upper chambers of the heart, also called the atrium.

Bacillus (bas-il'-us): Rod-shaped forms of bacteria.

Bacterium (bak-tē-ri-um): A synonym for micro-organism.

Bactericide (bak-te'-ris-īd): Destructive to bacteria.

Bacteriology (bak-te-re-ol'-ogy): The science and study of bacteria.

Baldness (bawld'-ness): Loss of hair.

Base (bās): The lowest part, foundation. In chemistry an element or radical that combines with an acid to form a salt. The electro-positive radical of a compound.

Battery (bat'-er-e): A series of cells producing electricity.

Benzoin (ben'zoin): A resin obtained from Styrox Benzoin, a tree of Sumatra. Used as an antiseptic.

Beriberi (ber'-e-ber-e): A disease due to a lack of water soluble vitamin B.

Bi: A prefix meaning two.

Bicarbonate of soda: Baking soda.

Biology (bi-ol'-o-je): The science of life and living things.

Bipolar (bi-po'-lar): Having two poles.

Blackhead (blak'-hed): See comedone.

Bleach (bleech): To make white or pale.

Bleb: See bulla.

Blood (blud): The fluid that circulates through the arteries, veins and heart.

Boil [noun]: See furuncle.

Boric acid: A crystalline acid used as an antiseptic.

Brain: That part of the central nervous system contained in the cranial cavity, consisting of the cerebrum, cerebellum, pons, and medulla oblongata.

Brilliantine: (bril'-yan-teen): A cosmetic compound of oily substances used to impart luster to the hair. There are liquid and paste brilliantines.

Bromidrosis (bro-mid-ro'-sis): An affection of the sweat glands in which the sweat has an offensive odor.

Bulb: An oval or circular expansion of a cylinder or tube. A swelling at the root of the hair.

Bulla (bul'-ah): A blister or bleb, consisting of a portion of the epidermis detached from the skin by the infiltration of a watery fluid beneath it.

Calory (kal'-or-e): A unit of heat, the amount of heat required to raise the temperature of one gram of water one degree centigrade.

Canities (kan-ish'-e-ēz): Blanching of the hairs. Gray hair.

Capillary (kap'-il-a-re): Hair-like; relating to a hair; to a hair-like filament or to a tube with a hair-like bore.

Capillus (kap-il'-us): A hair; specifically a hair of the head.

Capsicum (kap'-sik-um): Cayenne pepper.

Carbolic acid: See phenol.

Carbon (kar'-bon): A non-metallic element, occurring in the various forms of charcoal, lampblack, etc.

Carbuncle (car'-bun-kl): A hard, circumscribed, deep-seated, painful suppurative inflammation of the subcutaneous tissue.

Cardiac (kar'-de-ak): Pertaining to the heart.

Carotid (kar-ot'-id): The carotid artery. The principle large artery on each side of the neck.

Cartilage (kar'-til-aj): Gristle; a white, non-vascular connective tissue, softer than bones.

Castor oil: A fixed oil expressed from the castor bean.

Catabolism (kat-ab'-ol-ism): Destructive metabolism, disassimilation, physiological disintegration, breaking down of tissues.

Cataphoresis (kat-af-or-e'-sis): The introduction of drugs through the skin, by means of ointments or solutions applied by the electrode of a battery.

Caustic (caws'-tik): Very irritant, burning, capable of destroying tissues; a substance that destroys tissue.

Cell (sel): A granular mass of protoplasm containing a nucleus.

Cellular (sel'-u-lar): Pertaining to cell.

Centigrade (sen'-te-grād): Having one hundred divisions or degrees.

Cerebellum (ser-e-bel'-um): The inferior part of the brain, lying below the cerebrum and above the pons and medulla.

Cerebrospinal system (ser-e'-bro-spi-nal): Consisting of or pertaining to the brain and spinal cord.

Cerebrum (ser'-e-brum): The chief portion of the brain occupying the whole upper part of the cranium.

Cervical (ser'-vik-al): Pertaining to the neck.

Chemistry (kem'is-tre): The science of molecular and atomic structure of bodies. The study of the composition, properties and attributes of matter.

Chloasma (klo-az'-mah): A deposit of pigment in the skin, occurring in patches of various sizes and shapes and of a yellow, brown or black color.

Cholesterin: cholesterol (ko-les'-ter-in) (ko-les'-ter-ol): A single atom constituent of nervous tissue, egg yolk, and blood.

Chronic (kron'-ik): Long continued; of long duration. Opposed to acute.

Chyle (kīl): The milk-white fluid absorbed by the lacteals during digestion.

Chyme (kīm): Food that has undergone gastric digestion only.

Cicatrix (sik-a'-triks): A scar. The connective tissue which replaces localized loss of substance.

Cilia (sil'-e-ah): The eyelashes. Also the hair-like appendages of certain epithelial cells.

Circumscribed (sir'-kum-skrībd): Strictly limited, marked off, well defined, distinct from the surrounding parts.

Citric acid (sit'-rik): Acid found in lemons or citrons.

Clavicle (clav'-ik-l): The collar bone.

Coagulate (ko-ag'-ū-late): To curdle or form a clot, as of blood.

Coalesce (ko-a-less'): Grow together.

Cocci (kok'-si): Plural of coccus.

Coccus (kok'-us): A spherical bacterium.

Coiffure (kwa-fūr'): Hairdress.

Comedo (kom'-e-do) (plural, comedones): A chronic disorder of the sebaceous glands, characterized by yellowish or whitish elevations the size of pinheads or of pin points containing in their centers exposed blackish points.

Concave (kon'-kāv): Hollow and curved.

Conductor (kon-duk'-tor): A cord or substance that transmits electricity. Also applied to electrodes.

Congenital (kon-jen'-i-tal): Existing at birth.

Contagion (kon-ta'-jun): The process by which a specific disease is communicated, or the specific germ from which a communical disease develops.

Contagious (kon-ta'-jus): Communicable or transmissible by contagion, or by germs.

Contaminate (kon-tam'-i-nate): To soil, as with germs; to infect.

Contract (kon-trakt'): To draw the parts together, to shrink, also to acquire by contagion.

Contractile (kon-trak'-til): Having power or tending to contract.

Contour (kon'-toor): The line that defines a figure; shape.

Corneum (kor-ne'-um): The stratum corneum or the horny layer of the skin.

Cornification (kor'-nif-ik-ā-shun): The process of hardening or making horny.

Corium (ko'-re-um): The true skin.

Coronoid (kor'-o-noid): Crown-shaped.

Corpuscle (kor'-pusl): A small body or particle, a molecule or atom. A cell, a blood cell.

Corrosive (kor-o'-siv): Eating away; a substance that destroys organic tissue by chemical means or by causing inflammation.

Corrugator (kor'-ū-ga-ter): That which wrinkles.

Cortex (kor'-teks): The surface layer of an organ.

Cowlick: (See whorl).

Cranial (kra'-ne-al): Relating to the cranium.

Cranium (kra'-ne-um): The skull. The cavity that contains the brain, its membranes and versets.

Crista Cutis: A crest or ridge of the skin.

Cutaneous (kū-ta'-ne-us): Pertaining to the skin.

Cūticle (ku'-tik-l): The epidermis or scarf skin.

Cūtis (ku'-tis): The derma or true skin.

Cycle (sī-kl): A succession of events, a period in which a round of operations or events is repeated.

Cyst (sist): A cavity containing fluid and surrounded by a capsule.

Cytoplasm (sī-to-plaz-m): Cell plasm other than that of the nucleus.

Dandruff (dan'-druf): The scurf or scales formed on the scalp.

Debris (da-brē'): Loose pieces; fragments.

Decompose (de-kom-pōz'): To cause a compound to break up into its simpler constituents; to undergo putrefaction.

Deodorant (de-o'-dor-ant): A substance that removes or conceals offensive odors.

Depilatory (de-pil'-a-to-re): A substance used to destroy hair.

Depressor (de-pres'-or): A muscle that depresses or a nerve that lowers functional activity.

Derma, Derm: The true skin.

Dermal (der'-mal): Pertaining to the skin.

Dermatic (der-mat'-ic): Pertaining to skin.

Dermatitis (der-mat-i'-tis): Inflammation of the skin.

Dermatologist (der-mat-ol'-o-jist): A skin specialist (a physician).

Dermatosis (der-mat-o'-sis): A disease of the skin.

Dermic (der'-mik): Relating to the skin.

Dermis (der'-mis): The corium or true skin.

Desquamation (des-kwam-a'-shun): The shedding of the superficial epithelium.

Dessication (des-ik-a'-shun): Process of drying.

Detergent (de-ter'-jent): A cleansing agent.

Dexterity (deks-ter'-ity): Skill and ease in using the hands. Expertness.

Diagnosis (di-ag-no'-sis): The determination of the nature of a disease.

Diathermy (di-ath-er'-me): Elevation of temperature in deep tissues induced by high frequency current.

Diffuse (dif-ūz'): Scatter.

Digestion (di-jes'-chun): Those processes whereby the food taken in is made capable of being absorbed.

Disease (dis-ēz'): A disturbance of function or structure of any organ or part of the body.

Disinfect (dis-in-fekt'): To destroy or remove pathogenic substances.

Disinfectant (dis-in-fek'tant): An agent that destroys the germs of disease.

Disinfection (dis-in-fek'-shun): The destroying or removal of pathogenic germs, especially by chemical means.

Distal (dis'-tal): Extreme; at the greatest distance from a central point.

Duct (dukt): A tube or channel, especially one for conveying the secretions of a gland.

Eczema (ek'-ze-mah): An inflammatory disease of the skin characterized by an infiltration of serum in a part.

Edema (e-dē-mah): An infiltration of serum in a part.

Efferent (ef'-er-ent): Nerves carrying impulses away from the central nervous system.

Effleurage (ef-lu-razh'): The stroking movement in massage.

Electricity (e-lek-tris'-it-e): A force of nature developed or generated by means of chemicals, friction and magnetism.

Electrode (e-lek'-trōd): A piece of metal or other substance fastened to the conducting cords through which electricity is applied to the body.

Electrolysis (e-lek-trol'-is-is): The destruction of hair by an electric current.

Eleidin (e-le'-id-in): A material occurring in the form of granules in the stratum granulosum of the epidermis.

Element (el'-e-ment): Any one of the ultimate parts of which anything is composed. Tissue elements are cells. In chemistry, a body that cannot be decomposed into simpler substances.

Endocrine (en'-do-krin): Any internal secretion.

Endocrine gland: Secretes specific chemical substance which passes into the blood stream.

Enzyme (en'-zīm): Any ferment formed within the living organism.

Epi: Prefix signifying upon.

Epicranius (ep-e-kra'-ne-us): Occipitofrontalis muscle.

Epidermis (ep-e-der'-mis): The outer layer of skin.

Epilation (ep-il-a'-shun): The extraction of hair.

Epithelium (ep-e-the'-le-um): A term applied to the cells that form the epidermis.

Erythema (er-ith-e'-mah): A redness of the skin occurring in patches of various sizes and shapes.

Erythematous (er-ith-em'-at-us): An erythema-like condition.

Erythrocyte (er'-ith-ro-sīt): A red blood corpuscle.

Ethmoid (eth'-moid): Sieve-like bone at the base of the skull near the nose

Etiology (e-ti-ol'-o-je): The causation of disease.
and inner orbit.

Excrete (eks-krēt): To romove useless substances from the body.

Excoriation (eks-ko-re-a'-shun): Abrasion of a portion of the skin.

Exfoliation (eks-fo-le-a'-shun): A separation of bone or other tissue in thin layers.

Facial (fa'shal): Pertaining to the face. A term used here to denote a face massage.

Faradic current (far-ad'-ic): See faradism.

Faradism (far'-ad-ism): The electricity produced in an induced current.

Fat: A greasy substance; a compound of oleic, palmitic or stearic acid with glycerol.

Fiber (fi'-ber): A filamentary or thread-like structure.

Fissure (fish'-ūr): A groove or cleft, or the cracks in the skin.

Flaccid (flak'-sid): Flabby, relaxed.

Follicle (fol'-ik-l): A small secretory cavity or sac. Hair follicle: The depression containing the root of the hair.

Foramen (for-ā'-men): A perforation or opening, especially in a bone.

Formaldehyde (for-mal'-de-hīd): Formic aldehyde, used for antiseptic.

Freckle: See lentigo.

Friction: The act of rubbing, as in massage. Firm, circular manipulation.

Frontal (fron'-tal): Pertaining to the anterior part of an organ; belonging to the forehead.

Frontalis Muscle (fron-tā'-lis): The frontal portion of the occipito-frontalis muscle.

Fulguration (ful-gū-rā'-shun): Lightning stroke; burning by means of high-frequency sparks.

Fumigation (fū-mig-a'-shun): Disinfection by exposure to fumes of a vaporized disinfectant.

Function (funk'-shun): The normal or special action of a part.

Fungus (fun'-gus) (plural—fungi): One of the lowest orders of plants; the molds.

Furrow (fur'-o): A groove.

Furuncle (fū'-rung-kl): A boil.

Galvanic Current (gal-van'-ik): See galvanism.

Galvanism (gal'-van-ism): Primary electricity produced by chemical action.

Ganglion (gang'-le-on): A knot; a well-defined collection of nerve cells forming a subsidiary nerve center.

Gastric (gas'-trik): Pertaining to the stomach.

Germ (jerm): An ovum, spore, seed; a microbe or bacterium.

Germicide (jer'-mis-īd): An agent that destroys germs.

Germinative layer (jer'-mi-na-tiv): The growing or germinating layer of the epidermis lying on the corium.

Glabrous (gla'-brus): Smooth. Destitute of hair.

Gland: An organ which secretes something essential to the system or excretes waste material.

Glandular (glan'-dū-lar): Pertaining to gland.

Glycerine (glis'-er-in): A colorless substance of syrupy consistency, sweetish to the taste.

Glossopharyngeal (glos-o-far-in'-je-al): Pertaining to the tongue and pharynx or to glossopharyngeal nerve.

Hacking (hak'-ing): Chopping stroke in massage.

Halitosis (hal-i-to'-sis): Foul breath.

Hair: A delicate filament growing from the skin of mammals. A modified epidermal structure. Collectively all the filaments forming the covering of the skin.

Hamamelis (ham-a-mē'lis): "Witch-hazel." The bark and twigs of *Hamamelis Virginiana*, used in the perparation of witch-hazel.

Heart: A hollow muscular organ, the function of which is to pump the blood through the vessels.

Hemoglobin (hem-o-glo'-bin): The coloring matter of red corpuscles.

Hircus (her'-kus) plural—hirci (her'si): The axillary hair.

Histology (his-tol'-o-je): The minute anatomy of tissues. Microscopic anatomy.

Hormone (hor'-mōn): A chemical substance produced in some of the organs of the body.

Hydrogen (hi'-dro-jen): A gaseous element.

Hygiene (hi'-je-ēn): The science that treats of the laws of health and the methods of their observance.

Hyoid (hi'-oid): Having a "U" shape. Hyoid bone—A bone between the root of the tongue and larynx.

Hyperhidrosis (hi-per-hid-ro'-sis): Excessive sweating.

Hypertrichosis (hi-per-trik-ō'-sis): Excessive growth of hair on a part or the whole of the body.

Hypoglossal (hi-po-glos'-al): Situated under the tongue. Hypoglossal nerve or 12th cranial nerve.

Imbricated (im'-bri-ka-ted): Overlapping like shingles on a roof.

Immerse (im-murs'): To dip into a liquid.

Impetigo (im-pet-ī'go): An inflammatory disease of the skin characterized by pustules containing a yellow fluid.

Indigo (in'-dig-o): A blue or blue-violet pigment.

Inert (in-ert'): Devoid of therapeutic action.

Infection (in-fek'-shun): The communication of disease from one body to another. The disease-producing agent.

Infectious (in-fek'-shus): Communicating disease.

inferior (in-fe'-re-or): Lower.

Inflammation (in-flam-ma'-shun): A morbid condition with hyperemia, pain, heat and swelling.

Infrared (in-frah-red'): Below or beyond the red end of the spectrum.

Infra-orbital (in-frah-or'-bit-al): Beneath or below the floor of the orbit.

Ingredient (in-gre'-de-ent): Any substance that enters into the formation of a compound.

Inherited (in-her'-it-ed): Derived from an ancestor.

Ion (i'-on): An atom or group of atoms carrying an electric charge.

Insertion (in-ser'-shun): The point at which a muscle is attached; the more movable attachment.

Insoluble (in-sol'-ū-bl): Incapable of being dissolved.

Insulator (in'su-la-tor): A non-conducting substance by means of which insulation is effected.

Integument (in-teg'-ū-ment): A covering, especially the skin.

Inter (in'ter): Prefix signifying between.

Intercellular (in-ter-sel'-ū-lar): Between cells.

Interstices (in-ter'-stis-ez): Epaces or intervals; also pores.

Intestinal (in-tes'-ti-nal): Pertaining to the intestine.

Intestine (in-tes'-tin): The part of the digestive tube extending from the beginning of the pylorus to the anus.

Irritant (ir'-it-ant): An agent that induces irritation.

Involuntary (in-vol'-un-ta-re): Performed or acting independent of the will.

Kaolin (ka'-o-lin): Aluminum silicate, china clay.

Kation (also Cation) (kat'-i-on): Ion carrying a positive charge.

Keratin (ker'-at-in): The basis of horny tissues, hair, nails, etc.

Kilowatt (kil'-o-watt): One thousand watts of electricity.

Kneading (need'-ing): Same as petrissage.

Labial (la'-be-al): Pertaining to the lips.

Lacrimal (lak'-rim-al): Pertaining to the tears.

Lacteal (lak'-te-al): Pertaining to milk. Any of the lymphatics of the small intestines.

Lanolin (lan'-o-lin): Adeps lanae U.S.P. A cholesterin fat obtained from sheeps' wool; used as a basis for ointments.

Lanugo (lan-ū'-go): Downlike hair.

Lentigo (len-tĭ'-go): A freckle. A small circumscribed patch of pigment occurring mainly on face and hands.

Lesion (le'-zhun): An injury, wound, a morbid structural change in the body.

Leucocyte (lū'-ko-sīt): The white corpuscle of the blood.

Levator (le-vā'-tor): That which raises, as certain muscles.

Ligament (lig'-a-ment): A band of flexible compact connective tissues connecting the articular ends of the bones and also enveloping them.

Light (līt): Luminous wave motions that give rise to sensations of vision when the rays impinge upon the retina.

Litmus (lit'-mus): A blue pigment obtained from a lichen plant used in litmus paper.

Lobe (lōb): A more or less rounded part of projection of an organ, as lobe of the ear.

Lotion (lo'-shun): A liquid solution.

Lubricant (lū-bri-kant): Making oily or slippery.

Lucidum (lu'-si-dum): Clear.

Lymph (limf): The fluid in the lymphatic vessels.

Lymphatic (lim-fat'ik): Pertaining to lymph.

Lymphatic System: A system of vessels and glands accessory to the blood vascular system.

Macule (mak'ūl): A non-elevated spot, especially on the skin.

Magnetism (mag'-net-ism): The power possessed by a magnet to attract or repel other masses.

Malar (mā'-lar): Pertaining to the molar (cheek) bone.

Malpighian (mal-pig'-e-an): Malpighian stratum or layer of the epidermis.
Mandible (man'-dib-l): The inferior maxillary bone.
Manipulation (man-ip-u-la'-shun): A handling; the use of the hands for the purpose of performing some work in a skillful manner, as in massaging.
Massage (mas-ahzj'): A method of rubbing, kneading or stroking the superficial parts of the body.
Masseter (mas'-e-ter): One of the muscles of mastication.
Mastication (mas-tik-a'-shun): The action of chewing.
Matrix (mā'-triks): A cavity or the tissue into which any organ is set; the intercellular substance.
Matter (mat'-er): Physical substance.
Maxillary (maks'-il-a-re): Pertaining to the jaws.
Medulla (me-dul'-ah): The marrow, anything resembling marrow in structure or its relation to other parts.
Melanin (mel'-an-in): A pigmentary substance occurring in the skin and hair.
Mentalis (men-ta'-lis): The levator labii inferioris muscle.
Menthol (men'-thol): A crystalline substance derived from oil of peppermint.
Membrane (mem'-brān): A thin layer of tissue surrounding a part or separating adjacent cavities.
Metabolism (met-ab'-o-lism): The process of building up and breaking down within the cells of the body.
Microbe (mi'-krōb): A living organism of very small size.
Micron (mi'-kron): One thousandth part of a millimeter.
Microscope (mi'-kro-skōp): An apparatus through which minute objects are examined.
Milia (mil'-i-ah) (plural): A disease of the skin characterized by small pearly non-inflammatory elevations.
Miliaria (mil-i-a'-re-ah) (plural): Prickly heat.
Mitosis (mi-to'-sis): Cell division.
Mole (mōl): See Nevus.
Molecule (mol'-e-kūl): A minute portion of matter.
Morbid (mor'-bid): Pertaining to disease.
Mucous membrane: Lining membrane of cavities having the ability to secrete a fluid called mucous.
Muscle (mus'-l): A structure composed chiefly of muscular tissue and having the property of contracting.
Nape (nāp): The back part of the neck.
Naris (na'-ris): A nostril. One of a pair of nasal openings.
Necrosis (nek-ro'-sis): The death of cells surrounded by living tissue.
Neoplasm (ne'-o-plazm): New growth. A circumscribed new formation of tissue characterized by abnormality of structure or location.
Nerve (nerv): An elongated, cord-like structure made up of aggregations of nerve fibers and having the property of transmitting nervous impulses.
Neuritis (nū-ri'-tis): Inflammation of a nerve.
Neurology (nū-rol'-o-je): The study of the nervous system.
Neuron (nū'-ron): A nerve cell and its processes.
Neutralize (nū'-tral-īz): To render neutral or inert.
Nevus (nē-vus): A circumscribed area of pigmentation, usually elevated (mole).
Node (nōd): A knob, a swelling.
Non: A prefix meaning "not"—non-pathogenic (not pathogenic): non-striated (not striated), etc.
Nucleus (nū'-kle-us): The essential part of a typical cell, usually rounded and situated in the center.
Nutriment (nū'-tri-ment): Anything that nourishes.
Obesity (o-be'-sit-e): An excessive development of fat.
Obsolete (ob'-so-lēt): Out of date.
Occiput (ok'-sip-ut): The back part of the head.
Occipital (ok-sip'-it-al): Pertaining to the occiput.
Occipitalis (ok-sip'-it-a'-lis): The posterior belly of the occipitofrontalis.
Ohm (ōm): Unit of electric resistance.

Oleosa (o-le-o′-sa): Greasy.
Olfactory (ol-fak′-to-re): Pertaining to the sense of smell.
Optic, Optical (op′-tik, op′-tik-al): Pertaining to vision or eye.
Orbicular (or-bik′-ū-lar): A term applied to circular muscles.
Orbit (or′-bit): The bony cavity containing the eye.
Organ (or′-gan): Any part of the body having a definite function to perform.
Orifice (or′-if-is): An opening.
Origin (or′-ij-in): The beginning or starting point. Origin of a muscle:
    The point of attachment of a muscle which remains relatively fixed
    during contraction.
Oris (or′-is): Pertaining to the mouth.
Osmosis (oz-mo′-sis): The passage of liquids.
Osteology (os-te-ol′-o-je): Science of anatomy and structure of bones.
Oxygen (oks′-ij-en): A colorless, tasteless, odorless gas; one of the elements.
Palate (pal′-at): The roof of the mouth.
Palpebral (pal′-pe-bral): Pertaining to the eyelid.
Papilla (pap-il′-ah): The nipple, or a nipple-like eminence. Vascular papilla,
    papilla of the skin containing the capillary loops. Papilla of the hair, etc.
Papule (pap′-ūl): A small circumscribed, solid elevation of the skin; a pimple.
Parasite (par′-ah-sīt): An animal or vegetable living upon or within another
    organism.
Parasitiside (par-a-sit′-is-īd): An agent capable of destroying parasites,
    especially the parasites living on the skin.
Parotid (par-ot′-id): Situated near the ear, as the parotid glands.
Pathology (path-ol′-o-je): The branch of medical science that treats of the
    changes in the structure caused by disease.
Pathogenic (path-o-jen′-ic): Disease-producing.
Pediculosis (ped-ik-ū-lo′-sis): Lousiness; a skin affection characterized by the
    presence of pediculi (lice).
Pericardium (per-e-kar′-de-um): The closed membranous sac enveloping
    the heart.
Percussion (per-kush′-un): Rapid tapping or slapping movements in massage.
Periosteum (per-i-os′-te-um): A fibrous membrane investing the surface
    of a bone.
Phagocyte (fag′-o-sīt): A cell having the property of engulfing and digesting
    foreign and other particles harmful to the body.
Pharmacology (far-ma-kol′-o-ji): The science of the nature of drugs.
Phenol (fe′-nol): A chemical commonly called carbolic acid, used in highly
    diluted form for disinfection.
Physics (fiz′-iks): The science of nature, especially that treating of the
    properties of matter.
Physiology (fiz-e-ol′-o-je): The science that treats of the function of organic
    beings.
Physiotherapy (fiz-e-o-ther′-a-pe): The use of the forces of nature in the
    treatment of disease; such as heat, light, electricity, massage, exercise,
    etc.
Pigment (pig′-ment): A dyestuff; a coloring matter. Any organic coloring
    matter of the body, as in skin or hair.
Pili (pī-lī): Hairs.
Pilo (pī-lo): A prefix meaning relating to hair or hairy.
Pityriasis (pit-ir-ī′-as-is): A term applied to various skin affections; char-
    acterized by fine, branny desquamation.
Pityriasis Capitis (cap′-i-tis): Pityriasis of the scalp.
Pityriasis Steatodes (ste-a-tō′-dēz): Oily dandruff.
Plasma (plaz-mah): The fluid part of the blood.
Platysma (plat-iz′-mah): A thin flat muscle which wrinkles the skin of the
    neck and depresses the mouth.
Pledget (plej′-et): A small flattened compress, as of cotton.
Polarity (po-lar′-it-e): The state or quality of having poles or points of
    intensities with opposite qualities.
Posterior (pos-ter′-i-er): Placed behind or in back of a part.

Posterior Auricular (aw-rik'-ū-lar): The muscle placed behind the ear.

Pruritus (proo-rī'-tus): Itching, a peculiar uncomfortable sensation due to irritation of the peripheral sensory nerve.

Procerus (pro-se'-rus): The pyramidalis nasi muscle.

Psoriasis (so-rī'-a-sis): A chronic inflammatory disease of the skin characterized by reddish patches covered with silver scales.

Psychic (sī'-kik): Pertaining to the mind.

Puberty (pū'-ber-te): The age of capability of reproduction, accompanied by the development of body hairs and beards in the male.

Pustule (pus'-tūl): A small circumscribed elevation of the skin containing pus.

Putrefaction (pū-tre-fak'-shun): The decomposition of nitrogenous organic matter under the influence of micro-organisms, accompanied by the development of disagreeable odors.

Rash: A superficial eruption of the skin or mucous membrane.

Relax (re-laks'): To loosen or make less tense.

Relaxant (re-laks'-ant): An agent that diminishes tension.

Relaxation (re-lax-a'-shun): A diminution of tension in a part.

Rete (rē'-te): Any network or interlacing, especially of capillaries.

Reticular (ret-ik'-ū-lar): Resembling a net.

Sanitary (san'-it-a-re): Pertaining to health.

Sanitation (san-i-tā'-shun): The act of securing a healthful condition; the application of sanitary measures.

Scaly: Resembling scales, characterized by scales.

Scale: The dry, semi-opaque lamina of horny epidermis shed from the skin in health and in various diseases.

Scalp: The hairy integument covering the cranium.

Scar (skar): Cicatrix; a connective tissue which replaces a localized loss of substance.

Scarfskin (skarf'-skin): Term used to denote epidermis or cuticle.

Science (sī'-ens): Systematized and classified knowledge.

Scurf (skerf): A bran-like desquamation of the epidermis; dandruff.

Sebaceous (se-ba'-shus): Pertaining to sebum.

Seborrhea (seb-or-ē'-ah): A functional disease of the sebaceous glands characterized by an excessive secretion of sebum.

Seborrhea oleosa (ōl-ē-os'-a): Oily type of seborrhea.

Seborrhea Sicca (see'-ka): Dry type of seborrhea.

Seborrheic (seb-or-e'-ic): Pertaining to seborrhea.

Sebum (se'-bum): The secretion of the sebaceous glands.

Secretion (se-krē'-shun): The act of secreting or forming from materials furnished by the blood a certain substance which is eliminated from the body; the substance secreted.

Senile (sē'-nīl): Pertaining to or caused by old age.

Sensory (sen'-so-re): Pertaining to or conveying sensation.

Sepsis (sep'-sis): A state of poisoning produced by the absorption of putrefactive substances.

Septic (sep'-tik): Relating to sepsis.

Serous (se'-rus): Pertaining to serum; characterized by or resembling serum.

Serum (se'-rum): The clear yellowish fluid separating from the blood after coagulation; any clear fluid.

Shaft of the hair: The part of the hair above the skin.

Shampoo (sham-poo'): Synonym of massage; especially cleansing the scalp with lather and rubbing.

Sheath (shēth): An envelope or covering, as coverings of arteries, organs, muscles, nerves, etc.

Sheen: Gloss, brightness.

Singe (sinj): To burn the ends of hair.

Sinus (sī'-nus): A hollow or cavity; a recess or pocket.

Sinusoidal (si-nus-oid'-al) current: An alternating induced electrical current with equal current strokes.

Skin: The protective covering of the body, composed of the epidermis, corium and subcutaneous tissue.

Skeleton (skel'-et-on): A supporting structure, especially the bony framework of an organism.

Skull (skul): The bony framework of the head, consisting of the cranium and the head.

Soap: A chemical compound made by the union of certain fatty acids with an alkali. Green soap, soft soap made from linseed oil and potash.

Soapless shampoo: Sulphonated oil liquids or organic detergent liquids.

Spatula (spat'-ū-la): A flexible blunt blade for spreading ointment.

Spectrum (spek'-trum): A band of rainbow colors produced by decomposing light by means of a prism.

Sphenoid bone (sfe'-noid): A wedge-shaped bone in the fore part of the cranium.

Spirillum (spī-ril'-um): Corkscrew-shaped bacteria.

Spirochete (spi'-ro-kēt): Germs of bacteria. (See treponema.)

Spongy (spun'-je): Having the texture of a sponge; very porous.

Spore (spōr): Any germ or reproductive element less organized than a true cell.

Squamous (skwā'-mus): Of the shape of a scale; scaly.

Staphylococcus (staf-i-lo-kok'-us): A genus of micrococcus cells which are irregularly clustered, like a bunch of grapes.

Steatoma (ste-at-o'-mah): A sebaceous cyst.

Sterile (ster'-il): Free from germs.

Sterilize (ster'-il-īz): Render free from germs.

Sterilization: The act of rendering anything sterile, or the destruction of micro-organisms.

Sternocleidomastoid muscle (ster'-no-klī-do-mas'-toid): A neck muscle.

Stimulate (stim'-u-lāt): To stir up, increase functional activity.

Strain (strāne): Overuse of a part. The condition produced in a part by overuse or wrong use.

Stratum (strā'-tum): A layer.

Streptococcus (strep-to-kok'-us): A genus of micrococcus cells which are arranged in strings or chains.

Striated (stri'-a-ted): Striped.

Stroking: To pass the hands gently over an object, or a part of the body.

Styptic (stip'-tik): An agent that checks hemorrhage by causing contraction of the blood vessels.

Subdermal (sub-der'-mal): Same as subcutaneous.

Subcutaneous (sub-kū-tā'-ne-us): Beneath the skin.

Sudamen (sū-da'-men): An eruption of translucent whitish vesicles due to disturbance of the sweat glands.

Subjective (sub-jek'-tiv): Pertaining to the individual himself; of symptoms experienced by the patient himself and not amendable to physical exploration.

Sudor (su'-dor): Sweat.

Sudoriferous (su-dor-if'-er-us): Producing sweat.

Supercilium (sū-per-sil'-e-um): The eyebrow.

Superior (su-pe'-re-or): Higher or upper part.

Suppuration (sup-ū-ra'-shun): The formation of pus.

Supraorbital (su-prah-or'-bi-tal): Above the orbit.

Sweat (swet): The secretion of the sudoriferous glands, consisting of a transparent colorless, aqueous fluid.

Sycosis (sī-ko'-sis): An inflammatory disease affecting the hair follicles, particularly the beard, and characterized by papules, pustules and tubercules, perforated by the hair, together with infiltration of the skin and crusting. Sycosis barbae (bar-be), sycosis of the beard.

Sympathetic (sim-path-et'-ik): Conveying sympathy or sympathetic impulses.

System (sis'-tem): The body as a whole. A combination of parts into a whole as digestive system, nervous system.

Tan: A yellowish brown color. A brown color imparted to the skin by exposure to the sun.

Tactile (tak'-til): Pertaining to the sense of touch.

Tapotement (ta-pōt-man'): In massage, the operation of tapping or percussing.
Technic (tek'-nik): The method of procedure in operations or manipulations of any kind.
Temple (tem'-pl): The portion of the head behind the eye and above the ear.
Temporal (tem'-po-ral): Pertaining to the temple.
Temporalis muscle (tem-po-ra'-lis): Temporal muscle.
Tendon (ten'-don): A band of dense fibrous tissue forming the termination of a muscle and attaching the latter to a bone.
Tension (ten'-shun): The state of being stretched.
Tepid (tep'-id): About blood heat.
Terminal (ter'-min-al): Pertaining to the end, as terminal arteries. In electricity, sometimes used in the plural to denote the poles of a battery.
Texture (teks'-tūr): Any organized substance or tissue of which the body is composed; the arrangement of the elementary parts of tissue.
Theory (the'-o-re): The abstract principles of a science, also a reasonable supposition or assumption.
Therapeutic lamp: An electrical apparatus producing ultra-violet or infra-red rays or a combination of both rays.
Thermal (ther'-mal): Pertaining to heat.
Tinea (tin'-e-ah): Ringworm; a generic term applied to a class of skin diseases caused by parasitic fungi.
Tinea barbae: Ringworm of beard.
Tissue (tish'-oo): An aggregation of similar cells and fibers forming a distinct structure and entering as such into the formation of an organ.
Tissue fluid: The fluid in the intercellular spaces.
Toxsin (tok'-sin): Any poisonous nitrogenous compound produced by animal or vegetable cells (in nature).
Treponema pallidum (tre-po-ne'-mah pal'-id-um): Parasitical germ of syphilis.
Trichology (trĭk-ol'-o-je): The science of the hair and its diseases.
Trichonosis (trik-on'-o-sis): Any morbid affection of the hair.
Trichoptilosis (trik-op-til-o'-sis): Synonym of trichorrhexis nodosa.
True skin: The corium. The second layer of skin.
Tweezers (twe'-zers): A forceps for extracting hair.
Ungues (un'-gwēz): The nails.
Unit (ū-nit): A single thing; a group considered as a whole; a quantity with which others are compared.
Urticaria (ur-tik-a'-re-ah): A disease of the skin characterized by the development of wheals which give rise to the sensation of burning and itching.
Valve (valv): A device placed in a tube or canal so as to permit free passage one way, but not in the opposite direction.
Vapor (va'-por): A gas, especially the gaseous form of a substance which at ordinary temperatures is liquid or solid.
Vascular (vas'-kū-lar): Consisting of, pertaining to, or provided with vessels.
Ventrical (ven'-trik-l): A small cavity or pouch.
Vaso-constrictor: A nerve or drug that causes constriction of blood vessels.
Vaso-dilator: A nerve or drug that causes dilation of blood vessels.
Verruca (ver-oo'-kah): A wart.
Vessel (ves'-el): A receptical for fluids, especial a tube or canal for conveying blood or lymph.
Vibrator (vi'-brā-tor): A device for conveying mechanical vibrations to a part.
Violet ray: A term sometimes used to denote high frequency current.
Virulent (vir'-oo-lent): Poisonous.
Volatile (vol'-at-il): Passing into vapor at ordinary temperature.
Volt: A unit of electromotive force.
Wart: An unnatural increase of the papillae of the skin, forming a small projection.
Watt: An electrical unit of energy.
Whitehead: See millium.
Whorl (hworl): Cowlick; a spiral-like growth of hair.
Zygoma (zi-go'-ma): The malar bone or cheek bone.

REFERENCES

In the preparation of this Standardized Textbook of Barbering, the following works were consulted as authorities on various phases of Barber Science treated herein. The student who seeks amplification of points covered briefly in this book will do well to utilize these reference volumes.

Gray's Anatomy, Lewis.
Diseases of the Hair and Scalp, Hubbard.
Diseases of the Hair, Jackson and McMurtry.
Textbook of Anatomy and Physiology, Kimber and Gray.
The Ultra-Violet Rays, Lorland.
Light and Health, Luckiesh and Pacini.
Light Therapeutics, Kellogg.
Basis of Light in Therapy, Goodman.
The Cosmetiste, Blood.
Materia Medica and Therapeutics, Wilcox.
Essentials of Medicine, Emerson.
Fighting Foes Too Small to See, McFarland.
The Story of Germ Life, Conn.
Sanitation and Physiology, Ritchie.
Care of the Skin in Health, Goodman.
Diseases of the Skin, Sutton.
The Sales Promotion Handbook, Aspley.
Public Relations Principles and Problems, Canfield.
Advertising Principles, Latest Edition, Agnew and Hotchkiss.